PA ER

G NN

BRANDEN PUBLISHING COMPANY
Boston

Library of Congress Cataloging-in-Publication Data

Escape of the Pacific Clipper / by George L. Flynn.
p. cm.
Includes index.
ISBN 0-8283-2026-8 (pbk. : alk. paper)

1. Pacific Clipper (Airplane)
2. World War, 1939-1945--Aerial operations, Japanese.
3. World War, 1939-1945--Aerial operations, German.

I. Title.
D792.J3F59 1997
940.54'4952--dc21 96-47053
CIP

BRANDEN PUBLISHING COMPANY
17 Station Street
PO Box 843 Brookline Village
Boston, MA 02147

CONTENTS

PROLOGUE

In the morning of 2 December, 1941, the Pacific Clipper, Pan American Airways's newest flying boat, left Los Angeles on its maiden flight. The Clipper was the most sophisticated and technologically advanced plane flying anywhere in the world. She would island hop across the vast expanse of the Pacific Ocean to Auckland, New Zealand, then return. On December 8, 1941, one half hour after a 7AM take off from Noumea, French New Caledonia on the way to Auckland, the world of the Pacific Clipper as well as most of humanity turned upside down. The Empire of Japan, in a sneak attack, bombed Pearl Harbor. The United States went to war and few if any cared about the fate of an American commercial plane stuck in New Zealand. With the Imperial Japanese Navy having destroyed all its bases in the Pacific, and without maps, charts or any navigational aids, as well as being under strict radio silence, the men of the Pacific Clipper decided to try to return home.

This is their story.

To Jill, without whose belief in my ability to write this story and her spelling skills, this book never would have been finished. With love. Her husband, George.

Opening

Tanaka's Plan

The submarine rose slowly from the floor of the ocean. The dark, gray waters of the depths gradually lightened as the bright South Pacific sunlight filtered down through the soft green waters that surrounded the islands of New French Caldonia. The sub stopped its assent and leveled off as its periscope rose and softly broke a hole in the water. The man looking through the eyepiece of the periscope slowly rotated the viewer. Suddenly he stopped and with his right thumb, flipped the magnifying glass on the scope. As he watched, a small dot appeared at the top of the scope and gradually became larger as it approached the sub. In a few seconds, the dot became a form and it then soared overhead. The man smiled and turned.

"Down periscope," the man ordered and the steel viewer quietly slid into its housing cylinder. He turned to another man holding a note pad. "Radio Commodore Tanaka. The American plane has left Noumea. Note the time, 0705 hours, 8 December, 1941. As instructed, we will we will follow to Auckland and keep you advised of the American's movement." The man giving the orders wore the insignia of Lt. Commander on his uniform collar. The uniform was that of a member of the Imperial Japanese Navy.

The other officer took the message across the bridge to the radioman who began his transmission. The electric impulses shot up the sub's antenna and across the water to another submarine, submerged somewhere off the coast of Malasia, the Dutch East Indies. The message is transcribed by the radioman and given to another officer. The transmission is in code and only one man aboard the sub can decipher the code. The radioman walks quickly down the passageway to a closed door. Knocking respectfully, the door opens to reveal two men. One is clad in khaki, his shirt open at the neck and the shoulder boards indicate the rank of Captain. His name is Nagoma, Captain

Jintsu Nagoma, one of Japan's finest submarine commanders. His ship, the Arista, is the pride of the Japanese underwater fleet. It is a member of the "1 15" class, the largest Japanese subs ever built. Launched in 1939 by Mitsubishi, its displacement is 2,180 tons, and she carries 24 torpedoes. Her armament is one 5.5 inch gun and 2 MG ack ack guns on the sail. The Arista has two Diesel engines and can do 20 knots on the surface. Almost 350 feet long, she is 30 feet wide and rises 16 feet from the keel to the top of the conning tower. The Arista also carries a seaplane, folded and stored aft. Captain Nagoma commands a compliment of 60 officers and men. This was his cabin until the other man came on board.

The other man took the message from the radioman, who bowed and left. Nagoma looks at his guest, dressed in his full Naval uniform, indicating he is a Commodore in the Emperor's Imperial Navy. He is very tall for a Japanese, well over six feet, broad of shoulders and slim in the waist. His size makes Nagoma's cabin seem almost doll house like in size. His face is hard, with high cheekbones. The head is shaved, almost scraping the ceiling of the room. But even more impressive than the man's massive frame are his eyes. Not brown, typical of the Japanese nor any shade of blue or grey. They are green. Hard, almost metallic, and thus far in the few days the man has been aboard the Arista, Nagoma had never seen any softness in those eyes.

The tall man finishes reading the message and looks at Nagoma as he folds the paper and puts it in a manila envelope. "Ah, my good Nagoma. Our quest begins. The American plane, the Pacific Clipper is, as we speak, headed for her final out-bound destination, Auckland, New Zealand. As of now, they do not know that our planes are swiftly attacking all their bases from Pearl Harbor to Hong Kong. Soon, Captain Ford, the pilot will know what a devastating blow we have dealt them and when he lands in New Zealand, he'll know he can't return home the way he came. We don't know when the Americans will leave Auckland but they will. Our spies in New Zealand and along the Australian coast will keep us advised of the Pacific Clipper's movements. But I'm certain he will head for the small Pan Am base at Darwin, then try for Java. Surabaja. There is 100 octane fuel there. And that is where our esteemed Major Thu and his commando are waiting!"

His tone of voice indicated that he was just informing the Captain of the Arista of his plans and expected immediate obedience. And Captain Nagoma is prepared to give it. He knows that other than the family of the Emperor, the House of Tanaka is the most honored of all in Japan. And standing in his cabin, ten fathoms under the South China Sea is the nephew of the architect of Pax Nippon, Japan's plan for the conquest of Asia, Commodore Isodecki Tanaka.

The Commodore was a legend in Japanese diplomatic and military circles. For years he had infiltrated the highest levels of the American military establishment while posing as a member of the Japanese diplomatic corps at its embassy in Washington. It was his work that brought the Japanese high command vital knowledge of American military operations in the Pacific. Even Commodore Tanaka's escape from American military intelligence and their FBI was the stuff of fables. And Nagoma, like almost all the officers of the Imperial Navy, knew of the major conflict between his father and his uncle. They violently disagreed on the Baron's plans for Japan's future. His father, Count Tanaka was a close friend and advisor to the Emperor and fought against his brother on invading China and baiting the United States. But the Baron won and even though he was now dead, the War Party, led Prime Minister General Hidecki Tojo came to power because of Baron Tanaka. Even the Count, advising Hirohito, couldn't stop Tojo and his people from gaining control of the Japanese parliament and the government. Commodore Tanaka had sided with his uncle and it was widely understood that his father swore never to speak to him again. But as much as he admired the Tanaka family and the exploits of the Commodore, he was a Captain in the Imperial Navy, in command of a ship of the line, and when at sea, almost a god unto himself. He wanted to be sinking American ships. But he had been ordered to obey Commodore Tanaka and knew that the plans of man in his cabin seemed to be far more important in the overall strategy of the Imperial staff than his desires to torpedo Yankee ships. Respect was expected and fully given but obsequiousness was not a reason why Nagoma became the commander of the Arista. He has some serious reservations about their mission.

"Sir, maybe you could take the time to explain to an old sea dog why this American plane is so important that the Arista is denied the honor of joining our honorable sailors who are fighting the Americans," Nagoma asked with natural deference in his voice.

Tanaka's eyes turned cold and flared briefly at Nagoma's impertinence but he recognized that he needed Nagoma's complete confidence in the mission. To him it was simple but he had to sell Nagoma, a man who came up through the ranks to command.

"Captain, your question stands you in good company. It is the same one General Tojo and Admiral Yamamoto asked me when I first presented them with the plan to capture the Pacific Clipper. I'll be brief and ask you one question. Do we have any long range bombers?" Tanaka asked and waited.

"Our planes are bombing Hong Kong, Shanghai and Nanking," Nagoma answered.

"Indeed, but they are short range planes, two engine Mitsubishis from Manchuco or planes from our carriers off the coast of China. We can't expect to conquer and hold an area as vast as the Pacific without long range aircraft, planes that can fly thousands of miles, deliver a heavy load of bombs and return. And the technology, the engineering, her engines and the navigation equipment that the Pacific Clipper carries is years ahead of our talents. When we capture her and copy all her secrets, we'll build planes that will give our armies and navies an umbrella of protection that no enemy can penetrate. The American plane, in our hands, will give the Empire the technology to conquer Asia, and eventually the world," the nephew of Baron Tanaka explained.

Nagoma nodded in understanding. But he still had a major question. "Commodore, you stated that we are now destroying American bases where Pan Am has facilities. You also stated that there was no way for the American plane to return the way they came. So why in the world would the Americans leave the safety of New Zealand?"

"That would be the safe play, Captain Nagoma. Stay in New Zealand until the war is over. But I know this Captain Ford, the pilot of the Pacific Clipper. I've flown with him as a passenger, twice, in fact. Our intelligence people knew Ford would be the pilot of their new Boeing 314A. He is Pan Am's best. The Pacific Clipper is the finest plane in the world and who better to fly her on her maiden flight than Ford. And believe me, Ford will not stay in Auckland. No, he'll come out. He knows that soon we will control the skies over Asia and he'll be stuck in Auckland. So he'll come out and we must anticipate where he'll land. He needs aviation fuel and must land in deep water harbors where his plane can serviced. There are only a few place he can go once he leaves Auckland. Darwin first and then to Surabaja. As Ford is the best commercial pilot in the world, so you, my good Nagoma are our best submarine commander. No one knows the South China Sea as well as you or the waters around Malasia. And because you do, I trust you to get us where we must be when we decide to take the Clipper. We've guessed Surabaja in Java. If Ford doesn't go there, I depend on you to take me and the other commandos on the Arista to where he is so we can capture the American plane," Tanaka explained.

Nagoma smiled, stood and bowed. As long as he and his men would receive recognition for their part in the Commodore's plan, he was satisfied. And if this American plane was half as important at Tanaka said, the honor of being the commander of the submarine that helped capture her would far outshine what his contemporaries were doing. He was sold. As Nagoma left his cabin and headed for the control room, Tanaka closed the door behind him. He thought of his illustrious ancestor, the Baron and remembered the hours spent listening to his warnings that Japan had to control the skies with long range bombers if they expected to conquer and hold Asia. And he constantly stressed that only the Americans stood in the way of Japan's rightful place as masters of Asia. With the Pacific Clipper in their hands, Japan would soon have what his uncle said Japan needed. The tall man allowed himself a brief smile as he thought of the welcome he would receive when he landed in the waters of Tokyo harbor aboard the American plane. Then the smile faded as he thought of the odds against pulling this off. He knew that the Pacific Clipper would probably be shot down or crash because it ran out of gas long before he had his chance at it. The thought brought a wry smile to his face as he realized that his success at capturing the Pacific Clipper was in direct ratio to Ford's ability in getting the Clipper to Java. For it was there, in Surabaja, that the Commodore felt he'd have his best, and probably only chance at getting the Boeing 314A. Alone and speaking out loud, Tanaka laughed when he realized his fate was totally tied in with the Captain of the Pacific Clipper. "Yes, Captain Ford. My hopes are high for you to reach Surabaja. Good luck. I'd love to be there to welcome you but I sure you'll find the reception I've planned for you quite warm indeed. See you soon at Kota Bharu."

CHAPTER 1

Outbound: The Last Leg

7 December 1941-Lift off 0700, Noumea, New French Caldonia, climbing to cruising altitude, 8000 Ft. ETA Auckland, NZ 13:40

Navigator John Steers sat back and looked at his latest entry into the flight log. He took the paper from the Smith/Corona portable typewriter and began to file it in the black binder with the red, white and blue logo of Pan American Airlines embossed on the top right hand corner of the leather folder. He put the paper in and gave it one final perusal.

"Shit," muttered Steers. "We've passed the International dateline. It's 8 December, not the 7th!" He was tempted to erase the error but knew that Captain Robert Ford did not allow for any mistakes on his watch, including erasures in the log book. So Steers put in another clean sheet of paper, retyped the entry and filed it. Some Captains would have accepted a smudged entry. Not Ford. Steers didn't mind. He knew Ford was a stickler for details and also that he was the finest four engine pilot in the world. So Steers would put up with Ford's idiosyncrasies, grateful to be Fourth Officer on any flight Ford commanded, especially the maiden flight of the Pacific Clipper.

He rose and placed the typewriter and log book on the floor of his navigator's file cabinet. He walked over to his table and double checked the course he plotted that the Clipper would fly to Auckland. The crew had come aboard the ship at 0530, pre-flighted the ship and the passengers boarded at 0630. At precisely 0655, Ford started the engines of the giant plane and on the mark of 0700, began their run down the watery runway in the Coral Sea and lifted easily into the air. In a few hours, they would be landing in Auckland, then a couple days rest and begin their return trip home to the States. Thus far, their trip had been right out of the textbook.

Looking around the flight deck, Steers was pleased at the space they had for working. There was so much more room that a person as tall the Captain could stand erect and not hit his head. It was a great improvement from the Martin 42's that had been the backbone of Pan American's amphibian airships until Boeing built the 314s for Juan Trippe's airline. Now Steers and the rest were flying an improved version called the 314A and it simply was the finest commercial aircraft in the world. She could fly over 5000 miles before refueling, each of her Wright Cyclone engines had 1600 horses that gave them greater power, speed and range. Standing near his table, Steers could see the doors that led to the huge wings on the port and starboard sides of the plane. The Boeing engineers had designed them so that the flight engineers could walk inside the wings on a metal ramp to make any necessary repairs while in flight. The stairway from the flight deck down to the passenger level was directly behind the seat of the First Officer. The console for the radio operator and his station was on the other side of the stairway. To the left and ahead sat the Captain, Robert Ford.

To Steers, Ford was the bridge between the early seat-of-the pants pilots that flew for Pan Am, the fliers that experimented and risked their lives to find out what a four engine amphibian airplane could do and if it could be made into a profitable business. The new breed of pilots were trained aviators with degrees in engineering and aeronautics. Steers had heard stories about Ford's barnstorming days in the late Twenties while he was still in college and also knew that Ford had received his degree in Aeronautical Engineering from the University of Wisconsin, one of the few major universities in the country that were in the vanguard of scientific research in aviation technology.

All pilots must have excellent hand and eye coordination so most of them are good athletes. Ford was an end on the Wisconsin football team, an honorable mention All Big Ten his senior year and a star second baseman on the Badger's baseball team. Rumor had it that he'd been signed by the St. Louis Cardinals and was to report to one of their farm teams after he graduated. But Ford passed on going to the minors because he wanted to fly. Anyway, with the exception of a Bob Feller or a Joe DiMaggio and a few others, baseball players didn't make much money. Captains of Pan Am Clipper ships did.

Physically, Ford was 6'1" tall, about 185 pounds, his black hair free of any grey and while Steers wouldn't call Ford handsome like Robert Taylor or Tyrone Power, he was good looking. Steers knew that a Captain of a Pan American Clipper ship was welcomed in high society wherever they landed and Ford, he knew, enjoyed the respect and in some case, the adulation, that came from his rank and position. The story that all the Pan Am people thoroughly enjoyed was the one about Ford that had him involved with the daughter of a wealthy financier in Hong Kong. The girl was supposedly so beautiful that here parents would not allow her to appear in public. How Ford and she got together and exactly what their relationship was, if there was one, made for great conversation at Pan Am bases across the world. And stories about the parties Ford and his close friend, Bill Mullahey threw were legendary. Mullahey was one of the great characters in Pan Am, the man who cleared the lagoon at Wake Island and was now the Pan Am director in New Zealand. Those that had attended a Ford- Mullahey bash said that they gave new meaning to the term, bachelor parties!

But is wasn't Ford's off-duty life that impressed Steers and the world of aviation. It was his ability as a pilot that set him apart. To Steers, it was Ford's total confidence in himself, the sure knowledge that there wasn't anything Mother Nature or the aircraft itself that could daunt him. A sudden thunderstorm that could shake the rivets out of a plane or one of those unseen and unexpected wind tunnels that could drop a plane 1000 feet in seconds were challenges to all pilots. It was just that when it happened to the plane Ford was piloting, it didn't seem to be a problem. He never gave any indication of concern.

Many Pan Am people thought that Ford was a tough commander. But thus far in this maiden flight, except for the delay in Los Angeles, things had almost been too easy. This was

Steers's second tour with Ford but the first for all of them flying the Boeing 314A. The training flights they had gone through over Puget Sound helped get the bugs out of the plane and give the crew a good shakedown. But no training flights can ever duplicate the actual flying with passengers across the great expanse of the Pacific and all the inherent dangers.

Each of the officers on the flight deck of a Pan Am clipper ship was trained to handle every job from pilot to navigator to radio operator so that if one became ill during a trip, another could step in and do the job. This was the Pan Am way and one of the reasons they were the best commercial airline in the business. Even the military did it the Pan Am way. But that wasn't too surprising. Pan American planes were flying laboratories for the War Department and results of Pan Am's testing of equipment and new technologies were quickly assimilated into the latest designs of American fighter planes, bombers and cargo aircraft.

As Steers scanned the flight deck, he was again reminded of what an improvement the Pacific Clipper was aesthetically. No longer the dull, gunmetal navy grey of the older Pan Am planes. For this plane, the flight deck was painted a light blue, teal blue one of the ground crew had told him. With the sun streaming in from the flight deck windows, the cabin was bright and airy. The crew was dressed in their "whites," a takeoff on the British Royal Navy that plied the tropical waters of the world. Juan Trippe ran Pan Am like the Navy. It was the bridge or flight deck, not the cockpit, the co-pilot was the First Officer, the flight attendants were the Flight Stewards. Pan Am ran on military time: 3 PM was 1500 hours. Their dark blue uniforms were direct copies of the dress blues of the United States Navy. They were wearing their "whites" on this trip since they were in the Southern Hemisphere and even though it was December, in the South Pacific it was summertime. They had on their Bermuda shorts and white stocking that came up to just below the patella. On their feet they wore white oxfords and the white shirts they had on showed only the color of the blue and gold epaulets depicting the rank of each man. Although he took umbrage at it the first time he heard the crack from one of the passengers that they looked like some poor man's stock company playing in an off-Broadway production of H.M.S. Pinafore, Steers had to admit that the man had nailed it. Indeed they did!

Standing at the rear of the flight deck, Steers looked at the three men sitting at their posts doing the job. His best friend, John Mack was the First Officer. Like Steers, he was from Southern California. The same age, they had know of each other as high school stars at the their different schools in Los Angeles but Steers went to UCLA and Mack to Stanford. Mack was a star football player for the Indians while Steers had become a world class 100 meter swimmer at UCLA. However, it was when both entered the employment of Pan Am that they became fast friends. And there was no doubt in his mind that the next captain of a Boeing 314A for Pan Am would be John Henry Mack. John Mack was the best four engine pilot in the world, next to Bob Ford. But then there was no one in Ford's league. Not in Pan Am or any other airline. Steers felt very pleased thus far with this maiden flight of the Pacific Clipper. But it didn't start out like that.

He recalled that the Clipper had flown to Los Angeles from San Francisco. Their departure the next morning to Honolulu was delayed because Washington had called New York and New York had called telling the Ops manager in Los Angeles to hold the Clipper for a special passenger. Ford was steamed but there was nothing he could do about it. Finally, about an hour past their scheduled take off, a blue Dodge with a Navy insignia on the side door pulled up and three uniformed officers got out. One seemed to have more gold on his sleeve than the others. The trunk of the car was opened and one officers brought out a small, overnight suitcase while the other took a box out, square and about the size of a hatbox. The three turned and came down the ramp and entered the Clipper. Steers remembered that the first officer to board was a woman and from what he could see, rather attractive. In a few minutes, the two male officers deplaned and almost immediately, the radio cracked on the flight deck and the Pacific Clipper was cleared for take off to Hawaii.

That was on 2 December, 1941 and the crew quickly got word up to the flight deck that the female officer had been given the Master Suite, on orders from Juan Trippe. She never left the suite all the way to Hawaii, taking her meals in the room. When the Clipper landed at Honolulu late that afternoon, the plane was met by another group of Navy brass and the mysterious passenger left with them, one carrying the hat box and another her small suitcase. The crew got busy deplaneing the passengers and it was only later when they were alone on the plane that someone mentioned the mysterious Naval lieutenant. They wondered who she was and why she was so important that all that Navy brass made such a fuss over her. The next day, John Mack solved the mystery.

After the debriefing by the Boeing engineers that morning, 3 December, 1941, the crew had the rest of the day off before leaving for Midway Island the next day. Over coffee and cigarettes, Mack recounted his "solving" of the "Mysterious Navy Woman with the Hat Box."

"I was having a drink at the Officer's Club at Pearl Harbor last night. An old teammate of mine is a gunnery officer aboard the Arizona and I was his guest. We were sitting at the bar when this group of Naval officers came in, maybe seven or eight of them, with a couple of admirals in the group. In the center was our lady friend. And I'll tell you this, even in a uniform, she is something. As they passed us I asked Bill if he knew who she was. He didn't but a few minutes later, another officer came by and Bill hailed him, introducing me to a Commander Rochefort and mentioning that I was part of the Pacific Clipper's crew. Bill tells me that Rochefort is some kind of Naval Intelligence genius but the Commander waves that aside as he asks me where we are headed after we leave Hawaii. I tell him Midway, Wake, Guam and he stops me, smiles and hits me with this," Mack tells the crew. All are there, including Ford, and enjoying his story. "I might have a passenger for you, at least as far as Guam. In fact, she flew in with you today. Her name is Lt. Elmes, Kathleen Elmes and she is part of our Naval Intelligence group in D.C.," Mack continues, repeating what Rochefort said. "Do you return via Guam?" he asks and I assure him that we do. He then excuses himself and walks over to the table where the admirals and the mystery woman sit. He leans over and speaks to the man that seems to be the ranking officer. The Admiral leans back to look at me, then nods. Rochefort walks over to the Lt.'s chair, whispers in her ear and the two of them join Bill and me at the bar. Rochefort introduces Lt. Kathleen Elmes to us and explains that he'll cut orders for her to accompany us to Midway, Wake and Guam. So tomorrow, gentlemen, the best looking Intelligence officer in any man's army, I mean Navy, will be with again," Mack finishes with a very broad smile.

"There is nothing on those islands to attract anyone. Why is she going there?" John Steers asked.

"Rochefort said Lt. Elmes would be briefing the commanders of the installations on those bases. When we make our return trip, we'll pick her up and bring her back to Pearl and probably on back to the States," Mack answered.

Bob Ford had listened without comment. When Mack finished, the other nine members of the crew looked at him. He offered no comment, just looked at Mack, put out his cigarette, shrugged and walked over to the hanger door and through it. The crew knew their captain was not happy.

But they were. To a man, they were delighted that the lovely Lt. Elmes accompanied them and when she decided after briefing the brass at Guam that she'd like to continue on with the Clipper to New Zealand, the Navy granted her request for some R&R, knowing the Clipper would bring her back to the States when they made their return trip.

Kathleen Elmes was delighted. She knew she'd probably never get another chance to see this part of the world and the two days she'd been aboard, she and the crew had become fast friends. Except for Captain Ford.

But there was little Ford could do about it. He knew of Juan Trippe's close ties to the Navy and any protest by him would fall on deaf ears. He thought at first that his officers might spend too much time entertaining Miss Elmes but he had to admit that their performance was excellent even with her aboard. He kept his feelings to himself but the very few times he was in her presence, he knew she knew how he felt. But the Lt. was thoroughly enjoying herself and the flight to these exotic islands!

Not so First Radio Officer John Poindexter. He had been shanghaied by Bob Ford. He was sitting in Base Operations at Long Beach, California, which, along with San Francisco, was the major Pan Am base on the West Coast. His plane, the Manila Clipper had finished its round trip from the Orient. He was dead heading back to San Francisco, with a week's leave time coming and his third anniversary a few days away. He and his wife and her folks were planning to celebrate with dinner at Ernies. He never made it.

When the Pacific Clipper landed at Long Beach to pick up the mystery passenger, Ford came into Operations and told the Ops Manager his radioman had stomach flu and couldn't continue. He needed a replacement. None were available. Then Ops man spotted Poindexter sitting in the lounge reading the LA Times and Ford had his radioman. So everyday, Poindexter would radio a message to his wife, apologizing for the screw up. She was a good Pan Am wife and understood.

Now as they climbed to altitude after leaving Noumea, Poindexter was seated at his console, head set on, listening to radio traffic from the ships at sea. In this part of the world, the radio was still a new invention and since it was Sunday, there would be no regular broadcasting. Suddenly, Poindexter sat straight up in his chair. He checked his location finder. It read 220 degrees north, 15 degrees east. Hawaii area.

"Captain. Captain," Poindexter called to Ford. The urgency heard in his voice caused the others on the flight deck to stop what they were doing. Ford turned in his pilot's seat and looked back at his radio operator. He liked Poindexter's work and knew something must be important. Poindexter almost never spoke, very unusual for a radioman.

"Yes, John. What is it?" Ford queried.

"I'm getting strange noises, words, I can't recognize, sounds like rolling thunder, and people yelling but I can't make any sense out of it," the radioman replied.

"Put it on the speakers, but just here on the bridge," Ford ordered.

Poindexter reached up and flipped a switch on his console and suddenly the cabin was filled with strange sounds; voices yelling, noises that sounded like someone popping paper bags and a hum that reminded Ford of the sound of buzzing bees. And most mysterious, they could hear the voices of people speaking in a language that sounded familiar but that none of them could identify. They suddenly, the bridge was quiet. The four looked at each other and it was obvious that they hadn't the foggiest idea of what they had heard. Seconds later, it began again and the deck was filled with the more of the strange babble and eerie noises. Ford shook his head and signaled for Poindexter to shut down the speakers.

As the quiet surrounded the four men, Ford looked at John Mack and suddenly, he had an idea. "John, didn't you tell me that Lt. Elmes was a language expert, an Asian specialist?" Ford asked.

"Yes, Sir. Why?" Mack replied.

"Maybe she can help us decipher what we're hearing. After all, that's her job isn't it. Intelligence?" Ford asked, somewhat sarcastically.

Without a word, Mack got out of his chair and quickly moved down the steps to the passenger level. In what seemed like just seconds, he escorted Kathleen Elmes up to the bridge. Ford looked at her as she reached the top step and quietly admitted that she was indeed a very beautiful woman. Wearing a light green and white cotton summer dress, a green scarf holding back her blond hair and white sandals on her feet, Kathleen Elmes, even in casual dress was quite an eyeful. These thoughts flashed through Ford's mind as he rose and walked over to the radio console.

"Lt. Elmes, sorry to disturb you but I thought you might help us. We are hearing strange sounds over the radio, voices in a language we can't understand. Maybe you can help us figure out what is going on," Ford explained.

"Delighted to try, Captain Ford," she replied.

Poindexter flipped the switch to put the sound on the bridge's speakers but they were silent.

"Were you able to pinpoint where the sounds were coming from, Mr. Poindexter," she asked.

"In the general direction of Hawaii," he replied.

Just then the speakers blared again, the same noises but this time the voices seemed clearer but they still couldn't get a handle on what they were hearing. Suddenly Kathleen Elmes gasped, her eyes widened and she began to pale. She reached out for John Mack's arm to steady herself. She starred at the speakers, almost hypnotized as the noise continued. Then she shook her head.

"Japanese," she whispered.

"What? What did you say, Miss Elmes?" Ford asked.

"The voices are Japanese. I'm guessing that the popping noises are bombs exploding and the humming is probably coming from airplane engines," she whispered.

Before anyone could respond, the speakers spewed out more words and Kathleen Elmes groaned. John Mack grabbed her around the waist as she almost fainted. He helped her over to Steer's navigator's chair and grabbing the thermos on the table, poured her some water. Her face was completely devoid of color.

"Did you hear it? Did you?" she asked of no one but all. "Akagi. Didn't you hear it? Akagi!" she asked as her voice began to rise. "Akagi. The Akagi. It is the biggest aircraft carrier in the world. Don't you know what is happening. The Japanese are bombing Pearl Harbor!" Kathleen Elmes almost screamed at them.

Ford and the others just stared at her. When what she had said sunk in, Ford walked back to his pilot's chair, sat and reached down, opened a small safe and took out a white envelope marked "TOP SECRET-Code A" he opened it and quickly scanned his orders. He knew them by heart. Reaching over and turning off the automatic pilot, Ford banked the Clipper to the right, 10 degrees and turned to Poindexter.

"Mr. Poindexter. Please turn off that noise and raise Auckland. I want to speak to Bill Mullahey," Ford quietly instructed his radioman. Poindexter did as ordered and within a minute, Bill Mullahey's voice returned the Clipper's call.

"Mullahey here, Clipper. We didn't expect your transmission for another 2 hours. What can we do for you?" asked the famed hero of the construction of the Pan Am's Wake Island station.

"Bill. Bob Ford here. We are about 40 minutes out of Noumea and have garbled transmissions we think are coming from Hawaii. One of our passengers is a US Naval Intelligence officer and she thinks the noises we're picking up are caused by the Japanese bombing Pearl Harbor. Have you any information on that?" Ford asks.

"She? Japs attacking Pearl? Have you been hitting the Mai Tia's early? No, Bob. We haven't heard anything about an attack on Hawaii. Our receivers can't pick up Hawaii. Want me to try Darwin?" Mullahey offers.

"No, Bill. We'll raise Darwin. Pacific Clipper signing off," Ford responds and looking back at Kathleen Elmes, he shakes his head, then instructs Poindexter to call Pan Am's small facility at Darwin.

Three times Poindexter calls for Darwin to come in and silence is their only response. As he tries for the fourth time, the Clipper's speakers come alive.

"What the bloody hell is with you assholes! Don't you know there is a bloomin' war on. The Japs have bombed Hawaii, Port Morsby and they're on their way here. Get the bloody hell off the air!" Darwin answers.

Some fifty miles behind the Pacific Clipper below the waters of the Coral Sea, the Japanese sub that reported the Pacific Clipper's departure from Noumea hears the transmission from Darwin to the American plane. The radioman tells his superior officer who passes the information on to the Captain. The Japanese officer instructs him to radio the information to Captain Nagoma that the Americans flying the Pacific Clipper now know that Pearl Harbor is under attack. "And add that we'll wait off Auckland's coast as ordered and alert Commodore Tanaka when the American's leave. But I doubt we'll ever send that message. Where would they go?" the Japanese Captain asks rhetorically.

The atmosphere on the flight deck of the Pacific Clipper is funereal. Even the speakers seem exhausted and each man sit with his private thoughts as they try to understand what Darwin and Kathleen Elmes have told them. Ford flies mechanically, his thoughts a jumble, trying to figure out what is happening at Pearl Harbor and knowing that the other islands where Pan Am has bases are probably under attack. Like the rest of the crew, he has friends there. His mind races as questions explode in his brain. What was happening to them? Why is this happening? How are they going to get home? And how and why did the Japs do it? Ford turns in his chair and looks at the officer from Naval Intelligence.

"How in hell did this happen? Why are the Japanese attacking us? How come you intelligence types didn't know this was going to happen?" Ford almost shouts at Kathleen Elmes.

She looks at Ford and then the rest of the crew. Her color had begun to return to her face and the accusatory tone in Ford's voice speeds up the coloring. She had no answers but at least she did have the background to try to make some sense out of the senseless. She looked around the flight deck, took a deep breath and began.

"More than any group, you Pan Am people that fly the Pacific know of the continuing tensions between our government and the Empire of Japan. Your planes have been flying laboratories for our military. You know that and so do the Japanese. We have known for the past six months that the Japanese were planning an attack on American bases in the Pacific unless President Roosevelt backed down and gave the Japanese carte blanche in Asia. That would mean the enslavement of all Asia. The President couldn't do that and the Japanese knew it," she began. Before she could continue the background lesson, Ford exploded.

"You mean you knew the Japanese were going to attack us?" Ford asked incredulously, his anger and frustration beginning to target Kathleen Elmes. "Why in hell didn't you tell our people?" Ford spat out.

She held up her hand, palm out, as if asking for peace.

"We did. Only we didn't know where," she began. "We had broken the two most important of the Japanese codes last spring, their diplomatic and High Admiralty codes. But in November, they changed the Admiralty code. Later that month, the Japanese fleet left Tokyo harbor and we haven't been able to find where they went. Until now, unfortunately. It wasn't until 10 days ago that we were able to break their most secret diplomatic codes. A copy of the machine that did this was what I brought to Commander Rochefort at Pearl Harbor the other day. Then I rode with you to Midway, Wake and Guam to alert the commanders there on the different possibilities of what might happen if there wasn't a diplomatic settlement. Unfortunately, we have not been able to break their Admiralty codes. We never guessed that they would attack Pearl Harbor," she quietly summarized.

She looked at the four men and they looked back at her like she was from another planet. Ford had put the Clipper back on autopilot so he could face the Lt. as she tried to explain to them what was happening. But he couldn't seem to grasp it. Codes, diplomatic maneuvers, naval fleets moving and hiding. Finally, John Mack stepped in, sensing the growing conflict brewing between his Captain and the poor Naval Intelligence officer.

"Kathleen, how in hell can a fleet of warship and all their support vessels just disappear? It isn't like a tug boat or even a merchant ship was missing. You're saying a whole fleet vanishes! Carriers, battleships, cruisers, ...I mean, didn't anyone see them, a plane, a merchant ship, anyone?" he asked.

Kathleen was grateful for John Mack giving her a chance to regroup. "But where to begin?" She looked at Ford and thought, "OK, you son-of-a-bitch. I'll tell you what I know but you just fly your goddamn plane and get us to Auckland."

Another deep breath and she continued. "We passed all the information we had to Admiral King who passed it on to the President. Most of the intelligence we had up to the time we lost the Jap fleet indicated that they would attack the British at Hong Kong and then go down the South China Sea to take out Singapore. The Royal Navy still holds the upper hand with the Prince of Wales and Repulse based there. But the British Army is very weak, having been stripped of many men to fight Rommel in North Africa. So to most of us, it looked like the Japs would ignore us and go after the British. After taking them out, Indochina is an easy conquest and when they took Java, they'd have all the oil and rubber they need. They probably thought that with the British gone and controlling almost all of the important parts of Asia, they would then be so strong that we might consider detente," she explained. Somehow the grand design that she and others in Intelligence had formulated back at the War Department seemed very weak and shallow flying at 8,000 feet above the Coral Sea. She looked at the four men and saw that the hostility from Ford had ebbed and so she continued.

"The second place we thought they would attack, were our bases in the Aleutians. We only have a few small installations up there and their fleet could sweep across the Gulf of Alaska and down towards Puget Sound, threatening the West Coast. But they faked us out and hit Pearl Harbor," she sighed.

The four men looked at her trying to understand what she was saying. But they were still too stunned to make sense out of it. Then John Poindexter spoke.

"Captain, I have Mr. Mullahey calling. Shall I put it on the speaker?" he asked. Ford nodded his ascent and Bill Mullahey's voice boomed onto the tense flight deck.

"Bob, we have verification. This morning, at approximately 0730, Sunday, 7 December, 1941, in the States, 8 December here, the Japanese bombed Pearl Harbor. I just got off the phone with Ambassador Welch. It seems that the whole fleet was caught sleeping, literally. Most of the ships along Battleship Row have either been sunk or so badly damaged they'll never sail. We're waiting for you. Good luck and go to Code A. Auckland out," Mullahey ended the transmission.

Ford slowly banked the plane back to its original course. Giving himself a chance to think, his mind raced through his options. First to get to Auckland as fast as possible. Second, inform the crew and the passengers. Looking over his shoulder, he saw that the rest of the crew had come up the stairway while he was lost in thought. The two stewards stayed below, attending to the passengers. Ford looked at them and began.

"You all know the drill. No outgoing transmissions from now on. Mr. Poindexter, keep listening and alert me with anything important. Lt. Elmes, thank you for your help. Mr. Mack, please accompany the Lt. down to the passenger level. I will speak to the passengers on the intercom and tell them what has happened. Gentlemen, the United States is at war with the Empire of Japan. As of thirty minutes ago, so is the Pacific Clipper!"

CHAPTER 2

War

Thursday, 11 December, 1941, Base Operations, Pan Am Terminal, Auckland, New Zealand.

The long tentacles of the Japanese octopus reached everywhere across the Pacific as they brutally conquered lands held by the French, Dutch and the British. The American possessions where Army and Marine units were stationed were bombarded, invaded and began to fall like ripe peaches to the powerful, well trained Japanese armies. The American public, reeling from the treacherous attack on Pearl Harbor began hearing names like Guam and Wake Island and Midway and had no idea that American troops were even stationed there. The Philippines were somewhat better known but not Battan and Corregidor. Geography teachers opened their atlases and maps to parents and students to point out the tiny dots in the middle of all that water where their sons were fighting and dying. It made no sense. There was no reason for it, no reason to bomb Pearl Harbor, to invade these islands and kill American boys. Who were these people and why did they stab us in the back? At the Pan Am headquarters in Auckland, Bob Ford and the crew were asking the same questions. And one other. How in hell were they going to get home?

That they would consider even attempting to return to the States flew in the face of the reality of their situation. They were 25,000 miles from home and their regular route back across the Pacific lay in ruins, blocked by the Imperial Japanese Armed Forces. Wherever Pan Am had a base, the Japanese were bombing it or had already conquered the island. Hong Kong, Shanghai, Singapore were being attacked daily from the air. The Philippines were being invaded and Manila bombed. Guam had fallen and Wake Island and Midway were receiving daily attacks. Pearl Harbor was still burning and most expected the Japanese to invade any moment. As Ford sat looking at the map of the Pacific, he wondered if the Japanese were at war with the United States or Pan American Airways. As Ford mulled over their situation, Bill Mullahey came out of his office and joined his friend. When the others of the Pacific Clipper crew saw the tall Irishman join the Captain, they walked over to get the latest on the war. They had been in Auckland four days now and to a man they hoped that Mullahey had some solid information on what in hell was happening, especially to their fellow shipmates on the other Pan Am planes that were somewhere out in the Pacific when Pearl Harbor was attacked. They knew they were lucky that they were flying towards New Zealand when the Japs struck.

Without preamble, Mullahey began. "It has been four days since Pearl Harbor and I finally have an update on our planes that were out there when the bastards attacked us. First, the Hong Kong Clipper was caught at the dock in Hong Kong, fully fueled and about to take on passengers. Jap planes caught her sitting there and blew her out of the water. The crew escaped and is stuck in Hong Kong. So far, Hong Kong hasn't been invaded so they are safe. The Aztec Clipper was headed into Hawaii when they got word of the attack. They landed in Hilo Bay, refueled and got the hell out of there. Made it back to Frisco, all crew and passengers safe. This next you won't believe. The Philippine Clipper was aloft headed for Wake from Guam when she heard about Pearl but there was no way she could go back. She landed at Wake and refueled just as the first wave of Jap fighters hit. They caught her at the dock and blasted the hell out of her but didn't sink her! Those old Martins are tough bastards and when the first wave of Jap planes were finished, she took off with over 60 bullet holes in her. She reached Midway just as another wave of Jap fighters were blasting the hell out of the Marines there. So she landed on the far side of the island and when night came, snuck around to what was left of our base, refueled and flew to Pearl. She refueled there and is on the way back to Los Angeles. So that makes the score, one Clipper sunk and destroyed, two badly beat up but safe at home and you guys here. Not bad, I'd say, seeing all of you were caught, naked as jaybirds as my sainted Mother would say," Mullahey concluded.

"Bill, have you heard anything about our people at those bases?" the First Officer asked. Mullahey just shook his head. Ford, watching this interplay began to sense that his men were beginning to feel sorry for themselves and worry too much about things that they couldn't control.

"OK. There is nothing more that Bill can tell us and we know he will when he hears something. From now on, we are going to begin to plan our way back home. When word comes from headquarters I'll let you know. Each of you have your assignmentsso lets get busy and take care of them," the Captain spoke. Mullahey, picking up on Ford's move, spoke up.

"Bob, you and I have an appointment with Ambassador Welch at the consulate. He wants to discuss things with you. He's been here two years and hasn't had ten people visit. Now he is so swamped he can't even find time for a drink!" laughed the big Irishman.

Ford grabbed his cap and the two of them walked out the Ops door into the bright sunlight of another beautiful morning in Auckland. They walked over to Mullahey's Ford Model A, in mint condition and climbed in. Mullahey was his best friend in Pan Am and as he looked at him, he smiled to himself and he recalled the stories about Bill Mullahey and Wake Island.

Mullahey had graduated from Columbia University in 1934 and as he told Ford one time on one of their fishing trips, he didn't feel like joining the nine-to-five club, even if he could have found a job in the midst of the Great Depression. So he decided to take Horace Greely's advise and headed West to see the country. Like many others he hitchhiked or hopped rides on freight trains and found odd jobs along the way that fed him and gave him a place to sleep. When he finally hit San Francisco, he had a few bucks in his pocket and thoroughly enjoyed blowing it at the wonderful bars and eateries along Fisherman's Wharf. When his pockets were empty, he decided to get a job and heard that Pan Am was looking for construction people to build hotels and resorts on exotic islands in the South Pacific so Juan Trippe's planes could hopscotch across the great ocean to China, the mysterious and wealthy East. Trippe's people were looking for expert construction people but the place they were hiring was in Hawaii. Mullahey got passage on a tramp steamer, working as a deck hand. When he landed at Pearl Harbor, he spotted the Pan Am terminal and walked over to where he saw a long line of men waiting to be interviewed for jobs. Mullahey followed the others in and after an hour or so, he found himself standing in front of a table where the interviewer sat. The man Mullahey faced took one look at the 6'4" Mullahey and smiled.

"By chance, my tall friend, would you be of Irish decent," the man asked in a brogue so thick that Mullahey had to cock his head towards him to make sure he heard correctly. Smiling broadly and trying not to imitate the man's accent, he assure the interviewer he was. The man smiled and then quite seriously, asked Mullahey if he had any experience in working with dynamite. With total confidence and complete lack of knowledge about the explosive, Mullahey assure his fellow Irishman he did. And, in fact, he was an expert! The man jumped up and yelled to his friends behind the other desks that he had found Pan Am's dynamiter. With that announcement, Bill Mullahey became the official explosive expert for the Wake Island expedition.

One does not receive a degree from Columbia University without a modicum of intelligence and the big Irishman had more than enough to realize that saying he knew all about dynamite and how to use it was one thing and being able to perform on the job was quite another. So the next morning, Mullahey got on the bus at Pearl Harbor and asked for the offices of the Navy's demolition team. When he entered the building where they were located, he found a sailor seated behind a desk and asked for the man in charge. When the sailor, looking at a civilian asked why, Mullahey rose to his full height, looked down on the seaman and announced it involved national security. The seaman, immediately assumed someone so physically impressive had to be from Naval Intelligence, quickly moved from his chair into another office. In a second, he returned and, holding the door open, invited the presumed officer from Naval Intelligence into the office of the head of Naval Ordinance at Pearl Harbor. Mullahey entered and came to a complete stop, his mouth dropping open.

Seated behind the desk was a man so huge that he made Man Mountain Dean look like a pygmy. The name plate on his desk announced that this was Chief Petty Officer John Biggaman and the white sailor uniform he had on was stretched to its limits. Mullahey felt that if the giant man decided to flex his muscles, the buttons would become deadly missiles as they shot off his blouse. Mullahey looked at the man and thought that if this was the United States Navy's best, the country was in deep trouble. But Mullahey kept his thoughts to himself and accepted the offer to sit in the seat the man pointed at. Looking at the big man, Mullahey suddenly knew that behind that gross body was a brain of some consequence and he had better be careful. So, he fell back on the old canard that honesty is the best policy, he plunged ahead.

"Thank you for seeing me, Chief Biggaman. I know your busy but I need some help. I just signed on as the head dynamiter for the Pan Am construction crew that is going to Wake Island. And, to be honest with you, I haven't the foggiest fuckin' idea of anything about dynamite!" Mullahey began.

The big man looked at Mullahey for ten seconds and then smiled. "Needed a job pretty bad to become a dynamiter, right son?" Chief Biggaman responded. "Sorry friend. No offense but what you're asking is indeed quite strange. You want me to teach you in a short time all you need to know to clear that goddamn lagoon there. Yes, I know a lot about where you're going and what's facing you. So take that pencil there and here is a pad of paper. Professor Biggaman is about to give you a crash course on what you need to know to keep your job and your life."

In two hours, the Chief took Mullahey through the do's and don'ts, the whys and hows of the world of high explosive. Mullahey's respect for the Chief grew rapidly and he knew that he probably never had an instructor on the banks of the Hudson as insightful and concise as the big man in front of him. Huge as he was you don't become a Chief Petty Officer in the United States Navy without having brains and talent. Mullahey was sure his superior officers overlooked his physical condition because of his abilities. To Mullahey, Chief Biggaman was Prometheus, Aristotle and Carl Doran rolled into one huge body with a razor sharp brain. When the session was over, Bill Mullahey, recent graduate of a prestigious university had just been subjected to best training course he'd ever taken. His admiration for the Chief was total and as he rose to leave, the Chief passed on one last piece of advise.

"Big man, remember this. Dynamite is more treacherous than a great white shark in bloody waters. Never trust it. Treat dynamite like a woman scorned. If you fear it, you just might live long enough to see those planes land on your lagoon," the Chief concluded as he rose and shook hands warmly with his tutorial student. Mullahey left, on his way to an island he'd never heard of to do a job for which he had never been trained. Until now.

The reason Mullahey and the ship filled with the Pan Am construction crew were headed to Wake Island was that the man who ran Pan Am, Juan Trippe, wanted his airline to dominate the Pacific and to open up the Orient to American travelers. Pan Am could fly from the West Coast of the United States to one of the great natural harbors in the world, Pearl Harbor. But that was the end of it. No plane built in 1934 could fly from Hawaii to China, Trippe's ultimate goal. So he decided to work with the United States Navy and land on their islands in the Pacific, to hopscotch across the vast waters. The Navy fully cooperated. But only after Juan Trippe convinced President Franklin D. Roosevelt that his pilots and engineers would turn over all the engineering and technological knowledge gained from these flights to the

American military establishment. In the 1930s, the country was still totally mired in the Great Depression. The President faced a public and Congress that wanted nothing to do with the fighting going on in the Far East between Japan and China. And they certainly would never authorize any appropriations to modernize the American forces no matter how many dictators there were strutting across the face of Europe.

But the President, his military leaders and the most sober analysts of what was happening around the world knew only too well that another war was on the horizon and that it could involve the United States. So in quiet exchange for their assistance in helping Pan Am get exclusive rights to build facilities on American islands in the Pacific, Pan Am promised to become flying laboratories for the Navy and Army Air Corps. President Roosevelt, a Harvard man, told friends that his dealing with Trippe taught him that the Pan Am chairman was the "nicest gangster that Yale had ever graduated!"

But the Roosevelt Administration didn't promise to build bases for Pan Am. They had to do that themselves and when Juan Trippe looked at the huge globe in his offices atop the Chrysler Building in New York, he saw that he could get from Pearl Harbor to Midway Island but the next step was a hell of one. It was to Guam, 4,000 miles away from Midway.

The United States Maritime services assured Trippe that there was nothing between Midway and Guam. His own staff came to the same conclusion but Trippe wouldn't believe what he saw on the globe or what he was told by the United States Navy. They were on orders to help but even FDR couldn't order an island to pop out of the bowels of the Pacific so that Trippe and Pan Am could get to China. Of course, there were other islands but they were owned by the Japanese, who considered the Pacific Ocean the "Emperor's Lake" or other nations like England, France and the Netherlands. They were not about to cede landing rights on their islands to Trippe. They had their own plans for the lucrative Asian market. The other islands didn't have the natural harbors that could accommodate an amphibian plane.

Juan Trippe started Pan Am on a shoe string, in the early 20's, contract flying for the United State Post Office in an old trimotor German Fokker, taking the mail from Miami to Havana, Cuba and back. Through his guts and daring, by 1934, Pan American Airlines had become the unofficial airlines of the United States, flying the mail in Sikorsky 34's to Latin and South America, the American flag painted brightly on the fuselage of the plane, the Pan Am logo smaller but above the flag. But Trippe had to get out of the mail business to make money. He needed paying passengers. To grow, Trippe had to open up the Pacific and the Atlantic. He needed bigger, long range planes to carry more passengers but most importantly, he had to have places for his planes to land.

Trippe refused to believe that in all of the Pacific between Midway and Guam, there wasn't one island he could use. Then one day, on his way to his offices, he walked past the New York Public Library on Fifth Avenue and 42nd Street. He walked up the steps and past the granite lions guarding the entrance, thinking that if there were an island between Guam and Midway, this great library would know. He was right. They did.

He told them of his problem and asked for their help. An intrepid librarian took Trippe's problem personally, feeling the honor of the New York Public Library system was being challenged. Deep in the basement of the library, the librarian discovered some old maps that were relics of the days when the great four masted clipper ships sailed the Pacific. In the log of an American whaling ship, there was an entry that indicated that the ship had sailed past a small island about 18 degrees north by 120 degrees east, some 2000 miles from Hawaii. The log told the story that the captain put some men in a long boat to explore the island to see if there was fresh water and hopefully, fruits or vegetables. The crew returned in an hour saying the waters were so rough that they couldn't land. A year later, when the whaler came home to Plymouth, the log was entered into the company's records. However, there was no name for the island discovered so the company just named the island after the captain of the whaler, Frederick Wake.

Wake Island. When Trippe heard the news he was ectatic. He quickly called the Navy Department and asked if they had any ships sailing in that area and if, as a favor, check it out. The report came back a few weeks later. Yes, the island was there but it was worthless. The crashing waves on the coral reefs that surrounded the island made it almost impossible to enter the mouth of the lagoon. The island was about a mile in diameter with 80 percent of it taken up by a lagoon. The highest point on the island rose only 12 feet above sea level and a few palm trees lent what little shade to whomever would be crazy enough to live on that god forsaken piece of coral. When the report was received, one was routinely sent to the Navy Department and the other to Trippe at Pan Am Headquarters. The Navy Department immediately ordered the building of a Marine installation on Wake Island!

Trippe's needs were different from the military. Marines could put up tents and metal huts for the men. Pan Am had to have a luxury hotel for the passengers. But before they could bring any passengers to Wake Island, there had to be a place for the Clippers to land. They couldn't land outside the island and have boats bring the passengers to the island. The waves and currents would destroy any plane docked outside the lagoon and swamp any boats trying to enter the lagoon through the treacherous mouth. So to make Wake Island the key stepping stone to China, the planes had to be able to land in the lagoon. On the map, that looked easy. The lagoon was deep and long enough for the Clippers to land on. But when the survey team, brought in by the Navy, finally got to the lagoon, they found it impossible for Pan Am's needs. For beneath the placid surface of the lagoon, were thousands of coral pillars, geologically known as stalagmites, that would rip the belly of any amphibian plane landing on the lagoon. Forget Wake Island, they said.

Not Juan Trippe. There had to be a solution and Bill Mullahey, although he didn't know it, was it. Trippe's engineers told him that all that had to be done was blow the coral pillars up and clear a runway beneath the water so the planes could land safely. An easy chore for the Marines.

The Navy instructed the Commanding Officer of the Marine detachment on Wake to put some demolition experts on the job as a favor to Pan Am. The Marines were use to blowing up bridges and pill boxes and other military objectives. But these men had never worked under water before and knew nothing of the kinetics of underwater explosions. They planted the dynamite in the sand next to the coral growths, ran the wires up to the shore and attached them to the detonator. One marine raised the red handle, looked around at the others watching and shoved it down.

A giant explosion shook the sand and geysers of water shot high into the sky. The marines watching suddenly began to duck as dead fish fell from the sky, blown into the air by the explosion! When the water settled, the marines rowed out into the lagoon to see what their efforts had netted against the coral. Nothing. Not one single coral pillar was down. United States Marines are not easily discouraged so they tried the same techniques again. And again. The cook came running down to the lagoon's shoreline with a huge bathtub-like container and began gathering the fish! The men would eat fresh fish that night but the coral pillars were untouched.

The next day, the Marines came up with a simple solution. The charges had to be put inside the coral growths, near their base, a few feet above the sandy bottom, then detonated. That meant that a diver would swim down, stuff the explosives inside the coral, run the wires up from the growth to a detonator above, swim away and wait while the coral was blown up. The Marines estimated that about 1000 coral stalagmites had to be destroyed! The commanding officer demurred on committing his men to a civilian task of such magnitude. The Navy Department, concurred, reluctantly.

Enter Bill Mullahey. When the construction crew arrived, the survey team informed him of his task. Mullahey thought of Heracles and his 12 Labors, especially the cleaning of the stables of Augeas, king of Elis which hadn't been scoured in 30 years! Well, at least Mullahey had more than the one day Heracles did. Mullahey had been a 400 meter swimmer at Columbia but he never dreamed when he got his degree that he'd be making hundreds of dives to the bottom of a lagoon half way around the world for Juan Trippe.

Mullahey's equipment consisted of a bathing suit, a pair of canvas gym shoes, a canvas bag to carry the dynamite sticks plus a pair of diving glasses, picked up by him in a Honolulu gift shop. They were the kind used by Japanese pearl divers! The coral pillars that Mullahey would attack rose about 12 feet from the bottom, with a base of about four feet on the bigger ones. At its deepest point, the lagoon was 40 feet deep. The sandy base rose slowly away to a point where the tips of some stalagmites were just four to five feet below the surface. A Clipper ship, when landing could dip as much as twenty feet deep into the water before rising to eight to ten feet before taxing to the dock. Ignoring the coral pillars that were forty feet down, Mullahey and the Pan Am engineers figured that starting where the growths were twenty feet from the surface, Mullahey had to cut a swath through the coral pillars, about four football fields in length and width! Then there had the be another path cut to the landing dock.

Mullahey's partner on the daily excursion out onto the lagoon under a merciless equatorial South Pacific sun was John Flynn, an Irishman from Chicago who had escaped the cold and winds of that lake front city riding the rails to the West Coast and working on aboard a trap steamer to Honolulu. Broke, he joined Trippe's Wake Island band to keep body and soul together. He could handle a rowboat and was quickly trained in the art of dynamite detonations and assigned as Mullahey's assistant. And each day, he'd row Mullahey out to their area for work and they could easily see, because the waters were so clear, where they left off the day before. The big man would put on the goggles, throw the knapsack over his shoulders, sit on the edge of the dinghy, take a deep breath and roll into the water. Using the weight of the dynamite sack to help the decent, he'd quickly plant the sticks inside any hole in the coral near the bottom, cap the dynamite, then bring the wire back up to the surface. He'd hand them to Flynn, who would attach them to the detonator. Then Mullahey would climb in, Flynn would row them away and when far enough, twist the cap, firing the dynamite, destroying the coral pillar. It was efficient but it was very time consuming. Mullahey and the Pan Am construction team had a three month time limit to get Wake Island ready for the first survey flight from Midway Island. At the pace Mullahey and Flynn were moving, it would be three years before Wake was ready! There had to be a better way.

Mullahey felt that if he could wire four or five coral pillars at once and blow them together, it would speed up the number of demolitions. They tested their theory the next day. Mullahey dove and as fast as he could, placed the dynamite under a cluster of five pillars. His lungs almost bursting, he grabbed the wires from the five charges, kicked hard towards the surface and breaking the water, handed the wires to Flynn, climbed aboard and the two rowed away. Flynn twisted the detonator charge and the explosion almost drowned them. The force of the blast capsized the dinghy, flipping the two into the water. Mullahey quickly swam to the surface and treading water, looked around for the dinghy, and spotting it still afloat about twenty yards away, he began swimming towards it.

No one knew that Flynn couldn't swim. As Mullahey moved towards the boat, the Chicagoan's head broke the surface and his arms started flailing away. A few Marines on the surface saw that he was in trouble. They started racing along the shores of the lagoon, yelling and trying to get Mullahey's attention and knew it was useless. They were too far away but they kept running, yelling and hoping.

Later, Mullahey would not be able to explain what made him look back. It was just something he felt. He turned and could not see Flynn. Suddenly, he realized his partner was drowning. Turning, he kicked his swimmer's body into a swift churning of the water that left a frothy wake as he raced to where he thought Flynn might be. He saw his partner's hand and wrist above the water and then they disappeared. Mullahey body leaped across the water and diving under the water, he saw his friend's body sinking. In a second, he grabbed Flynn's waist and dragged him up and into the air. With his left arm holding his face above water, Mullahey, with one arm began to swim slowly to the shore, making sure no more water was swallowed by his friend. In a few seconds, the Marines arrived and help bring the two of them out of the water. Mullahey was too spent to give mouth to mouth recusation but one of the Marines did and after a frightening few seconds, Flynn began to cough, rolled his head and opened his eyes. Laying in the sand, the two men looked at each other and Mullahey began to shake his head. Flynn smiled, weakly and rolled his eyes, telling Mullahey they were going back to the old way!

But within three months, Mullahey and Flynn had cleared 80 % of the landing area. Two months later, regularly scheduled flights began into Wake Island. Bill Mullahey, John Flynn and the rest of the Pan Am crew who built the terminal, the hotel and the landing area were gone. But the people of Pan Am heard the story of the lagoon at Wake Island and to this day, it is known as "Bill Mullahey's pond,"

Ford, looking at Mullahey as they drove down Auckland's main thoroughfare towards the American Embassy passed on his thoughts about the war. "Bill, if I didn't know better, I'd be bound to think that the Japanese were at war with us, with Pan Am. Think about it. Pearl Harbor bombed. Guam gone. Wake Island and Midway under constant bombing. Plus Hong Kong, Singapore, Shanghai and Manila all under some form of attack. If we had a base up in the Aleutians they'd probably be shelling that too!"

Mullahey didn't respond, knowing his friend was just making conversation, letting off a little of the frustration he felt. Mullahey pulled up to the wrought iron gates of the American Embassy, where two Marines in khaki shirts, blue ties, blue pants with the red stripe down the side stood guard. Their garrison caps were also in blue with the bronze globe emblem in front. Recognizing Mullahey they saluted smartly and waved the two Americans into the Embassy parking lot. In a few minutes, they were inside the building and it was exactly as Mullahey had described, utter chaos.

There were people everywhere, assembled in front of different desks and the noise was ear-shattering as people shouted questions at the clerks. Down the hallway the two walked until they spotted another bracket of Marines, standing on either side of a wide double door. To the left on a stanchion was the American flag and on the other side, the banner of New Zealand. This was the office of the American Ambassador to New Zealand. To the left of the door in front of the American flag, a matronly woman sat behind a desk. Spotting Mullahey, she rose,

rose, smiling broadly as Mullahey picked her up in his arms and gave her a big hug.

"May, you look wonderful. Meet my friend, Robert Ford, Captain of our Pacific Clipper. Bob, this is May Evans, Ambassador Welch's major domo. Without May, the American Embassy would cease operations," Mullahey stated.

"Bill Mullahey, you have the Irish gift of blarney. And Captain Ford, don't pay attention to him; he's told me all about you and I didn't believe a thing he said," she said, giving her hand to Ford.

"May, thank you for such discernment. I know the big Irishman has a way of expanding on the truth. I'm pleased to meet you," Ford expressed.

May Evans walked back behind her desk and quickly became the secretary of the Ambassador of the United States to the Commonwealth of New Zealand. "Gentlemen, the Ambassador is busy but is expecting you. Please do not be shocked about the mob scene inside. Everyone is trying to find out from him what is happening across the world and we have no more information than they do," Smiling, she nodded to the Marines who opened the door for the two Pan Am people.

Mullahey and Ford entered the main reception room of the Embassy and stopped. People were shouting at a husky man sitting behind a desk covered with papers and maps. And each person seemed to think that if he or she yelled loud enough, the man would recognize them. And the object of their bellowing sat calmly with his hands on the desk, fingers slowly tapping as he waited for the din to subside. Slowly the cacophony began to lessen as the others began to realize that yelling was useless. When reasonable quite was restored, the man rose and addressed the audience.

"Ladies and Gentlemen," Ambassador Welch began softly, so that if they wanted to hear him, they had to stifle themselves. And they did. "I appreciate why you are here. And we will do everything to answer your questions. In a few minutes, our press secretary, Mr. Goodyear will hold a conference in the amphitheater where all of you will be brought up to date with the latest information we have. Now if you all would please follow Mr. Murray, Mr. Goodyear's assistant into the amphitheater, you'll know everything we do. Thank you."

As the crowd followed the press secretary's assistant into the amphitheater, the Ambassador remained standing. Ford got a good look at the Honorable Walter R. Welch. A large man, not tall but well built with broad shoulders and a little bit of a belly. And that didn't surprise Ford, knowing a little something about the life of an Ambassador since wherever he brought his Clipper ship, he always had at least one dinner with the American Ambassador stationed there. Welch's hair had more than a little grey but that figured with what was going on across the globe. Ford liked him. He seemed as Mullahey had described him, a "meet-the-people" ambassador. Now with the Japanese headed towards Australia and New Zealand, he had one hell of a lot more to worry about than meeting the people!

The Ambassador spotted the two Americans standing in the rear of the room. He rose and motioned them to come over and as they did, he walked around the desk to greet them, shaking hands with Mullahey first and then Ford.

"Bill, good to see you and this must be Captain Ford," he stated as he looked at the two men. "Sorry Captain Ford that we meet here rather than at the party we had planned the other night for you and your crew. What say we do it after all this is over?" the Ambassador offered. Both Ford and Mullahey laughed, knowing it wouldn't happen.

"Thank you Sir. Bill told me of your plans and on behalf of the crew, I thank you. Maybe next time we fly into Auckland, we can do it then," Ford responded.

"Delighted you think there will be a next time, Bob," the Ambassador stated, leading the two across the room towards a wall that had a magnificent map of the world hanging in a beautiful mahogany frame. The map was, in cartographic terms, a polar projection map, where the planet is viewed as if you were standing atop the North Pole and looking at the Earth as it spread out from you in circles. 12 feet tall and eight feet wide, it hung rectangularly from near the ceiling to a few feet from the floor. Looking at the map, the three men saw that the continent of Australia was at the top of the map and at the bottom, South America. And they could all see that all that separated New Zealand from the United States was water, the waters of the Pacific Ocean. Small dots with names next to them were sprinkled here and there so that it seemed to the untrained eye that one could almost hop scotch from one island to another all the way across the Pacific to the States. It just seemed that way.

"No way, my friend," Bill Mullahey said, reading Ford's mind. "It is over 6000 miles from here to Hawaii. Even with her great range, the Clipper can't do that distance. And there is one other little matter. The Imperial Japanese Navy,"

Ford looked at the map. "You're right, Bill. I can put the Clipper on any body of water in the world, but unless I can beg, borrow or steal aviation gas, so what! And we don't know where the Japs are headed!" Ford said in a voice of measured frustration filled with anger.

"Yes, we do," a voice from behind them declared. Both men spun and there, in her Navy uniform stood Kathleen Elmes. She smiled at the two of them and laughing, moved towards them.

"After we landed the other day, I explained to Mr. Mack that I should report to the Embassy so they could advise my Headquarters of where I was. Since you were busy securing the Clipper, I figured I'd get out of your way and come here. The Ambassador was kind enough to invite me to stay here until things settled down. The other morning he asked me to see if I could help in the code and message center. So I have. You didn't miss me, Captain Ford?" she asked, a wry smile on her face, knowing very well that Ford hadn't the slightest idea where she had gone or even thought about her! And Ford's rueful look showed her how right she was.

"Sorry, Lt. Elmes. John Mack did tell me that you had come here and I'm glad the Ambassador has taken good care of you." Ford said. "But you said you know where the Japs are headed?"

Kathleen was livid. "You cold fish," she thought. "You didn't even care enough to even realize I'd left the group at Base Ops or wonder where I was! You bastard! Some day, I'll get you for this!" But her anger was brief. She had more important things to do that worry about why Ford didn't miss her.

"Yes, Captain Ford," she began, very coldly. "Our guess that they would come down the South China Sea from Manchuria was accurate. Right now, land and carrier based planes are bombing all the major Chinese cities along the coast, from Nanking to Hong Kong and even Singapore. But their Naval forces have not yet come as far down as Singapore. So that is one bright light in a very dark picture. A major Japanese force is attacking the Philippines and the invasion there has begun. Guam has fallen and Wake Island is under attack. Another task force is headed for New Guinea and their land based bombers, the two engine Mitsubishis from Bougainvilleand Guadalcanal are bombing Port Morsby. If they take New Guinea, they could be here in a few weeks. To make matter worse many natives across Malasia are burning and looting towns, villages, plantations and destroying crops. The Japanese Fifth Columnists have done a great job sewing the seeds of revolution."

"Kathleen," Bill Mullahey broke in. "What did you mean, with the exception of Singapore, when talking about what was happening in the South China Sea."

"Bill, the British have two battleships at Singapore, the Prince of Wales and the Repulse," Kathleen responded, walking over and pointing to Singapore on the big map hanging from the wall. "The Japs have nothing that can match those two monsters. So it is unlikely they will try to land at Singapore until they can neutralize the British Navy there. Lets hope they can't because if they do, the rest of Southeast Asia will fall like a ripe apple to the Empire of Japan."

"Kathleen, thank you for the update. And since it is almost noontime I think I'll have a little bourbon and branch water. Anyone wish to join me?" the Ambassador finished and leaned over to give Lt. Elmes a fatherly kiss on the cheek. As he walked away for his morning drink, the other three turned and looked at the map.

"Any word from your headquarters in New York, Captain Ford?" Kathleen asked and this time Ford paid attention to her. What she had told them about what was happening across the Pacific brought home the harsh reality of what they were up against. Sitting in Base Ops talking to the crew and Mullahey and the other Pan Am people had briefly insulated him from the actuality of his situation. If her intelligence was right, and he knew it was, in a matter of days, maybe even hours, he'd be trapped in Auckland.

"No, not yet," Ford sighed in response to Lt. Elmes's question. Mullahey, who considered Ford indefatigable, was shocked at the despair in Ford's voice. He turned and was about to say something to cheer up his friend when Ford suddenly turned to both of them, this time with fire in his eyes.

"Goddamit! I don't give a shit what Intelligence says. I'm not going to sit on my ass here and let those slant-eyed bastards dictate to me where I can go. There has to be a way home and I'll find it. They are not... I repeat, not going to keep me here and get my plane. I'm going home. Now. I mean now," he finished and to his undying embarrassment, those still in the Ambassador's office began to clap and cheer. "Go get'em, Yank" and "Way to go, Capt'n" and "We're with you, Mac," were a few of the comments Ford heard from the others and as he blushed slightly, Kathleen Elmes and Bill Mullahey smiled and began to applaud. Suddenly, the gloom of the previous minutes was over and whatever tensions and dislikes there were between the Navy's Intelligence officer and the Captain of the Pacific Clipper were gone. And big Bill Mullahey knew he was losing a friend to a very beautiful woman who was every bit Ford's match. And although he knew it, he wondered when and where Ford would discover the same.

CHAPTER 3

Going Home

Monday, 16 December, 1941, 0845 hours Pan Am Base Ops., Auckland, NZ

A week had passed since Pearl Harbor. There were no flights in or out of Pan American Airways station this day and there probably wouldn't be for months or maybe years. But the Operations center was crowded with Pan Am employees just sitting around having coffee and Danish, discussing the war. All they knew was what little their home radios told them but here, at least they had the chance to hear directly from other Pan Am bases and especially New York. But thus far, they had all been disappointed. New York hadn't said diddly. Bob Ford and his crew were part of the scene, doing the same, sitting around, waiting. Suddenly, Bob Ford rose and strode over to Mr. Mullahey's office and walked through his door.

"Bill, I'm going home. The Clipper is ready and we're going to try it," Ford calmly stated.

"Bob, I know how you feel but you can't make it. Every base we have in the Pacific is either destroyed or under fire. So forget it. There are no other places where there are people that can service the Clipper or where you can get aviation fuel. You're screwed," the head of Pan Am operations replied.

"Bill, logically you're right. But something woke me early this morning, something I saw on that big map at the Ambassador's office. I think I know a way home," Ford stated.

"Bob, I was looking at the same map and all I saw were Pan Am bases being overrun by Japanese forces. What did you see that I didn't," Mullahey asked as he rose and followed Ford out of his office as the Captain of the Pacific Clipper walked back to where his crew sat. With Mullahey standing by, Ford looked at his crew and began.

"Look. I think I know of a way to get home. But what I plan is very dangerous, almost crazy. Because of what is involved, I want each to decide for yourself. I can't order you and I sure as hell can't fly the Clipper by myself. So talk it over and let me know who wants to try," Ford concluded. He paused and waited for the men to disperse and talk it over. No one moved. No one said anything. They just looked at him. Finally, John Mack spoke.

"What are your orders, Captain Ford?" the First Office asked.

Ford didn't say anything, just kind of ducked his head to the side, looked at Mullahey and a brief smile crossed his lips.

"Thank you. Now, here is a map of the world," Ford began. "I want all of you to look at it, including you Mr. Brown and tell me which route you would fly," The Mr. Brown he referred to had joined the Clipper in Honolulu, replacing the Boeing Tech Rep that had flown with them from Seattle to Hawaii. The Boeing man had kept pretty much to himself, spending most of his time with the engineers, Swede Rothe and John Parish. That was natural and none of the other members of the crew thought anything about it. Ford hadn't paid much attention to the new Brown except to ask Norm Brown about him one afternoon as they were sitting around the Ops room. The Second Officer kept all the records on each member of the crew as well as the Boeing Tech Rep.

"Nice guy. Keeps to himself. Graduate of Cornell... BE in Mechanical Engineering... was a Saturday Hero like some others on this flight," That got a laugh from some of the crew sitting near by, knowing Ford and Mack had played college football. "Came to Boeing last year... from Boston, has family in the Navy. That's it," Norm Brown finished up. "What's his first name?" John Mack asked.

"Giles," Mr. Brown had answered.

The crew fell to looking over the map and soon the room was filled with different reasons for one route or another but as each man had his say, the others shot him down. The two engineers' opinions carried the most weight but even they could not come up with a route that everyone felt safe flying, knowing that the skies across the Pacific were controlled by the Japanese. Soon, very soon, it became apparent to all of them the route Captain Ford had decided on and suddenly, they wished they had a chance for a two out of three vote about leaving New Zealand.

While the men were going over the map, Ford went back into Mullahey's office and came back wheeling a large blackboard. The others had returned to their seats and sat quietly as Ford brought the blackboard to their table. He picked up the map off the table and with the help of a couple of small pins, nailed it to the wooden frame of the blackboard.

"You've figured it out," he stated and the groans from the crew indicated they had! Ford's snort was his response, saying in essence that "you're right, it is crazy."

"Ok. So now you know. This is our route home," And turning to the map, he began pointing to the places he planned to try to reach. "As of now, we'll await word from New York before we take off but if we don't hear today, we'll head for Darwin tomorrow. There is a small Pan Am station there and they should have 100 octane. That is the easy part, unless the Japs surprise us there. And if they do, then we'll not have to worry about the rest of the trip, will we?' Ford began. "After Darwin, we'll be going where very few people have ever seen an amphibian airplane, and at some places, an airplane itself. You all know the problems we'll face so I won't bother to dwell on them. The biggest will be gas. While I hope we can top off the tanks with high octane in Darwin, there is no guarantee they have any. If not, Swede, those engines of yours are going to take a beating because we'll be using automobile fuel, if we can get that! You all know we can't break radio silence, from the moment we leave Auckland till we land in New York. And since we can't break radio silence, we'll have to very lucky all the way to not get shot down by some over eager defender at any one of these places where I plan to fly.

"And Captain, after Darwin, where?" asked John Steers.

Ford looked at the map and put his finer on a spot just above Darwin. All the crew were too experienced to think the dot was as close to Darwin as it seemed. The dot had to be 1,000 miles away and when Ford told them its name, they had trouble pronouncing it.

"Give that to us again, Captain?" Steers asked.

"Surabaja. It is a major city in Java and I'm told there is a Dutch Air Corps detachment there, as well as the biggest oil refineries in Asia,. So we should be able to get 100 octane for the Clipper in Surabaja." Ford answered.

"How do you pronounce and spell that, Skipper?" Steers asked.

"Su ra ba ha. Surabaja." Ford explained. "Why?"

"Captain, I'm responsible for the log of this flight and we are going to places no one ever heard of. So if we ever make it home, I want whomever reads the log to be able to pronounce the name," Steers responded. "And if we don't make it, well..."

Ford looks at Steers, pauses and then shakes his head.

"Ok. The British still control the Singapore area and as long as that holds, we should be able to get to Darwin, then to Surabaja, refuel and get the hell out of there. It doesn't take a General MacArthur to see where the Japs are headed and that is the Dutch East Indies and all that oil and rubber on Java," as Ford explained his haste.

"And from there, from Surabaja, Captain?" John Mack asked.

Ford looked at him and the map and pointed to Ceylon. The men whistled and Mack came over and put his thumb on Surabaja and his middle finger on Ceylon.

"Make it 3,000 miles, Captain," Mack said casually.

"Closer to 3,500, John. Any one else have a comment," Ford asked.

He waited as the crew looked at him and waited. They all knew another would speak. And finally, Second Officer Roderick Norman Brown rose to voice his opinion. None that had flown with Norm Brown before were surprised. Ford would have thought Number Two was ill if he hadn't spoken. He was an excellent officer and fulfilled his duties admirably. Of all the men that Ford had flown with in Pan Am, Norm Brown was probably the most knowledgeable about the laws and customs of the lands where they landed. He could tell Ford the background of a Viscount, how to greet a Maharajah and which fork to use at the garden party given by a Chinese mandarin. He was a very valuable member of Ford's crew. And Roderick Norman Brown was also a giant pain in the ass. He would not have been Norm Brown without raising an objection to Bob Ford's plan.

"Mr. Brown?" Ford asked, yielding the floor.

"Captain, I'd like to express my objections to leaving Auckland now. As you have pointed out, our regular routes home are probably cut off. But we have not received any definite instructions from Headquarters and until we do, I suggest we stay here, in relative safety. The Pacific Clipper is the most technological advanced plane flying in the world today. It is far too valuable to risk just to try to get home. Maybe President Roosevelt and Emperor Hirohito are talking now to see if things can be solved. I don't know. But waiting seems far more sensible than flying off to places where there are no services for our plane and probably no high octane gasoline for the Wrights. I say lets wait till we hear from New York. As long as the British Navy at Singapore can stop the Japanese from dominating the South China Sea, we are safe here," Roderick Norman Brown stated. "But whatever you decide, Captain Ford, I am with you."

"Thank you Norm. I appreciate your view of the situation. I wish I could share your feelings that things can be settled by diplomacy but I'm not that optimistic. And I have to think that New York has more to worry about than us. So, as far as I'm concerned, we are on are own. Anybody else have a comment?" Ford stated. There were none. Then he looked at the group.

"OK. I know that each day here all of you have checked and double checked all that you can about the Clipper. But I ask you to do it again, if for no other reason that to keep busy. If we have to move quickly, I don't want to hear from any of you that you forgot something!" Ford finished as the rest laughed.

"But one final thought before Bill and I return to the Embassy. Think of where we are going. Look at the map. Remember, at no time can we break radio silence the whole way home We have no maps, no charts, no information about winds and tides where we are headed and landing. Look at the impossible happening and prepare for it. You are the best Pan Am has otherwise you wouldn't have been put on the Pacific Clipper. Because of that, we can make it home. Any questions?" Ford finished. Silence.

"Thank you," Ford responded.

The plane that would carry Ford and the crew to their fate, sat inside a giant hanger just off the Operations room. First Engineering Officer Homans Rothe his assistant, John Parish had again completed their pre flight check of the giant bird. She was as ready as they could make her. When the time came for the real thing, leaving Auckland, the two of them would do it again, this time with Captain Ford leading the inspection. When they finished, the plane would be wheeled outside and 5000 pounds of 100 octane fuel would be poured into her tanks and the Pacific Clipper would be ready to take them home.

Now she sat in splendid isolation, alone in the big building but her very size made the hanger seem almost too small to contain her. When the hanger was empty, the support personnel could play softball inside her, which they did on rainy days. With the Clipper inside, her wingtips almost touched the red brick side walls of the building. From port to starboard, the monowing stretched 152 feet. Housed in the wing were four massive 16 cylinder Wright engines, each delivering 1600 horses of thrust. The propellers, when rotating, cut a 15 foot swath through the air. These were the most powerful engines in all of aviation and gave the Clipper her immense range of over 5000 miles. From bow to stern, the Boeing 314A fuselage measured 106 feet and the distinctive tri-rudder rear wing rose 28 feet from the hanger floor.

Her hull measured 13 feet across and with the stabilizing sponsons on each side, the Clipper measured 40 feet across at the waterline. She was a triple decked plane, with the lower level used for storage of cargo, luggage and parts, the middle level for the passengers and the top deck, or flight deck, reserved for the pilot and flight officers. Looking at the huge plane sitting idle with the morning sunlight streaming through the four skylights, her silver body reflecting the rays around the room, illuminating the walls, ceiling and floor with an eerie glow, the Pacific Clipper looked like an ugly duckling. But when she was in her element, on water, and began her run down a watery runway towards her takeoff, there was no more beautiful sight in all of aviation.

The Pacific Clipper was the Queen Mary of the airways, the most luxurious plane flying. Pan Am had spared nothing to make her the beau ideal of airplanes. Her galley served gourmet meals that connoisseurs claimed rival the best restaurants in New York, Paris or New Orleans. Spread throughout the passenger cabin were seven compartments, each seating ten people, six on the starboard side and four on the port. At the rear of the plane was the Master Suite, reserved for movie stars, captains of industry or people like General Douglas MacArthur. The dining salon could serve as an extra compartment when the plane was filled, as they always were. The Clippers usually carried 40 passengers during their daylight flights and when flying at night, the compartments broke down into Pullman type berths and could accommodate 34 passengers. Getting a ticket for a transcontinental flight aboard a Pan Am Clipper ship was tougher than opening night at the Met.

Transoceanic flight had always been a dream of Juan Trippe and back in the late 20's, flying his World War I German Fokker trimotor, Trippe's dream seemed the stuff of Buck Rogers and Flash Gordon. But he had one very major ally in his quest for American domination of the commercial airways. The most famous man in the world, Charles Lindbergh, preached the message that America had to lead the way in developing a successful commercial aviation industry, that the aircraft was the future of transportation and in case of international conflict, the country that had domination in air power would control the world. Lindbergh joined Trippe at Pan Am as a consultant and together, in a little more than a decade, Pan Am became the most successful commercial airline company in the world. With the American flag painted on her fuselage and under her sponsons, flying across the oceans of the world, Pan Am became the "unofficial airline of the United States."

When Pan Am began regular mail flights into the Pacific, the Japanese government lodged an official protest, claiming that they had "special" rights in the Pacific Ocean. As Pan Am bought newer planes, first from the Sikorsky Corporation then later from the Glenn Martin Company, those planes expanded the range of Pan Am flights and each time they flew into a new location, the Japanese were almost pathological in their attacks on Pan Am through diplomatic channels. In 1939, when Pan Am unveiled the Boeing 314s, the Empire of Japan labeled Trippe " a gangster and threatening the peace of the Pacific," They demanded that the American Government force Pan Am to stop flying into Hong Kong, Manila, Singapore and other Far Eastern ports. Of course, the State Department explained that Pan Am was a private company and free to do business any where in the world. The Japanese knew that and they also knew that the Pan Am planes were flying research labs for the American military forces. A diplomatic attache at the Japanese Embassy had infiltrated the highest sources of American military intelligence and knew of Pan Am's work. The man who filed those secret reports was Commodore Isodecki Tanaka of the Imperial Japanese Navy.

The American Intelligence community knew of Tanaka's activities but because of diplomatic immunity and in the hope of keeping peace between their two countries, the American's did nothing to push the capture of the nephew of the former Prime Minister of Japan and the son of Count Tanaka, closest advisor to Emperor Hirohito. But in the summer of 1941, as the threat of war with Japan deepened, Military Intelligence and the FBI brought their reports to the State Department, who took it very seriously but did nothing, feeling the arrest of such a prestigious member of the Japanese entourage would only acerbate an already dangerous situation.

But it was the Japanese themselves that took the American State Department off the hook. Commodore Tanaka had submitted a very audacious plan that whetted the interest of the Prime Minister of Japan, General Hideki Tojo. Their own intelligence alerted them that the Americans were well aware of Tanaka's activities and only the American's desire not to rock the diplomatic boat kept them from throwing Tanaka out of the country. So the Prime Minister simply ordered the attache home, to protect him from the embarrassment of being caught and expelled. But more importantly, to have him explain in detail the plan that so captivated him.

Ford knew nothing about a man named Tanaka or his plan. He climbed into Mullahey's Ford, his thoughts on the upcoming trip. He wanted to wait for instructions from Pan Am headquarters but as each day passed, he became more nervous. The decision to try for home was easy, the choice of the route was forced on him but the decision of when to try for it was becoming more and more difficult to figure. He needed more information about where the Japs were, especially in the South China Sea. Mullahey driving, kept his own council. He wanted Ford to stay but understood his friend wanting to try for home. Mullahey was tempted to join them but he had adopted New Zealand as his new home and was happy here. Then a brainstorm hit him. He looked at Ford; knowing his feeling about the subject, he knew he had to tread carefully or Ford would reject it out of hand.

"Bob," he began. "You know you're flying blind into places where none of you have ever been and where the people that live there have never seen a flying boat. After Darwin, most the people where you'll be landing don't speak English. Not that the Aussies do. But that aside, you're biggest problem is the Japanese, Bob. You have to know where they are and what they are doing. So why not have someone on board that speaks their language, can decipher their codes and looks like Madeline Carroll?"

Ford looked at his best friend and was about to react negatively when his Midwestern pragmatism took over. "Bill, you're right. Lt. Elmes speaks Japanese and we could rig up a radio where she could listen in on their transmissions and tell us where they are and she probably decode some of their messages. That is a great idea. But do you think she'll come? I've been pretty rough on her."

The object of their discussion was busy in the message room on the second floor of the American Embassy. Kathleen had become invaluable to the Ambassador and his staff. With the approval of the Communications Officer, she had reorganized the staff into two departments, most of the people working on the diplomatic codes but the best ones working with her on military transmissions. The preponderance of the incoming traffic was military.

Any transmissions from military sources were brought to her for decoding and then taken to the Ambassador's staff for their intelligence. And there was quite a bit coming in from Wake Island, Hong Kong, the Philippines, French Indo-China, New Guinea and Midway. The messages were grim. The Allies pleading for help, for troops, planes, anything that would give them a fighting chance. But from the Japanese, it was almost always "Banzi!" She was beginning to cringe every time she had to translate that word. As she read the overwhelming evidence of the totality of the Japanese conquest of the Pacific,

Kathleen Elmes began to lose faith and wonder if there was force in the world that could stop this juggernaut!

She rose from her desk and walked over to a window that looked out upon a lovely garden. A few people were sitting on benches along the walk path, reading. But her eyes didn't focus on them. Rather her mind brought back the color of yellow, the color on the Ambassador's map for the Japanese Empire. And that color was growing daily as the Emperor's hordes swept across the Pacific like locus. The Japanese like to call the Pacific Ocean the "Emperor's Lake," "Well, it's almost that now," Kathleen thought. There were only two forces she knew of that threatened the Japanese, the American carrier fleet under Admiral Halsey and the British fleet at Singapore.

"Where is Halsey? Thank God the Japs haven't yet followed up with an invasion at Pearl. We have nothing to stop them and they could have been sitting in Honolulu with no effort. But where is Halsey?" she asked to herself.

Suddenly, her reverie was broken. One of the clerks came to her with a coded message. Kathleen saw that it was from Singapore and her heart leaped. Quickly she went to her desk and began to decode it. This time she wouldn't need the Purple machine she'd delivered to Commander Rocheford at Pearl. She quickly wrote down the decoded information and her heart stopped!

Honorable Admiral Isoroku Yamamoto Commander, Imperial Japanese Fleet Headquarters, The Admiralty, Tokyo

Sir, on behalf of the Imperial Army Air Corps, please be so kind to announce to his Highness, Emperor Hirohito, that his pilots have sunk the British battleships, Prince of Wales and Repulse plus other enemy vessels in the South China Sea off the shores of Singapore. Our planes from the recently captured island of Kota Bharu destroyed the enemy dreadmaughts in a two hour battle. Only a few of the Emperor's planes were lost. Banzi! Banzi! Banzi!

General Tomoyuki Yamashita

Kathleen Elmes looked at the message. There was more but she didn't bother. She was numb. A feeling of total helplessness crept over her. She wanted to cry but for some reason her mind went back to a movie she had gone to with Jim Seifert earlier in the fall. They waited in line to get into the magnificent Capital Theater and it was a spectacular fall evening in Washington, just a nip in the air and the smell of burning leaves lent a tang to the soft breezes. The movie was *Mrs. Minever* and it was the most popular movie of the year. And standing in line, talking with perfect strangers seemed quite natural. And the movie was wonderful. Her favorite scene was as the end of the movie with Greer Garson standing on the edge of a jetty as Walter Pidgeon and the other British civilians manned their small boats and headed across the Straits of Dover for the beaches of Dunkirk to rescue the soldiers trapped there by the Germans. She wondered if there were any boats with civilians going out from Singapore to rescue the survivors of those sunken battleships. The coded message said nothing about survivors.

She opened her eyes, sighed and wanting with all her heart just to get up and walk away, to go somewhere. Where, she didn't care. Instead, she walked to the door. The rest of the people had stopped working, just looking at her. She knew they wanted to know what had happened but there was nothing she could say. "Christ," she thought as she turned the knob to open the door. "Haven't they had enough bad news? New Zealand is still part of the British Empire and to tell them that two great symbols of their Empire's strength in Asia, the Prince of Wales and the Repulse were lying at the bottom of the South China Sea is too much. Let them hear it from someone else."

Pulling the door open, she walked down the stairs, knowing she had to see Ambassador Welch. With the Repulse and Prince of Wales gone, she wanted his help in convincing that jerk Ford to take her with him when he left. She knew he wouldn't ride out the war in New Zealand and she didn't care where he was going, she wanted to be on that plane. It was the only way she could get back to the States. She didn't expect Halsey to send a destroyer to get her and her usefulness here ended five minutes ago. Breaking codes might be fun for Charlie Chan but there was a war on and she wanted to be in it. Neither New Zealand or Australia could withstand an invasion by Japan. The Japs could send a couple of cruisers to sail outside the Great Barrier Reef and neutralize both nations.

As she came to the side door leading into the main floor of the Embassy, she could see through the glass window that the room was again full. Opening it, she tried to spot the Ambassador and saw him standing by the great map on the far wall. With him were Mullahey and Ford. She ducked back in behind the door, not wanting them to see her. She had be alone with the Ambassador to ask for his help in convincing Ford to take her along. Even though there was a mild truce between them from the other day, she knew how he felt. She was about to go back upstairs and wait until the crowd left when she looked down at the message in her hand.

"Whee!" she screamed out loud and then quickly placed her hand over her mouth. "That's it. He has to see me. I've got the message and I'm the only one that can decipher it for him!" Slowly she opened the door. Straightening her blouse and brushing her skirt, she threw back her shoulders and strode confidently across the room towards the three men. As she neared them, she could hear the Ambassador talking to Ford and Mullahey.

"Captain Ford, I admire your moxie but there is no way a flying boat can circle the world going the way you propose. God, there are no services once you leave Darwin. Japanese planes dominate the skies and you're flying right into their strength. Look how close Singapore is to Java and they are bombing that daily. What happens if a Jap fighter spots you. You can't outrun one. That big plane of yours couldn't out run a Piper Cub!" the Ambassador concluded.

As the Ambassador warmed to his subject, out of the corner of his eye he caught sight of Kathleen approaching. Even in a Navy uniform, the Ambassador couldn't help but feel a little lift in his libido.

"Gentlemen, here comes my confidant, the only one in all of New Zealand that really knows what is happening in the rest of the world, who tells me what the Japs are doing and what we are not. Ah, Lt. Elmes you make these awful days bearable."

Kathleen smiled at the Ambassador while Bill nodded at Ford.

"My dear, I have been trying to explain to our stubborn Captain Ford that he can't... what is it, Kathleen. What is the matter?" he asked, seeing the paleness of her face.

She looked at him and then at Ford and Mullahey and slowly brought the message from her side, still gripped in her left hand. She opened the paper, looked at it and passed it over to the Ambassador, without comment.

He looked at it and began to read when it dawned on him that it was still in code. He smiled and passed it back to Kathleen. "Sorry, you'll have to decode it for me. From your expressions, I'd guess it isn't good news."

Taking the message back from the Ambassador she began to read the coded words verbatim.

"Honorable Admiral Isoroku Yamamoto. Commander, Imperial Japanese Fleet. Admiralty..." her translation was interrupted by Ford.

"Forget all that ceremonial bullshit. Cut to the message. What the hell does it say?" Ford barked at her.

"Damn you, Ford. The Repulse and the Prince of Wales have been sunk off Singapore. There! Now you know," she hissed at the Captain of the plane she had hoped would take her home. Her anger at Ford had made her voice rise and those standing nearby heard the deadly news. Quickly, they spread the news that the Repulse and Prince of Wales were sunk. Behind hands raised to shield their whispering voices, the news raced from one group to the next.

"Repulse and Prince of Wales have been sunk," said one to his neighbor next to him, who passed it on. "The Japs sunk the Prince of Wales and the Repulse off Singapore," As the news passed from one group to the next, the gasps of shock slowly gave way to another sound, almost like mild cheering.

"The Japs were sunk off the coast of Singapore by the Repulse and Prince of Wales," Others heard that "The Repulse and Prince of Wales sank the whole Jap invasion fleet near New Guinea" and by the time the story reached the back of the room that Repulse and Prince of Wales had sunk the Japs at Port Morsby, the people broke into cheers. Those in front turned and looked at those in the back as if they had totally lost their minds. The Ambassador signaled to some of his aids to clear the room and as the people began to exit, each was asking another what really happened.

The four just stood there in silence, looking at the map, each with their individual thoughts. Other than what happened at Pearl Harbor, this was the worst possible news Ford could have received. His plans were based on the assumption that the British would keep the Japanese at bay above Singapore while he flew to Darwin, then on to Java and be gone across the Bay of Bengal before the Japanese broke out. Now he knew there was nothing to stop the Japanese Armed Forces from going wherever they wanted.

"Kathleen, I'm sorry I yelled at you," Bob Ford apologized. "A perfect example of killing the messenger because of the message. But there it is. There is nothing left in the South Pacific to stop the Japs. Nothing between them and here and Java. Mr. Ambassador, I want to thank you for all you have done for us but now it is time for me to return to Ops and get ready to leave."

Ford put out his hand and the Ambassador grabbed it with both of his, neither saying anything. Ford turned to leave but a cough from Kathleen stopped him and brought him up short. He had again exhibited bad manners by not saying goodby to her.

"I'm sorry Miss Elmes. Forgive me for not saying goodby. You were a great help translating what was going on at Pearl and I wish you luck. Have you heard from Washington, yet?" Ford asked as he began to lean towards the door to leave.

Kathleen shook her head in answer to his question about Washington. Her eyes pleaded at him to wait and Ford noticed that and it triggered something he knew he had forgotten to do.

Kathleen noticed and she blurted it out. "Captain, I want to go home with you on the Pacific Clipper.!" she began. Taking a deep breath, she began to give her reasons why Ford should take her.

"Great. We can use you, Lt," Ford responded. "Mr. Ambassador, Lt. Elmes is Navy but I doubt that with what's going on they'll be terribly concerned about orders and chain of command regarding the Lt. No reflection on your importance Lt. Mr. Welch, as the American Ambassador to New Zealand if some day the United States Navy asked you what happened to that Intelligence officer, just say that you took it upon yourself to send her home with us because she was a valuable asset. After all, you are the American Ambassador, right? And Lt. Elmes, you can close your mouth now," Ford commented.

The Ambassador laughed and nodded his agreement as she blushed.

"Kathleen, Bill and Captain Ford, if you could delay for a few minutes, please stay to have a bit of the bubbly with me. Behind that bookcase across the room is a refrigerator stocked with more than a few bottles of Dom Perion. Shall we pop open a couple to wish you bon voyage?" the Ambassador asked.

Hearing no rebuttal, he marched the three of them over to the bookcase, and pressed a button just to the right of a red leather bound edition of Washington Irving's "The Legend of Sleepy Hollow." He grinned as the bookcase slid backwards into the wall, and a small bar rose out of the floor and behind the bar, a refrigerator. He walked behind as the others stood on the other side. After taking out two Dom Perion bottles, he placed four goblets in the refrigerator to chill them. Peeling the gold wrapping off each bottle, he slowly twisted the cork on one and placed his two thumbs under the cork and pushed up. The soft whoosh of air rushed out. He repeated the same deft opening of the second bottle and retrieving the four goblets, poured the champagne into each. Looking at his guests, he raise his in salute, and then they all touched theirs to his and sipped. No one spoke.

CHAPTER 4

First Stop: Darwin

Tuesday, 17 December, 1941, 0800, Pan Am Base, Auckland, New Zealand

From the waters of the Hauraki Gulf, the Pacific Clipper, clad in her new grey camouflage paint, climbed towards her cruising altitude of 8000 feet. Out across the South Pacific, she gradually rose as the shores of New Zealand faded behind her. All on board were silent, each with their own thoughts, filled with trepidation but the fear was heavily laced with excitement of the unknown facing them. Captain Ford had made it quite clear that what they were attempting had never been done by a commercial airliner before, much less an amphibian one. New Zealand and security was gone. Ahead lay Darwin, the last vestige of possible safety for them. After that, who knew.

The farewells at Base Ops in Auckland had been swift and the pain eased by being so busy and caught up in what they were doing that when they were alone on the Clipper, the finality of leaving the comparative safety of New Zealand caused all to reflect. They knew that Captain Ford was committed to going all the way to New York and Darwin would be a quick overnight stop to refuel and get some rest, assuming the war hadn't arrived while they were in flight.

Normally Ford would have flown the water route to Darwin; north from Auckland, then across the South Pacific Ocean until he reached the Coral Sea. Then he would head directly east across the Great Barrier Reef, over the Gulf of Carpentaria. They would stay over water until the came to the Timor Sea and then drop down into Darwin. But these were unusual times and the most precious cargo Ford carried was 100 octane gas in the four Clipper tanks. He could not assume that Darwin would not be under attack or that there would be aviation fuel available for them. He had to assume that the only aviation gas they were going to have was what he had in the tanks now. Flying the ocean route would add 1000 miles to his flight. So he decided to fly the "crow-flies" route, a straight shot to Darwin across the heartland of Australia and some of the most rugged territory on the face of the earth. Ford knew the dangers of flying across lands where there was no water to land. Not good for an amphibian!

Ford, Mack and Steers stood at the navigator's table and looked at the open atlas. "About 2600 miles, Captain, from Auckland to Darwin, as the crow flies," Steers answered Ford's unasked question. "Well within our range, Sir. We'll save about 600 miles flying this route."

Ford nodded and continued to look at the map. He wasn't concerned about the distance. It was that there wasn't a place to set the Clipper down if they had an emergency. No rivers or lakes between Brisbane and Darwin. Was the safety of the plane more important than the savings on gasoline, Ford asked himself as he looked at the atlas. For most of their trip they would be crossing part of Australia that was know as Queensland. Looking at Steers, he asked how big it was?

"Queensland is bigger than Alaska," the navigator answered. "Surprisingly there is quite an agricultural industry there, kind of the breadbasket of Australia. After that, we'll be over what the call the "Northern Territories," probably the most rugged part of the continent. It is somewhat smaller than Queensland, but bigger than Texas. It does have snow in the mountains and therefore some rivers and small lakes. But nothing that I can see where we'd be able to put the Clipper, if we had to," Steers advised his Captain.

"Very good, John. That was most informative, I mean, looking at a third grader's atlas and coming up with all of that information. I appreciate it," Ford smiled at his navigator, impressed.

"Thank you, Sir. I figured you'd want to do the "crow-flies" route so I thought you should know something about the lands we'd be flying over," Steers explained.

"Very good, John. I hope Bill's coded message got to Darwin. With the Japs coming straight towards them, they probably will be ready to shoot anything that flies out of the sky. So lets hope the winds are favorable and we get there before dark," the Captain stated. The two Johns moved away, leaving Ford alone.

Looking at the map, Ford felt suddenly very depressed. "Christ, 2500 miles across some the vilest land in the world, in a flying boat. Nothing but mean, cruel earth. One screw up, one breakdown and we're history. But this is one hell of a plane. If anything flying can make it, she can. So stop feeling sorry for yourself and get to work,"

Ford lectured himself. Turning he walked over to his chair and began flying his plane home to America. First stop, Darwin.

The crew settled down into the routine of flying. The engineers, Rothe and Parish checked the instruments that monitored the engines while Steers fed information to Ford about the course across Queensland, the Northern Territories and into Darwin. The flight stewards, Barney Sawcki and Verne Edwards prepared breakfast for the crew and after preparing the Master Suite for Kathleen Elmes, there wasn't much to do but look out the portholes at the vast lands below them. Poindexter was prepared to rig a radio receiver in Kathleen's suite so she could listen in on the radio transmissions coming from across the Pacific but she wanted it near the stairway leading up to the flight deck. That made it easier for the two of them to listen to the transmissions and compare notes. Poindexter found her a class act. Unlike some other beautiful women Poindexter had met, Kathleen Elmes had no airs about her. She knew she was attractive and Poindexter was impressed at how easily she kept her femininity while she quickly became accepted as a member of this team of men. Poindexter had no trouble explaining to her how to use the radio, not to someone who could decode Japanese. With the longitude and latitudes on the face of the double spread in the atlas that Mullahey had purloined for them, she could plot transmissions of coded messages by triangulation of the places where the messages came from and from where the answers originated. Combining with the clear transmissions Poindexter would be picking up, the Pacific Clipper should have an ear to almost everything message being across the South Pacific.

They had reached cruising altitude and the noise from the engines was barely noticeable. The sun was on the starboard side so she could, without straining too much, see the smooth, deep blue waters below. The excitement of the takeoff, the pangs of leaving the new friends they made in Auckland and the wonder of what faced them soon faded as the monotony of flying began to permeate the plane. With no passengers to attend, there was little for the cabin crew to do. Ford and the others on the bridge were busy as were the two engineers and G. Brown, the Boeing Tech rep. He had joined the crew where Kathleen had, in Pearl Harbor. If Kathleen had said more than ten words to the guy, that was a lot. He was quiet, athletic looking but kept to himself, except when with the other engineers. He was Boeing's man carefully watching the performance of their star. But something about him told Kathleen that the man wasn't exactly what he said he was. She had no reason at all to feel like this and mentally shook herself to forget about the man. Which she did.

Ford had his coordinates from Steers and expected to cross the coast of Australia within an hour. They would be north of Brisbane then cross into the air space of the world's seventh continent. Although the flight would be one of their longest hops, it should be relatively uneventful. Ford hoped.

It was. The only excitement was when they approached the Great Barrier Reef. Brisbane was below and to the port side and the crew and Kathleen looked out to the starboard to see one of nature's truly awesome creations. a watery version of the Grand Canyon. Except you couldn't see into the depths of the reef. But even at 8000 feet the stunning colors of the reef mesmerized them. Teal greens merging with light blues and the many colors of the coral beneath the water provided a backdrop that a Van Gogh or any artist would literally give an ear to be able to capture on their canvas. And the mystery and fear from the stories of the denizens of the Great Barriers Reef, especially the Great White Shark gave those looking down a feeling of fear and reverence at the same time. They knew that few people would ever see the reef as framed from the windows of the Pacific Clipper. Within minutes, the startling panorama of the Great Barrier Reef faded as the ship passed over the water and began their flight across the lands of Australia. Now their view was of the dry, red clay of Queensland. Steers said this was farmland but it was foreign to Ford. This wasn't the land or the soil of the black, rich loam of the Middle West or the rolling, green hills of his Wisconsin. As far as he could see, the land was bleak and barren, reminding him of the lands of Nevada, Arizona and Death Valley that he flew over when test flying some of the fighter planes manufactured by Curtis Wright, Lockheed, Martin as well as Boeing. Ford was one of the few pilots in America that was checked out as a test pilot in single engine as well as four engine planes. Pan Am lent him to all the manufactures when his schedule permitted but only if Ford wanted to do the test. It wasn't that Pan Am was that altruistic, it was just that the planes Ford was testing were for Pan Am friends, the military.

Ford loved flying these hot, single seat planes, doing acrobatics and pushing the smaller planes past their limits. Alone, with a stripped down plane and an empty sky for him to cavort, Ford had a ball. He couldn't describe the feelings except to another test pilot. And the military even paid him for it!

"Captain, Lt. Elmes has some information for you," John Poin-dexter said, interrupting Ford's brief reverie. Ford looked at his radio man and for a second, couldn't place Lt. Elmes! Then it dawned on him and he shook his muddled head.

"Thank you John, please have her come up," Ford ordered and rose, tapping John Mack to take over the controls. As he walked towards the stairwell, Kathleen's head appeared and as she entered the flight deck, Ford greeted her.

"Good morning. Mr. Poindexter tells me you have something for us," Ford stated, in a matter of fact voice. "What is it?"

"I've picked up some coded messages from the Australians and British at Port Morsby to Darwin. They say massive Japanese forces are gathering in the Bismarck Sea, preparing to land on New Britain. According to them, troops from the Japanese islands of Bouganville and Guadacanal are on transports coming to New Guinea for the invasion. They are begging Darwin for help," she reported.

When she finished, Ford reached over for one of Mullahey's atlases and flipped through the pages until he came to a double spread that showed Australia, New Guinea and most of Indonesia and the islands of the Bismarck Archipelago.

Kathleen had paused in her briefing of what was happening in New Guinea and it became obvious to her that Ford couldn't have cared less. Yesterday, she would have taken umbrage at Ford's attitude towards her hard work and incisive analysis of what was happening in the war but now she realized that what she had to say was unimportant to Ford. And, surprising even herself, she understood his attitude. He had no control over what the Japanese were doing. Once they sank the two British battleships, all of Indonesia opened up to them and they could waltz to Java. That was Ford's problem and she didn't help by all this stuff about what the British needed in New Guinea. Ford and the plane had to get them home. It was that simple. So all this traffic between losing armies pleading for help held no importance to him. She wanted to call him cold and uncaring but she realized that he was right. The hell with what was happening across the world. Somehow, he just was going to get them home. She promised herself that the next time she asked to see him about what she had deciphered, it would be about them, not the rest of the world. So she stood there, waiting for his comments, knowing it wouldn't be very complimentary.

Ford looked at her. "Thank you, Lt. That was very informative. But the Japs are bombing here, and invading here. And all of that is over a thousand miles from us. Right? And since we are flying away from these areas, am I safe in thinking the Japs are not headed for

Darwin? Or do you have any intelligence about what is happening there that would effect us?" Ford asked.

His tone was not combative as Kathleen had expected but there was enough of a bite to it that she realized something else. She had been talking down to him and the others. They weren't Navy and subconsciously she'd been acting superior, being smug and condescending with all this stuff about where the Japanese Army and Navy were headed. She looked at Ford and he looked back at her and she suddenly realized that he was reading her mind. She had been putting on airs and he knew it!

"You bastard, Ford," she thought. "You let me run off at the mouth and be patronizing and you nailed me. We'll, I'll never admit it to you but I know you know I was an ass. I've been acting like Admiral Nimitz and you let me play the big fool. I'll get even. Someday, I'll get pay you back."

"Your analysis of what is happening in Darwin and Australia is quite accurate. Nothing is happening," she summed up, furious at herself and knowing he was laughing at her pretensions.

"Thank you, Lt. Please keep me informed if you hear anything about Darwin or Surabaja," Ford stated and with a nod, dismissed her and returned to his pilot's chair.

The Australian coast had fallen far behind them as they sped across Queensland. Ford checked the pitch on the props of the giant Wright engines, knowing that just the proper pitch could save them a small amount of gas. Although apprehensive, Ford felt that there probably little to fear from Japanese fighters roaming this far south from New Guinea. He hoped that Darwin had received the coded message for Mullahey so they would be expected. He'd only been to Darwin once before, a brief refueling coming over from Pago Pago on the way to New French Caldonia. He'd heard it was a great leave town but with things being as they were in this part of the world, he knew Darwin would be shut down totally. That suited him. Just get in, refuel, get some sleep and then on to Surabaja. He leaned back in his chair, stretched a bit and thought that thus far, the trip had been easy, except for Kathleen Elmes reminding him that he wasn't Navy. He had to laugh to himself, knowing she'd figured out he knew she was acting like a female Halsey, someone far superior to them with her in-depth understanding of "the big picture." But he didn't care what she thought. They were on their way home.

The hours passed and the day wore on. The transmissions that Poindexter and Kathleen monitored added little to their knowledge of what was happening across the South Pacific. So unless something was happening at Darwin, they should arrive there with their status unchanged. Except they would be 2,600 miles closer to home! Kathleen Elmes was getting fidgety. No matter how many times she looked at her watch, it seemed as if time stood still. All there was to look at outside the Clipper were blue skis with an occasional cloud floating by to break up the monotony. She was beginning to believe that flying really was as boring as John Mack and the others had told her. If the trip to Darwin was the rule, they were right. Then she felt a subtle change in the actions of crew and she noticed a quickening to their movements. Looking out the porthole by her table she noticed that the sky had begun to darken, the sun was to the stern and its rays were bouncing off the clouds giving the sky a pink hue. Slowly the giant plane began to descend and she forgot about listening for coded messages. She leaned against the porthole, straining to see Darwin but all she could see was the ecru colored desert lands of the Northern Territories. Had she been on the flight deck, her view would have been much more exciting.

Ford and the rest of the flight deck crew could see Darwin straight ahead and they looked at each other in total wonder. Instead of the sun setting on a city about to be invaded and where war time "lights out" were standard operating procedures, Darwin was lit up like New Years Eve and Ford suddenly grinned as he remembered that just a week ago someone from Darwin was swearing at them, yelling that "don't you blokes know a war is on!"

Keeping Darwin to his port side, Ford brought the Clipper over the shoreline of the Territories, banked left over the Clarence Straits and slowly pushing forward on the yoke of the steering column, he brought the huge plane into its decent mode. Down from 8000 feet across the Beagle Gulf, he descended by increments of 1000 feet as he slowed from 150 knots by 10 knots each thousand feet. At 2000 feet, he turned on his landing lights and slowing the speed, he dropped the plane towards the water. Ford was about 1000 yards away from the Pan Am dock, doing 70 knots when he eased onto the water. The landing was so smooth that had the crew not been expecting the touchdown, they never would have noticed the slight bump that told everyone the Pacific Clipper had landed in Darwin. Ford reversed the engines slowing the Clipper and easily brought her under control. Ford then pushed forwards on the stick and cut the power on the interior engines. Ahead, on the dock, they could see the docking crew waiting. When Ford had the Clipper within thirty yards of the end of the dock and about twenty yards to the starboard side, he cut the port engine and let the Clipper slowly drift towards to the dock, using only the outside starboard engine for control. Barney Swacki had popped open the hatch of the anchor room and climbed up the small step stool ready to toss his line to the landing crew. Vern Edwards now opened the cargo door on the lower level and walked out on the port sponson, docking rope in hand. When the docking officer, standing about 10 yards ahead of the Clipper's nose made sure that the Clipper's angle and drift would keep her parallel to the dock, he signaled Ford to cut the starboard engine by the slashing motion of his open palm across his throat. As Barney and Vern saw that, they tossed their lines to the dockhands and the men pulled the Clipper to her berth. The crew remained on board while Ford, Mack and Swede Rothe completed their post flight check. That was quickly accomplished and while there still was enough natural light, Norm Brown joined Vern Edwards on the dock to check the exterior of the plane. There were no apparent problems but at the first light of dawn tomorrow, the pre-flight check would be much more detailed.

They had flown over 2,500 miles and used more than half of their 5000 pounds of aviation fuel. That to the layman would mean about 30,000 plus gallons of gasoline since a gallon of aviation fuel weighs about 6 pounds. That was Ford's big concern and as he deplaned, he saw the dock master, Andy Gibbs, a Pan Am oldtimer waiting to greet him. As Ford moved towards him, Gibbs read his mind and broke into a big grin, nodding yes to Ford's unasked question. The two shook hands and he was assured that the tanks would be topped off this night before Ford and the crew were ready for bed. Relieved, Ford assigned John Steers and Jim Henricksen to supervise the refueling. Ford wanted the two radio men, Poindexter and Oscar Hendrickson to try to jerry-rig a radar system to help them the rest of the way.

Ford assigned Second Officer Norm Brown, and the two stewards, Barney Swacki and Verne Edwards to go into Darwin and secure more supplies, especially drinking water, more flashlights and batteries for the ones they had. And he wanted them to find medical supplies, especially quinine pills that they could put in the water to help offset any diseases that might strike them. Ford knew enough about the health perils of Asia and he'd read about the terrible living conditions in India, the Middle East and Africa that he wanted to protect the crew from those dangers. Malaria was his biggest worry. The quinine tablets would help and somewhere along the way, maybe they would run into a doctor that could give them the shots necessary to immunize them.

As the crew began to disperse to carry out Ford's orders, a member of the dock master's crew came forward and handed Mr. Gibbs a message. He whispered in Gibbs' ear who looked at Ford and then at the message and handed it to the Captain. Brown and the others waited to see what the message was, knowing Ford would read it to them.

"Sorry, Captain. I'd forgotten that the harbormaster called and said a message for you had been delivered to him from Melbourne. Since it is in code, he had it sent down to here for you," Mr. Gibbs said handing the message to Ford.

Ford opened it and since it was in Pan Am code, he didn't need the services of Kathleen Elmes, who stood by his elbow, hoping he'd ask her to translate the message. He didn't. He read it and laughed. He passed it over to John Mack who quickly read it and also smiled. The rest stood by waiting.

"Ok," Ford began. "This is from our leader, Juan Trippe. Pausing to add the necessary importance, Ford cleared his throat and began. "Captain Ford of the Pan American Airlines plane, the Pacific Clipper. You are hereby ordered to return to the United States with your crew and plane. Under no circumstancesis the Pacific Clipper to be allowed to be commandeered by enemy forces. As per your sealed orders, you will maintain complete and total radio silence. Good luck. Juan Trippe," Ford looked at the crew, Kathleen and Gibbs and with out comment, folded it and put in his pocket. Then he lit a cigarette.

"Mr. Mack, Lt. Elmes and I will visit with the Harbormaster. Those of you going into Darwin, be back by 2100 hours. Unless I find that there are better accommodations available, we'll all sleep aboard the Clipper tonight. And looking at how lit up Darwin is, maybe the war is over," Ford concluded as the rest of the men gave a kind of wry snort. "And questions?" he asked. There were none.

The different parties went their ways to complete their duties. The three going into Darwin were greeted by a young Aussie named Jerry. He was part of the docking crew and was told by Mr. Gibbs to take the Yanks into Darwin to get their supplies. And to make sure he brought them back. Verne Edwards climbed into the back seat with Barney Swacki while Mr. Brown took the passenger side. All three noticed that there were very few people on the street once they left the Pan Am docks while ahead they could see the lights of Darwin burning brightly.

"How come the streets seem to be deserted, Jerry?" Norm Brown asked. "But the city looks like it is lit up for a holiday."

"Not to worry, Mate. The women and children were packed and sent into the hills when we heard about Pearl Harbor," Jerry responded.

"It don't take no Iron Duke Wellington to figure the Japs are coming Darwin's way. We ain't got shit to stop them so we sent the families into the hills. Figure that's the best place for them if the bastards come here. So with the exception of the ladies of the night, Darwin is womanless. And to add to our pain, the town's been as dry as billiebog for six weeks. But yesterday, the ship with the good stuff, whiskey and beer arrived from Brisbane and the whole town has been on a one big blast since then."

Jerry turned onto a street that led toward the town. Now they could see that it wasn't only the lights of the city that had her illuminated to brightly, they could see flames and smell the smoke. Up ahead there was a barricade manned by the local police and they signaled Jerry to stop. One officer, dressed in khakis with a white hat and gloves, a Colt .45 in his holster approached. Jerry rolled down the window to explain where he wanted to go and why.

"Sir, may I be of help?" the officer asked politely.

"Yes, sir. I'm with Pan American Airways and these three Yanks have to get into to town to get some supplies. So I've been assigned to take them to a supply store and bring them back" Jerry explained.

The officer looked into the car and at the three Americans in their white uniforms and nodded to the driver.

"Son, be careful. Make sure you stick close to these men and watch out because a lot of our blokes have gone past the point of sobriety," the officer warned Jerry. Then leaning in to speak to Norm Brown, whom he recognized as the officer in the group, he tried to explain.

"Sir, our people ain't bad. It just that you can't expect an Aussie to go six weeks without a drop, and with the Japs coming down here, when the booze arrived, it was like putting a light to timber that ain't tasted water in months. Darwin exploded. So be careful. Go ahead but get back soon or we'll come looking for you," the officer concluded, waving them through the barricade. Jerry moved them out and as they came to one corner, he turned and what they saw absolutely stunned them. Store fronts with broken windows, some burning, men fighting in the street and the police standing tensely on the side, trying to make sure no one was killed. Australians loved to fight and as long as no one was shot, the officers of the law let those that wanted to brawl, have at it. To the Americans, it was barbaric, but fun to watch.

In the meantime, Ford, Mack and Kathleen had walked with Gibbs to the office of the Harbor Master. Gibbs knocked and when bade to enter, came in with the three to introduced them to Jocko MacDonald.

Gibbs nodded to Jocko and then at Ford and the group and left. The three looked around the room. It was fairly large with a bay window on one side, with a vista of the harbor. Although it was dark, they could see a tanker riding high in the water, its cargo unloaded. Ford and Mack looked at each other and smiled. This must have been the ship that brought the booze to Darwin! The room was decorated with paintings of sailing ships and Mack saw it first. He touched Ford's arm and nodded at the painting that hung behind MacDonald's desk. It was magnificent oil of a ship at a dock showing men were walking down a gang plank from the deck of the ship. You could see that each had a chain around his neck and his hands tied behind him. The dock was set against the background of heavy trees and the artist let you know that there was no escape into the woods for these poor souls. On the prow of the three masted schooner, painted in white against the blue black wood of the ship were the words, "Botany Bay," The three Americans knew the story of the prisoners from England that were brought to Australia to build a nation out of the wilderness. Darwin was just one example of the heritage left by those few men that came to the land down under in chains over three hundred years ago and built a great nation.

MacDonald walked around the desk, his hand outstretched to Ford. "Captain Ford. Welcome to Darwin although I wish it were under different circumstances. I received Bill's message from Auckland and big Irishman told me to treat you guys special. Of course. And this must be Mr. Mack. How are you, Sir?" MacDonald said shaking hands with the First Officer. As Mack was about to respond, he noticed that Jocko's eyes were feasting on Lt. Elmes so he just kept quite.

"Ah. Lt. Elmes. God bless Mary, Queen of we Scots. She must have taken pity on this old sot to bring you visiting. Just looking at you makes me forget what is happening across the water. There is no war and your being here makes it so!" Jocko MacDonald says as he bends his head over Kathleen's hand, briefly touching his lips to it.

Looking up, the Harbor Master winks at her and the four of them have a good laugh. With a wave of his hand, he asked his guests to sit. Looking at the Harbor Master as he walks behind his desk, Ford silently agrees that Jocko MacDonald was probably everything Mullahey had described; freebooter, smuggler and a hell of a man to have on your side if things got very rough. Jocko had put on some pounds and they showed around the waist but the breadth of his shoulders and depth of his chest made Ford realize that he would still be a very formidable opponent. He was a man Ford would want on his side in any kind of scrap. Still standing, MacDonald looked at the four of them and coming to attention, in a very clipped, formal English, addressed them.

"Captain Robert Ford, at the behest of His Majesty, the King of England and governments of the Commonwealths of Australia and New Zealand, I am hereby instructed to request that you consider staying in Australia and assist our forces in the fight against the Empire of Japan," MacDonald stated. Looking at the startled expressions on the faces of his three guests, Jocko broke up laughing.

"OK, that was my formal request as dictated to me not an hour ago from Melbourne. So I've done the King's bidding as well as the Prime Minister's. But as for me, Jocko MacDonnald, I say go for it son! And anything this old sea dog has that can help you get back home is yours. I don't have much but I do have some maps and charts of the islands you'll be flying to that, old as they may be, might help. You're welcome to them. Now, how about a drink. Although Darwin has been dry for six weeks, thanks to the largess of the captains of the tankers and cargo ships that come here, I have a healthy larder of Scotch and gin. Lt.Elmes, you first. What can I fix you?" Jocko asked.

Walking around the desk to an old wooden chest, made of ebony wood with iron straps girding it, looking like something out of Treasure Island, the Harbor Master opened it. And sure enough there was treasure inside. As he raised the lid and pushed her back, a small bar slowly rose from within the chest. There were crystal glasses on tiny wooden racks fixed to the underneath part of the top of the chest and red velvet lining to protect them. The whiskey, Scotch to Americans, and gin filled two Waterford crystal decanters, each set to one side of the chest. A silver bucket, with tongs sitting in the ice sat center in the bottom of the chest.

"Lt. Elmes?" Jocko asked.

"Oh, if you would be so kind, a martini, Mr. MacDonald," Kathleen responded.

"Jocko, Lt. Elmes, please" he requested.

"Kathleen, please, Jocko," she answered.

The four of them laughed and even Ford seemed to enjoy the banter. Jocko poured the silver liquid into a cocktail glass and added the ice. In the lower left hand side of the chest was a small bottle of Stock white vermouth and opening it, he looked at Kathleen as he splashed a drop in. She nodded her approval and Jocko passed over to her one of the driest martinis he'd ever made and her wishes met with his hardy approval. Too much vermouth gave one a hangover. For the pilots, he filled a six ounce crystal highball glass with Scotch, offering a little bitters or water. Mack nodded at the water while Ford just asked for his on the rocks. MacDonald did the same as Ford and taking his drink, walked over behind the desk and sat down. Raising his in toast, the other three did the same and sipped their drinks. Jocko lit his pipe and pushed a thermadore filled with American cigarettes and Cuban cigars over to them. Kathleen took a cigarette as the two men selected the Havanas. John Mack did the honors for Kathleen. Ford lit his own. Then they sat back and relaxed and enjoyed the early few minutes of their first landing on the way to America.

"Ok," Jocko began. "I have some maps and charts of these waters. They are old and nautical but these shouldn't be a problems since your plane is really a flying boat. Captain Ford, you'll probably leave here for Surabaja in Java. They have a beautiful harbor there, deep and wide so you'll have no trouble landing and taking off. It is a straight shot from here, maybe a thousand miles. But that next step is a doozy. If I'm not the navigator I use to be, then you'll be heading for Ceylon. Bob, that is one hell of a leap even in something as superb as the Pacific Clipper."

"I know Jocko but we haven't even gotten to Surabaja so lets not worry about getting to Ceylon. My problem is gas. Can I get it in Surabaja," Ford asked.

"That's the shipping point for Royal Dutch Shell and there will be plenty of aviation fuel there for you. I'm told that the Dutch have a squadron of fighter planes there. Now that the British Navy is a toothless tiger in the South China Sea, the Japs will be in Java in no time. But you should be able to get the fuel there and gone before the Japanese arrive," Jocko MacDonald explained. The visit continued for a few more minutes with small talk about Darwin and the coming invasion by the Japanese. Finishing his drink, Ford signaled to the others that time had come to leave.

"Jocko, thank you for the drinks and the maps. I'm sure they will be of help. Next time you speak to Mullahey tell him for the first time he hadn't exaggerated when he told me about you," Ford said as he shook hands with MacDonald.

Suddenly, the distinctive roll of thunder cascaded down to them and the four quickly looked at the skies outside the big bay window of Jocko's office. To the west, they could see the huge black clouds of a major thunder storm gathering.

He escorted the three of them to his door. "By the way Captain. If you have time in Surabaja, make sure you stop at the Black Swan for a drink. It is the best bar in the South China Sea." As he was about to open the door, John Mack spoke.

"Jocko, we still have a few hours before that thunder storm hits and I was wondering if there was any place nearby you'd recommend for us to go for dinner," he asked.

MacDonald looked at the three of them and shook his head.

"Didn't you notice the fires in the city as you flew in? Good God, man. Those weren't started by Jap bombers! When the word circulated that the tanker with the booze had docked, the town went crazy. No, Mr. Mack, I would strongly recommend that you go nowhere near this part of Darwin tonight," Jocko warned.

"Jocko, three of my men went into town to get some supplies? Do you think they're OK?" Ford asked. But even before the last part of his question had left his lips, MacDonald was running for his desk. He snatched up the phone and began jiggling the tone bar, telling the operator to get him the Chief of Police. When the gentleman came, MacDonald told him what Ford had said.

"What do they look like" Jocko asked, obviously in response to a question from the other end of the phone.

"Like us," Ford answered. "They left from the dock with a driver named Jerry," Ford answered beginning for the first time to be concerned about the three in Darwin. Jocko passed the information on and then he let go of a wry laugh and repeated the "white uniforms" description. Nodding to the phone, Jocko ended the conversation by promising to buy the drinks for whomever was on the other end of the conversation. Hanging up, he looked at the three.

"They are probably alright but the Chief will put out a special alert to find them and bring them back. I wouldn't worry. Unless they go into one of the pubs they should be waiting for you when you get back to the Clipper," Jocko said, trying to allay the fears of the Americans while he quietly wondered how daft some people could be to wander into a town half on fire. "And please, don't think you can help by going into town looking for them yourselves. Then we'd have two parties trying to find six Yanks and I couldn't let the honor of Darwin and Australia become besmirched if anything happened to any of you, especially the lovely lady," Jocko summed up, trying to relax Ford and the others two. Ford knew he was right so he and Mack shook hands with the Harbor Master, thanked him for everything and Kathleen kissed him on the cheek. As soon as they had closed the door behind them, Jocko raced to the phone and began screaming at the Chief of

Police to rescue those three dumb Americans that had wandered into the dock areas of Darwin!

Norm Brown, Verne Edwards and Barney Swacki had picked up the supplies the Captain had asked for. The store manager, warning the three Americans to be careful, watched as they left and then picked up the phone and called the police.

As the three started for the place that Jerry said he'd pick them up, a pub called the King's Gateway that was just about a block down the street, a couple of Aussies standing about ten feet away began to fight. One man got knocked down and as he got up, he picked up a bottle and rushed the other. Before he got two feet, a police officer stepped in front of him and with his billy club, knocked the bottle out of the man's hand and then brought it down over the poor bastard's head. As the guy slumped to the ground, the other brawler took off down the street. The policeman picked the unconscious man up by the shoulders, he pulled him over to a store front and popped him up there. Turning, he tapped his billy club to the brim of his cap in salute to the Americans and sauntered on his way. The three from the Pacific Clipper just looked at each other. Barney laughed as the other two shrugged.

They spotted the King's Gateway up ahead and when they got there, Jerry hadn't arrived. So they entered the tavern and stood at the door, looking in to see if they could spot a space at the bar. The place looked like the set of a bar room in a B western, with yelling and shouting and laughing. The three, carrying their supplies pushed through the crowd to the bar and, getting the bartender's attention, signaled for three beers. They were served in big steins. As they began to drink, the noise in the place suddenly stopped. Looking in the mirror, Barney saw that a semicircle of seven or eight of the patrons had gathered behind them. Elbowing Verne and nodding at the mirror, Barney could see that the rest of the crowd had also gathered but far enough away that there was no threat from them. The other seven, yes.

"Hey, you blokes ever see altar boys in short white pants, drinking in a man's bar?" a voice directly behind Barney asked the crowd. There was a roar of laughter with hoots and whistles and one of the men way in the back yelled, "Take it easy on the kiddies, Archie. We don't want their Mommies spanking them for getting their white uniforms dirty," More laughter as the three American just sipped on their beer, deciding to ignore the crowd. No way!

"Little Lord Fauntleroys, they are. All dressed up for scones and tea! They look old enough to drink. Are they men enough to fight?" the one called Archie challenged. Now the crowd began to laugh and taunt the Americans and with that, the three turned. The bar became very quiet. The crowd sensed that the Americans were not going to back down and that hum of anticipation when a good fight is about to begin spread through the bar.

Barney Swacki had experienced more than a few of these before. Growing up in a tough Polish neighborhood on the West Side of Chicago helped as did the years flying with Pan Am. While the Captain and the officers of a Clipper ship may wine and dine with the society crowd at their ports of call, Barney and Verne hung out with the working stiffs from the cargo ships and tramp steamers that docked at the same ports as their planes. And Barney knew that talking was a waste of time.

Looking at the "voice", the one they called Archie, Barney saw a well built man, a little taller than he and the obvious leader of the gang. Barney put his left hand out, palm open and up in the sign of peace as he moved away from the bar. With that the "voice," Archie began to laugh, snickering to his buddies. As his head turned just slightly, Barney unloaded a hard right to Archie's nose and the sound of crunching bone told all that the "voice" would be speaking a note higher after this was over. The force of Barney's shot knocked Archie into his mates and as they pushed him up, they came at the three. Brown and Edwards kept the bar to their back and gave as good as they got. Archie proved to be more than just a mouth and he got in a couple of good shots to Barney's head. The First Steward ducked another roundhouse right and got inside to Archie's belly where he delivered a hail of blows to the stomach. But the Aussie brought his knee up and into Barney's groin, knocking his wind form him. As Barney backed up, gasping for breath, another of the Aussies tried to land a blow on the American's head but he stepped on Archie's foot, knocking both a little off balance. Barney shoved the second man into Archie and grabbed the shirt collar of one of two men beating up on Norm Brown and pulled him away. With just one to face him, Brown got in a couple of good pokes and took some. Edwards, like Barney an experienced bar room fighter saw Barney being jumped by two more, grabbed the man in front of him, and as the guy swung, Verne ducked and pushed the guy into the others going after Barney, knocking them away. Barney threw a left at Archie who took it on the shoulder and started a right at the American when a shot rang out. Everything stopped as the fighters and the rest of the crown saw the owner walking along the bar, an Army .45 in his hand. The crowd began to groan, knowing that Bertie was putting a stop to a hell of a fight. "Come on Bertie, let 'em have at it," some yelled while others laughed and kidded. "Bertie, give Archie a chance. He ain't going to beat that Yank by himself!" Another shouts at Barney, "Hey Yank, don't blacken Archie's eyes. He's our best shot and we'll need him when the Japs arrive!" And as the crowd breaks up laughing, Bertie speaks over the din.

"This will be fair fight or none at all. Seven against three ain't me idea of fair so back off or I'll toss alls yo outahere," the owner stated, waving the .45 at the crowd for emphasis.

The crowd began to boo and they weren't buying Bertie's decision but the three Yanks were. Archie wasn't about to quit, not with a busted nose and he started at Barney, who again held up his left hand in a sign of peace. Archie wasn't falling for the same trick again and kept coming until Barney spoke.

Wiping some of the blood off his hands onto his Bermuda shorts, he began. "Look, rather than any more of your guys getting busted up...," but before he could continue, the crowd broke up in laughter and derision, booing the Yank. But Bertie yelled for silence, got it and Barney continued. "As I was saying, lets settle this one of two ways: pick out your best fighter and he and I will go at it. No sense having the others get beat up," he offered to the crowd of non-fighters, who, being at no risk, booed heartily. Then they began to chant, "Archie, Archie." The object of their cheers clasped his fists above his head and nodded to the crowd.

"Ok, Yank. You got him. I'm the best man here and I'm ready to prove it," With that Archie pulled back his right but before he could throw it, Bertie, yelled at him. Looking at Barney, Bertie asks him for the alternative, knowing a brawl between these two might be good for story telling but would play hell with the fixtures.

"Pick out your best drinker, we'll fill a couple of those three foot pilsner glasses behind the bar with your best beer and the first one to finish wins and the loser buys a round of drinks for everyone!" Barney suggests.

With the mention of free drinks, the crowd roars its approval and again Archie steps forward. "Again, Yank. It's me. I'm the best drinker here," Then looking at the crowd, he asks, "What'll it be mates? Want me to give this altar boy a good whipping or beat his arse drinkin' so youse gets a freebie?

"Fight. Fight!" some yell. Then a lone voice from the crowd is heard.

"Better drink, Archie. He's already broken your nose and he might really hurt you next time!" Peels of laughter greet the idea and even

Archie laughs. Nodding his agreement to Bertie, Archie and Barney move to the bar, with the crowd behind them and Edwards and Brown to Barney's left. As the owner fills the tall glasses and the crowd begins to wager, Barney winks at his crewmates. Bertie fills the glasses and brings them to the two combatants. Three feet of beer is a lot of suds and as each man takes his long pilsner glass, the crowd fall silent. Bertie nods to the two and they begin. Worldwide in these drinking contests, the rule is that once the glass has touched the drinkers' lips, they can not take it away for any reason. If one does, he loses. They must keep drinking until one finishes. So the two began sipping slowly, watching each other over the rim of their glass. The crowd, silent at first, warms to the struggle and as the beer disappears into the throats of the two, they begin cheering for one then the other. First Barney is ahead but Archie catches him and leads but Barney comes back and as the glasses empty, the two men finish. It is a tie. The crowd roars its approval of the outcome and Archie reaches over and raises Barney's hand like a referee at a championship fight signalling the winner. Barney does the same to Archie and with the crowd yelling its approval, Bertie stuns one and all.

"Gentlemen, it is a tie! The drinks are on the house!" he yells. There is silence. The men look at each other, totally nonplussed. Never before had Bertie ever bought a drink for anyone, let alone the house! As they stare in disbelief at each other, the doors of the tavern fly open and in burst three of Darwin's finest, billy clubs drawn. The crowd erupts in laughter and when the police see Archie with his arm around one of the Yanks and the rest bellying up to the bar, they signal to Norm Brown that the car is waiting and walk outside.

Taking his drink in hand and pounding on the bar for attention, Archie signals for silence. Turning to Barney, he puts his arm around him and says, "You're a good man Yank. Even if you do dress funny!" With that the rest begin cheering and the two fighters walk to the door with the crowd behind them. As they get into the car, one of the spectators rushes out with their packages and gives them to Brown. Archie and Barney shake hands and the crowd yells "good luck" as Jerry pulls away from the curb. Barney looks back and laughs as he sees Archie, with a big grin on his face, pointing to his nose and shaking his fist at the departing Barney.

In the car, Jerry wants to know everything that happened. But looking at the smiles on their three faces, he knows. He'll get the details tomorrow night at the bar and by the time he hears all about it, the fight at the King's Gateway will make the Battle at Gallipoli seem like a cake walk.

Ford looked over his shoulder but it had disappeared. The thing was back. He was in San Francisco and walking west on a dirt path in Golden Gate Park towards the Pacific. He could feel the sweat running down his armpits, his chest was damp and his undershirt clung to his body. Looking in the mirror he could see that his white uniform was torn and dirt covered his face. He reached up to take off the pith helmet to wipe his brow and the thing had him! A white and yellow cloud began to choke him and he began coughing as he bent over, waving his arms to fight through the cloud. Suddenly he was free. And Phil Collins was waving to him to come over and go fly kites.

Ford loved kite flying and as he ran across the ball field towards his best friend, he could feel his sox sliding down his legs and saw that he was still wearing his school clothes. His corduroy knickers had fallen below his knees and he pulled at the blue tie the good sisters at St. Ignatius insisted the children wear at school. When it came loose, he threw it in the sand and kicking off his black gym shoes, he raced towards the shore of Albion Beach and dove headlong into the cold waters of Lake Michigan. Kehoe, Clark and Finn were already in, with their shoulders below the water. This was the only way to get warm in Lake Michigan; dive in, get the shoulders below the water and paddle fiercely. In a while the numbness wore off and you could swim. He headed for his friends and behind their heads he could see the plane, just sitting in the water. It was silver and long, without wings or an engine and as he swam towards it, it began to move away, bouncing along on top of the water. He knew he had frightened the thing so he dove under the water and doing the breast stroke, approached. As his head broke water, a door on the side of the thing flew open and men jumped out, carrying rifles and shouting something he couldn't understand. He dove under the plane to escape and coming up, he found himself standing by the giant statue of Buddha in the Lamin Temple on a hill over looking Hong Kong.

Lin Wan was running towards him, smiling and he felt such happiness watching her. She was wearing the traditional white silk sheath dress with the slit along her legs and had a red flower in her hair. He saw that she had been crying and as he moved towards her, the cloud came again, yellow and white but this time he could see something else, dark grey like the inside of an oyster. The grey thing had a mouth without lips, a hole with claws inside it. And Ford knew that if he didn't run, drawing the cloud away from Lin Wan, she would die. He yelled at the thing and it turned towards him and he ran, hard, down the hill but his legs gave way and the thing caught him. He could hear its laughter and the oyster had a face, that same face from that first dream that he had never seen before but he knew he knew it. And the face was going to kill him. The face came closer and the yellow and white mist suddenly became crimson and black and the face reached for him. Life was ebbing and Ford knew he had to smash that face before it killed him. He swung his right fist as hard as he could and watched as his arm uncoiled like a trout line flicking towards some pool in the side waters of a rushing stream. The face laughed at his puny attempt to hurt it and the laughter became a roar as Ford's fist disappeared into the folds of that awful face. Then the laughter stopped and the cloud and the face rushed towards him, reaching!

Ford woke, covered with sweat, convinced that if he had not willed himself to wake, he would have died. He lay on the small bed in his cabin, his heart pounding, trying to make some sense of what he had just dreamt. It took him a few seconds to remember where he was and he reached over to the table and fumbled for the lamp switch, and finding it, flipped it on. The small light illuminated his Pullman-like berth off the flight deck. He swung his feet out of the bed, took a Chesterfield from the pack, lit it and took a very deep drag. The smoke tasted wonderful and he let it roll around his mouth before inhaling. The he blew the smoke out through his nostrils and repeated the ritual. Putting the cigarette out in the small ashtray, he field-stripped it as he had been taught by his Dad on their fishing trips in the pine forests of northern Wisconsin. Checking his watch, he saw it was a few minutes before 0400. He knew he had to get more sleep so he swung back under the covers.

He couldn't. His mind raced over the dream he'd just had. It was the second time in a month he'd had it. Not about his old gang in Chicago but the cloud, the face and the sheer terror he'd felt. The first time he chalked it up to the fact he'd gone to the movies and seen Peter Lorie in a Mr. Moto movie and that he was tired from all the test flying of the Clipper over Puget Sound. Now, just a few weeks later, almost the same dream. Ford scoffed at people who put stock in dreams, that they were omens or something. But he had traveled to many places in the Orient and seen many strange things that couldn't be explain by logic or science. He snuggled under the covers, trying to get back to sleep.

But it wouldn't come. His pajamas were damp from the sweat the dream had caused and as he tossed about, he knew he was awake.

"Anyway, I've had five hours. That is enough," he told himself justifying getting up early, trying not to admit that the dream had shaken him. He dressed and took his windbreaker with him. Walking down the stairway to the passenger level, he quietly entered the anchor room. popped open the small door and climbed out on the dock. It was summer in Australia and in a few hours, the temperature would be in the 80s but now, the breeze coming off the waters of the Timor Sea chilled him so he put on the windbreaker and walked quickly towards the end of the dock, about one hundred yards away. As he walked along, he looked across the mouth of the harbor and knew that in a few hours, he'd take the Clipper out of this safe harbor into Harm's Way.

Auckland to Darwin. 2600 miles. It had been easy but as he looked to the East, he thought he could detect a slight change in the darkness. He recalled a line from Homer's "The Odyssey," about 'as Dawn with her rose-tinted hands had lit the East' and remembered that story of the Greek wanderer had been one of his favorites. Now he wondered at their predicament. Were they to be like Odysseus and his ill-starred crew? Then he snorted. That was mythology, this was real. 1000 miles from this dock was another in a place called Surabaja. It sounded exotic enough but would they find the gasoline they needed to keep going? Now as he looked at the sky, he could see Dawn's pink hands at work and he felt his stomach churn in the excitement of what was coming. Ford loved the morning because it brought the start of who knew what. That he would take the Clipper across the bay and out over the Timor Sea was a given. Surabaja was something else. What would happen when they got there he wished he knew. Then again, as he thought about it, Ford knew if he knew he probably wouldn't go! "Maybe ignorance is bliss and God protects the blind and the dumb. Well, we sure qualify," Ford mused.

He started back towards the plane and as he did the events of last night made him smile and his chest swelled with pride for his crew. Until you have actually flown with men, a captain couldn't really know the group he commanded. Sometimes they came together naturally but more often than not, seldom did ten men mesh smoothly. Not this crew. After last night, Ford knew he had a winner here. He laughed to himself about what had transpired.

The three of them had just returned from the meeting with Jocko and Swede Rothe fixed some coffee. Kathleen Elmes had gone to the Master Suite and he and Mack were having a cup when they heard the squeal of wheels coming inside the gate, telling them that the group for Darwin were back. When they entered the lighted cabin from the dark outside, the men started laughing. For the three men looked like hell! Their uniforms were torn and bloody and Barney's right eye was beginning to close. He looked like he'd gone a round with Joe Louis without a headguard! Edward's lip was swollen and also had a cut over his left eye. As for Norm Brown, he was grinning from ear to ear. A few seconds later, another car pulled through the gate and in came Jocko MacDonald, carrying a case of champagne! He had heard the story of the fight from the Chief of Police and he had to hear it from the combatants.

Ford and the rest sat in the lounges and listened while each of the fighters regaled them with his version of the epic battle at the King's Gateway. While they talked, Kathleen Elmes came out and quietly tended to their wounds. Even though they would be flying the next morning, Ford allowed the crew to enjoy the champagne that Jocko had brought to celebrate what the three did to uphold the honor of the Pacific Clipper and Pan Am! When the three were patched up and the champagne finished, Ford rose with a big smile on his face and signaled that it was time to call it a day. And what a day!

The Harbor Master bade them godspeed and asked Ford for a second of his time out on the dock. They walked over to the Operations shack where Jocko took out a slip of paper and handed it to Ford. On the paper were Jocko's notes from a conversation he had after Ford had left. What jumped out at the pilot were the words, "Pan Am."

"What is this, Jocko" Ford quietly asked.

"Right after you left, I got a call from one of our Army types. We've known that if war started in the Pacific, Australia would be involved. And Darwin is the closest place for the Japs to land. For the last few months, our intelligence people have been aware that the Darwin area has been infiltrated by Japanese spies. This evening, about an hour after you landed, a transmission went out from the hills back there. Since we don't know their codes, seldom does the Army get anything they can pass on. But obviously they haven't a code word for Pan Am so when this was picked up, they called me. It could mean anything but it is obvious that the Japs reported your landing here. I wanted you to know," Jocko summarized.

Ford just looked at the piece of paper then at the Clipper. "So much for camouflage and radio silence. The Japs know we're here. But was this just some soldier that was bored and wanted to impress his supcriors? Or is someone trailing us? And if so, why?" Ford mulled out loud as the Harbor Master just waited. "Thank you Jocko. Do me a favor. Alert your Army people to let you know if there is any transmission about us when we leave tomorrow. And since you're going to have a coded message sent to your consulate in Surabaja alerting them that we are coming, include anything that the Army may hear. Ok?" Ford asked. Jocko nodded and the two shook hands and walked to the gate. Jocko looked over Ford's shoulder at the Clipper and suddenly began to laugh.

"What's so funny?" Ford asked.

"Just the thought of the look on some native's face when he sees a huge silver bird come out of the sky, land on water, not sink and then men walk out of her belly. And when he tells the Chief what he saw, they'll have him for dinner!" Jocko said and began laughing at his own thoughts. Ford joined him and again they shook hands and as the Harbor Master walked over to his car and got in, waving goodby as he started up the car. Ford watched him speed the short distance, turned and strode back to the Clipper, looking up at the night sky. The thunderstorm had passed through and cleared away the clouds and the sky was filled with stars. He knew the names of some of them, quite a few in fact, but as he was about to name some, he yawned and headed back to the Clipper. Before climbing in the anchor hatch, he looked back at the sea. In a few minutes the crew would be awake and they would leave Darwin for Surabaja. Before them was the greatest challenge any of them had ever faced. Ford said a small prayer, figuring that with so much going on around the world, God didn't have time for a long one.

0815 hours-18 December, 1941-Aboard the Arista-Java Sea

A Japanese radioman, a piece of paper in his hand, walked down the aisleway to the cabin of his Captain. Knocking, he waited until the door opened. He passed the paper on to the officer and returned to his duties. Inside, Commodore Tanaka read the message. "American plane left Darwin, 0645, 18 December, 1941," Tanaka looked at the message and smile. Last night's transmission told him the Americans had landed in Darwin. Now Ford was leaving. The Clipper had the range to go to Batavia and that there probably was aviation gasoline there but Ford couldn't risk it. Only at Surabaja would he be assured of aviation gasoline. Royal Dutch Shell was just a few miles up stream from the city and there was a small contingent of the Royal Dutch Air Corps station at Surabaja and he knew Ford knew that. Tanaka again checked him map, did a couple of what if's and stood, smiling. Ford was flying into his trap. It was time to alert Major Thu in the mountains overlooking Surabaja.

CHAPTER 5

Next Stop: Surabaja

The takeoff from Darwin was perfect and Ford brought the plane up to the cruising altitude of 5000 feet. He thought it would conserve gas at this level and since the instruments indicated that there was a slight tailwind, there was no need to climb to a higher altitude. Ford turned the plane over to John Mack and joined Steers at his navigator's table. The charts Jocko MacDonald had give him last night were laid out but they were of the harbor and when Steers did an in-depth analysis of them, he found some data, the different depths in the harbor would help but basically without wind charts, they faced the problem that would dog them all the way home, bringing an 82,000 pound plane down onto the water without knowing anything about the cross winds.

Steers remembered one time he took his date to the dock in Seattle to look at one of the earlier Boeing's. When she commented about how landing on water must be much easier and safer than on land, Steers' gave her a lecture of the problems with head winds, currents, underwater debris, and the rest of the dangers faced when landing a plane on water. Information about the winds at a harbor when landing an amphibian plane was vital. Steers recalled the next time he called her for a date, she made some lame excuse and he never saw her again.

"John, looking at the map, we have an easy shot to Surabaja. Across the Timor Sea, over the Lesser Sunda Island, past Bali and into Java. Jocko's maps show a harbor that is deep so we don't have to go over some mountains and throw her down on the water. It should be easy. And if all goes well, the Dutch will have the fuel ready for us, we'll spend the night there and then on to Ceylon. Right?" Ford stated.

"Right, Sir," Steers responded. "Nothing to it. We fly 1000 miles by the seat of our pants, with no charts or radio signals trying to use land masses as markers, lands none of us have ever been to much less see from the air, and then just drop down into a harbor that we know nothing about and land. Right Captain, nothing to it."

0945 hours 18 Dec. 1941-aboard the Arista, Sea of Java

The Arista was on the Karimata Straits. Captain Nagoma was atop the sail and the third group of 15 men were resting on the deck. Nagoma wanted his men to get some fresh air so each group was allowed a half hour out of the confines of their work areas, free to relax in their bunks or on top. All but a few opted for the deck. The officers also accompanied their men. Nagoma knew that there was nothing to fear from any enemy planes or war ships. With the sinking of the Repulse and the Prince of Wales, there was little the British had that could threaten them and, much to his surprise, the American Navy had disappeared from the Pacific. None of their Intelligence groups had reported any sightings of the carrier fleet that was commanded by the one man most of the Japanese Navy feared, Admiral William Halsey. Taking a deep breath before he had one of his men invite Commodore Tanaka to come up, Nagoma could smell land off to the port side. He knew the aroma was coming from Borneo and that was another island that would soon fall to the Emperor's forces. Already, the Japanese Army had invaded Malaya at Kota Bharu and was coming down the isthmus from their beachhead there towards Singapore. Yes, things could not have been better for Japan. Everything had exceeded even the wildest dreams of the Imperial Staff. His admiration for the success of the Japanese armed forces was interrupted by a signal from his second in command. Commodore Tanaka awaited him. Nagoma, grasping the rails, quickly slid down from the sail to the bridge and walked down the passageway to his cabin, knocked and entered.

The big man rose from the small table he was seated at in Nagoma's cabin and as he was about to stretch, he stopped. His head was already bruised from the two times he banged it against the ceiling earlier by standing up too fast, forgetting about how small the space was in a submarine. Without preamble, Tanaka began. "As you know, the Americans have left Darwin, my good Nagoma. I have already prepared my instructions for Major Thu so please have it transmitted on these frequencies. There is no need for a response," Tanaka ordered and the Captain bowed, took the piece of paper and left for the radio room.

Tanaka sat down on the small chair next to the desk. It was time to put his plan for the capture of the Pacific Clipper into operation. If all went the way he had planned, the American plane would land in

Surabaja in late afternoon and probably refuel before bedding down for the night. Sometime in the early hours of the next morning, Major Thu and his commandos would board the plane but not try to take her. The plan called for them to hide in the cavernous holds on the Clipper. Tanaka guessed that the only thing down there would be extra parts and maybe some other materials. Since the Clipper would have no passengers, therefore no luggage and therefor no reason for any of the crew to check the hold. When the Clipper left the next morning, Thu and his men would commandeer her, fly the plane to Kota Bharu where he would meet it and then fly on to Tokyo. When they landed in Tokyo Bay, he would turn the Pacific Clipper over to the Prime Minister Tojo. Tanaka smiled to himself. Ford was coming to Surabaja and Thu was there, waiting and ready. Now he rose and opening the door, strode towards the operations center of the Arista. As the tall man arrived, without a word, the whole crew knew he was there and that the real mission of the Arista was now beginning.

1200 hours-18 Dec. '41-aboard the Pacific Clipper headed for Java

The Clipper was moving along at 180 knots. They were four hours into the flight and so far it had been uneventful. Even the radio transmissions that Kathleen Elmes and John Poindexter had been monitoring were infrequent. Both had been instructed by Ford to report any incoming or outgoing traffic from Surabaja. Thus far, they had nothing important to report. Steers, checking the maps that Jocko and Bill Mullahey had given them, thought that they were probably about 400 miles from Surabaja. The Clipper was purring along and there should be no problems. This was their first landing on uncharted waters in an unknown land. Steers was at once excited and apprehensive. He had one more check point that he felt he could recognize from the air and that would put them directly on course to Surabaja. It was the Island of Bali and even Steers had heard of this jewel of Malasia and the beautiful people that lived there. As he looked out of the small porthole by his navigator's table, he could only see the waters of the Timor Sea. Walking forward and standing behind the two pilots, he looked to his left and at about 1130 high, he saw the small island he was looking for.

"Bali?" Ford asked.

"Better be!" Steers answered. Both Ford and Mack laughed and the First Officer checked his directional finder and compass and nodded. The Pacific Clipper was on course. In another half hour or so, the coast of Java should be on their left and following the shore line should lead them to the harbor at Surabaja. Now Bali loomed larger in the waters.

And on the island itself, the arrival of the Pacific Clipper was of great interest to another. In a small hut near the edge of the water, a large man lay on a cot, snoring. He was flat on his back, hands folded over his immense belly. His tan shirt was streaked with sweat and the shorts he had on once were white but now were a grey something. The man's name was Bimbo and he was the official coast watcher for the British and Dutch governments on Bali and his job was to alert the Dutch garrison at Surabaja when Japanese forces appeared in the Java Sea.

Bimbo was a bum. He hadn't begun life in England to become one but circumstances and his own efforts over the years brought him to his present position, flat on his back sleeping off a drunk. During the Great War, he had been stationed in Turkey and although Bimbo's stories of what he did in the war often got him free drinks from fellow countrymen, in truth, Bimbo's job was to bring the better things of life to the officers, like women and liquor. When the war ended and he returned to England, the talents he had honed in the service of His Majesty's Army were not in great demand in polite society. In a few years, Bimbo's activities came to the attention of Scotland Yard and before they could place him in a quiet home, for five years, Bimbo escaped to the Continent. Across Europe his talents brought him to the attention of the police there and soon he was in the Middle East practicing his art. With each move, Bimbo's clients went down in stature as did their ability to pay large sums for the Englishman's talents. Finally he arrived, uninvited in the Far East. For a few years, dressed in tweeds and carrying a walking stick, his performance as a landed British nobleman brought him easy pickings among the stuffy Dutch and gullible English in Hong Kong and Singapore. But Bimbo liked to drink and his prowess with cards in a gentleman's gathering began to fade as the booze took the nimbleness from his fingers. Soon he was hustling tourists for a shot and a beer. He escaped Hong Kong just a few minutes ahead of the Chinese police that were coming to arrest him. He had made a friend of a first mate on tramp steamer and they took him on as a stoker. By the time the steamer docked in Okinawa, Bimbo decided that working in a boiler room was one step below being in prison. When the steamer headed for Korea, Bimbo stayed to see what the picking were in Naha, the major city on the island. For a few weeks, he did well, skimming at poker games, taking the locals. They knew he was cheating but couldn't catch him at it. One poor loser went to the police who decided the Englishman was guilty and threw Bimbo in jail. The next day, visiting dignitaries from the main island, Honshu, came to see how the police handled things. So they brought Bimbo out, beat him, then left him out in the prison yard as an example to all Occidentals of how the Asians treated criminals. The temperature was over 100 degrees. The routine was repeated daily until the Japanese left the island. Then they released Bimbo, ordered a ship headed for Borneo to take him or they wouldn't be able to land in Okinawa again. From Borneo, Bimbo somehow found his way to Java and Surabaja.

With Pearl Harbor, the Dutch and British on Java realized that it would only be a matter of time before they were invaded. They had few military assets but were determined to fight. They needed some advance notice of when the Japanese were coming. They knew that Bimbo had served in the British Army in the First War and although they didn't believe his stories of his exploits, he did have military experience. And anyway, who would miss a wharf rat?

So here lay Bimbo Halliday, a former Lance Corporal in His Majesty's Army, sleeping off another drunk in a hut on the shores of the island of Bali. He had been on the island for two weeks and nothing had come by or flown over. Now his own snoring woke him. He rolled over on his side and the cotton inside his mouth moved him to reach for the pitcher of water on the little table next to him. As he brought the water to his mouth, his hand shook and the water splashed over his legs. Swearing, he pulled his body up, swung his legs over the edge of the cot and with both hands, brought the pitcher to his mouth. Slurping loudly, he rolled the water around his mouth then spit it out onto the sand. As he took another swig, he heard something, a muffled sound he couldn't identify. Thinking it was coming from some motor launch, he walked out into the sun that immediately blinded him. Shielding his eyes and shaking his head, he looked across the water but couldn't see anything. Pouring the remaining water in the pitcher over his head, he looked up into the sky. Shading his eyes with his right hand, he saw nothing. But he could hear the sound, only it was getting louder. Suddenly, he saw a flash in the sky. Then it was gone. But he knew he'd seen something and the beating in his head was forgotten as he moved quickly back into the hut and returned with his binoculars. Moving to the shade of a palm tree and leaning against it to steady himself, he brought the glasses to his eyes and searched where he thought he'd seen the flash. Nothing.

Frustrated, he closed his eyes and turned his head from side to side, trying to locate the noise. It was to his left, ahead of him. Bringing the glasses back up, he looked out and slowly panned up towards the sound. There! He saw it. Spinning the focus knob, Bimbo Halliday almost fainted. There, maybe ten miles away was the biggest plane he'd ever seen! Bimbo scanned behind the huge aircraft to see where the rest of the Japanese air fleet was. He could see nothing but looking back at the one plane in the sky, he concentrated on it before running back to report.

"Blimey, when did the Japs build that thing? No wonder they only sent one. It can level Surabaja by itself," Halliday thought. Then, racing for the hut, he grabbed for the mike sitting next to the radio. He dropped it in the sand and as bent to retrieve it, he banged his head hard on the edge of the small table. It hurt but he ignore it, reaching for the crank on the side of the machine and began turning it as fast and as hard as he could.

"Bimbo Halliday calling Surabaja. Bimbo calling Surabaja. Come in. Come in! Goddamn it. Biggest fuckin' plane you ever saw headed for you. Jap bomber headed for you. Come in, Jap bomber coming your way. Come in, for Christ's sake!" he screamed.

He pushes in the receive button but the radio is silent, Running outside, he brings the glasses up and in a few seconds, locates the plane. His first report was unprofessional and he wanted Surabaja to know they have a good man as their coast watcher. So studying the plane as calmly as his beating heart would let him, he made mental notes of her structure and other important aspects.

"Four engines in a wing longer than anything I've ever seen. Single wing tail with three stabilizers. Big bastard, 70-80 feet. No markings that I can see. Funny lookin' body, never saw anything like it... reminds me of a boat... maybe a ship's bottom," the coast watcher mumbled to himself. Then the radio in the shack crackled and he rushed to respond.

"Come in Bimbo. Come in Bimbo. What in hell is this about a Jap bomber? Come in, Bimbo" the voice at headquarters insisted. Bimbo entered and flipped on the sending switch.

"Base. Bimbo here. The plane is a four engine bomber, single wing, three stabilizers on the tail. Huge, maybe 70 feet long. Bomber headed right for Surabaja. Altitude a guess but make it 4000 feet. Speed I don't know. Funny body... big, big plane... never saw anything like it. Blow the bastards out of the sky. Bimbo out."

"Thank you Halliday. Good work. Keep us advised on other planes coming. Out."

The man transmitting the message to Bimbo sat at the radio console in the Royal Dutch Air Corps base just outside Surabaja. His training had him write in detail all Bimbo had told him so he could deliver it to the commanding officer. He need not have bothered. The Commander was there, so were the four pilots, and every other member of this small detachment assigned the task of defending Surabaja and the Royal Dutch Shell oil refineries with six Brewster fighter planes, built in 1930. The name of the commanding officer was Alphonse VanGelder, His rank was Colonel, and he was a farmer, not a military man. The title was honorary until the Germans invaded his fatherland and when the government in exile in England realized they needed military men to protect their empire in Indochina, they activated VanGelder and put him in command of the defenses of Surabaja. He and the rest of the Dutch in Java knew that they had nothing that could stop the Japanese but they were willing to sacrifice their lives for their homes. As a young boy he had come to Java with his father and family as part of the continuing colonization of the Netherlands East Indies. The first time his parents took him into Surabaja and he was amazed to see shops and streets so similar to those in his hometown of Amsterdam. And over the years, as the VanGelder family fortune grew and the farm prospered, he watched with growing impatience the rumblings for independence from native groups like the Butio Utama or the Muslim led Saraket Islams. He knew how much the Dutch had helped uplift the lives of the natives and was disappointed that they didn't understand what that Dutch leadership had meant in making Java the envy of all of indonesia. But he wasn't blind like some of the other Dutchmen to what the natives of Java wanted. Freedom. Independence. Now the time they had all dreaded was here. A Japanese bomber was on its way to begin the invasion of Java and he had six old Brewsters, four pilots and a couple of anti-aircraft guns down by the harbor to stop them. The Japs were coming to destroy their harbor, their homes and their way of life and enslave the people of Java.

"Not this time, Tojo," the Colonel thought to himself. "Our planes may be old but they are faster that your big bomber and we'll blow you bastards back to your ancestors."

He didn't need to call the pilots together. They were just a few feet away. "Gentlemen," the Colonel began, "The Japs think so little of us that they are sending in an unescorted bomber to begin their invasion. If she is half as big as Bimbo says, she'll have a lot of guns to defend her. But that won't stop you. There is nothing I can tell you about flying or what you'll find when you get up there. Captain VanderKellen, your planes are ready and I know you and your men are. Good luck and blow the bastards out of the sky," the Colonel ordered. He stood ramrod straight and saluted his pilots. The four returned the salute and turning, walked from the shack for their planes. Six Brewsters were sitting in a row on the grass, with the first four tended by ground crew members. They were single engine fighters with 50 caliber machine guns mounted on each side of the fuselage, just back of the engine. The wing sat below the cockpit, fanning back slightly from the body of the plane. They were solid, plodding planes, not fast like Jap Zeros or maneuverable like the Spitfires or powerful like the German Messerschmitts.

Captain VanderKellen led his men to their planes and as they began to climb into their cockpits, he looked at his three comrades. He was the only of the four that had even flown in combat and while he knew that the others were good pilots, now they were going to face the real enemy. They would face gunfire from an enemy, from a plane that was the biggest thing flying according to Bimbo Halliday. How big it was didn't mean a thing to VanderKellen. It was an enemy plane and they had to shoot it down. For the three others, Andrews, Blab and Heyden, those days of training under the Captain were invaluable but now they would be facing the enemy, an enemy that would be shooting back. This would be their moment of truth.

For Rolph VanderKellen, there was no elation. He'd been there before over the coast of England, what they were now calling the Battle of Britain. For three months as part of the Free Dutch forces, he'd flown his Spitfire and attacked the German Luftwaffe. He never did recall being blown out of the sky. All he remembered from that morning was that they had taken off from Dover when the alert came and Captain Jenks spotted a formation of Junker bombers below them and they spun down to attack. He'd made one pass, thought he'd hit one of the bombers but as he climbed for a second pass, his plane suddenly began disintegrate around him. He hadn't felt a thing but the cockpit was filled with flames and something was burning. When the unbelievable pain hit him, he knew it was he on fire!

Everything after that was a blur and even now he couldn't honestly say he remembered bailing out or landing in the freezing waters of the Channel. Later, the doctors and nurses told him that it was the coldness of the water and the salt in it that helped his body quickly form scar tissue so they didn't have to do a skin graft on his hands, face or chest. He had stayed at the base hospital at Margate, just up the coast from Dover. When he was about to be released, Major Burton from the Squadron came by and asked if he'd consider another assignment. The Dutch government in exile needed experienced fighter pilots to train and lead the pilots that they had stationed at their bases on the islands of Indonesia. Given his choice of assignments he opted for Java. A few nights later, the evening before he was to ship out to Microasia, pilots of his squadron from Dover threw him a small party. When one of them asked why he'd chosen Java over India, his replay left all of them scratching their heads.

"Komodo Dragons," VanderKellen replied. The rest of his fellow pilots looked at him, and being British and naturally reticent, they let the explanation suffice. And now, sitting in his seat inside the Brewster as Sgt. Cole read off the check list and he mechanically repeated it, VanderKellen was happy he was sitting in a Brewster. It was slow, had little speed and wasn't very maneuverable. The Brewster was a flying pillbox. It was as solid a fighter plane built anywhere. VanderKellen knew they were going up against a bomber and as slow as the Brewsters were, they were far faster than any bomber. It was almost impossible for a gunner to shoot down a diving, flashing fighter plane.

Sgt. Cole completed the check list, pulled on Rolph's shoulder harness to make sure it was tight, tapped the Captain on the shoulder, pulled the canopy down, checked the lock, climbed down and walked forward to the front of the plane and grabbed the tip of the propeller with both hands, looked up at the pilot and nodded his head. Vander-Kellen switched on the ignition, counted to ten, then pulling on the choke, nodded to the Sgt., who, bracing his legs in the turf to give him leverage, pushed the propeller to his right and ducked away as the engine roared to life. Cole stepped back, saluted to Captain Vander-Kellen and looked down the line at the other three planes. All propellers were spinning and he joined the rest of the ground crew at the edge of the grass as the Captain moved his Brewster ahead and rolled down the grassy field. In a few seconds, the plane was racing along and the other three were following. There was no place marked for the Captain to decide where to lift off, just his instincts and instrument telling him it was time to pull back on the stick and leave earth. Slowly VanderKellen climbed into the sky and the other three Brewsters closed up behind him, forming a diamond pattern as they climbed out over the harbor and headed for their rendezvous with the first Japanese plane sent to attack Surabaja. The battle for Java had begun.

As Captain VanderKellen led his squadron into the sky, about two miles past the mouth of the harbor, the jungle began. In that jungle over looking the harbor, a small group of Japanese commandos led by Major Seishu Thu of the Japanese Imperial Army, were encamped. His goal wasn't the capture of oil fields or rubber plantations or blow up radio stations or even throw panic into the populace. In fact, it had nothing to do with the usual assignments to commandos. No, Major Thu's specific objective was to capture a plane, an American made plane that was suppose to land in the harbor at Surabaja. Because of Pearl Harbor, she couldn't fly her regular route back to American. He and his commandoes were to board and capture that plane. He remembered laughing at the idiocy of the whole idea until he was told that the nephew of Baron Tanaka had thought this up and Prime Minister General Tojo had approved. After that, he kept his own thought to himself. And Thu thought that if one could be part of plan so audacious that the high command of the Japanese Imperial Forces supported it and that it was the brain child of the illustrious Commodore Tanaka, well, it made sense to join, especially if it succeeded! .

Thu was an experienced combat officer. He'd cut his teeth in China but soon tired of the wretched experience of watching the pride of the Japanese Imperial Army reduce itself from the awesome, fast striking modern army to butchers practicing bayonet techniques on the bodies of women and children. The conquest of China wasn't as easy as the High Command had assumed. Yes, they took Manchuria but China was like a pillow. You push it in one place and it puffs up in another. You kill the people, rape the women, bayonet the leaders and nothing changes. The Chinese never even ask for mercy. Maybe that was the one thing that led him to ask for reassignment. There were far too many Chinese to kill and no matter how horrible the tortures and degradations, even with mass executions, they never gave up! Thu, like many officers, begged his commanding officers to transfer him somewhere else. One day, his commanding officer told him to report to Naval Intelligence in Tokyo. He was stunned and delighted. Now he was in Java, in the jungle overlooking Surabaja, awaiting the landing of the American plane, the Pacific Clipper.

Just a few days earlier. Lt. Ashi Auho of His Imperial Army Air Corps reported to Major Thu at his camp in the mountains. Auho was part of the flight group that would attack the American forces at Guam at the same time that Admiral Yamamoto's forces attacked Pearl Harbor. Two days before he had the chance to join the turkey shoot at Guam, he had been ordered to board a submarine and head for the coast of

Java. The Captain of the sub told him that he was to be part of a combined Navy and Army operation. All he was told was that he would be told what his assignment was when they got there. Now he knew and like Major Thu, he had his doubts but if General Tojo supported it, who was he to question the plan.

Thu, Lt. Auho and his commandos were in camp in the early afternoon when a runner from the revolutionary Sakarta group entered camp. His news changed everything. The Dutch were scrambling their fighter planes to shoot down a Japanese bomber attacking Surabaja! Thu was incredulous! He knew something was terribly wrong. He and Auho walked away from the camp to the edge of the tree line and looked down on Surabaja. Thu scanned the sky with his binoculars for the Dutch fighters as Auho looked with his out away from the city for the bomber.

"By Buddha's balls. It isn't one of our planes. It can't be!" Thu swore to himself. "What could panic the Dutch so much to send up their fighters? I know! I know! It has to be the American plane, the Pacific Clipper. Didn't the transmission from our people outside Darwin say the Americans left this morning? It must be them!" Thu knew that if the Dutch fighters shot down the American plane, their mission was ended. And they knew that unless the Dutch bullets were blanks, the Americans were dead. Suddenly, Major Thu saw the face of Commodore Tanaka flash across his mind and he laughed. "Sayonara Commodore. Tojo won't forgive this, even if it isn't your fault!" Thu signaled for his Sergeant to come to his side and when the big man arrived, dictated a message to alert Commodore Tanaka aboard the Arista what had happened. The message was short.

"Dutch fighters attacking Pacific Clipper. Will keep advised. Thu."

The Dutch planes began to climb to their attack position. Captain Rolph VanderKellen pushed his throttle in to increase his speed as he climbed to the attack altitude of about 4,000 feet. If the plane they were after was planning a bombing run on Surabaja, they would be probably be descending to that altitude.

But VanderKellen was no longer sure there was a threat. He'd been caught up in the excitement of the sudden appearance of the enemy bomber but even when he was sitting in the cockpit as the Sgt. was strapping him in, there was something that didn't feel right about all of this. As he continued his climb to altitude and searched the skies for the intruder, he reviewed the events of the past half hour. They had been told by their coast watcher that a big plane was headed for Surabaja, to bomb it. So since the only threat to Java was from the

Japanese, it seemed logical that the plane approaching was a Japanese bomber, given the description from Bimbo Halliday. Knowing of Halliday, the Dutch pilot had his doubts.

As far as VanderKellen knew, the Japanese were not given to making poor judgements like sending in a lone plane without proper protection, no matter how big and well armed it was. It didn't figure. As he continued his steady climb towards the west where he expected to see the bomber, VanderKellen reevaluated the report. He had studied all the intelligence available about the Japanese Air Forces and he couldn't remember anything that showed that they had a four engine bomber. As the locals would say "it was a puzzlement," But he had to fly and shoot down the invader so he shifted his thoughts to see where his squadron was and they were exactly where they should have been, in formation, two hundred yards below him, spaced about one hundred yards off each wing.

The attack plan was simple. When they spotted the enemy, they would climb above him and then, the other three would peel off and fly directly at the bomber, cutting over the top of the plane, drawing the fire from their gunners. After the three had flown by and reformed behind him, he'd lead the attack or send the three back over again to draw more fire. Then, as their gunners were regrouping from that sortie, he'd come in alone, below the bomber, hitting her in at the most vulnerable part of the plane, that space between the tail and the lead wing, the belly of the bomber.

Suddenly. there it was... at 10 O'Clock! Just a few miles away to his left almost parallel to them. And she was huge. "God, she is big... and beautiful. How in the world did the Japs keep something like this secret?" VanderKellen thought as something vaguely familiar registered in his mind but he dismissed it. His group prepared themselves for the attack. He watched with pride as his untested pilots followed his instructions to the letter and peeled off to race over the bomber, hopefully drawing her fire and leaving the monster exposed to his attack. He whispered a small prayer and 'good luck, men' as he watched them and got himself in position to shoot down the enemy.

"So far, so good," Ford thought. The island of Bali was beginning to disappear behind them and the chart that Jocko had given them showed the entrance to the harbor at Surabaja began over the Straits of Madura, just fifty or so miles from the end of Bali. Ahead he saw the tip of a small mountain and knew that it marked the opening into the Maduran Straits. If the atlas was accurate, all he had to do was bear slightly to the left and then head directly into Surabaja. "There probably will be some kind of reception boat in the harbor to show us where to taxi after we land. Jocko's chart shows the harbor to be very wide so we shouldn't have any trouble with the sea traffic. I hope they have the 100 octane there,"

"Whoram!"

Ford instinctively ducked as something roared over their head. He heard Poindexter yell. "Holy shit! What was that?"

Ford knew what it was. A fighter plane. But whose?

"Whoram!"

"Whoram!"

Suddenly, two more buzzed the Clipper, coming so close that their passing shook the big plane for a few seconds. Ford grabbed the wheel and steadied the ship. Steers had rushed into his navigator's cabin to look out back and was shouting to Ford.

"Four of them, Captain! Fighter planes! They're circling. Looks like they are going to make another run at us. Here they come!" Steers yelled as he watched, fascinated, knowing that there was nothing he or anyone could do to keep the Pacific Clipper from being shot down!

"Mr. Poindexter. Open up the radio to see if we can hear them," Ford coolly instructed. "John, see if you can come up with something to signal them that we are friends."

Mack jumped out of his chair and moved to Steers' table with the charts, grabbing a white piece of paper waving it from inside the port window!

"Here they come!" Steers yelled.

"Whoosh! Whoosh! Whoosh!" The Clipper again began to shake from the force of the air as the fighters roared past them again.

"They are Dutch fighters, old Brewsters. " Ford said easily to the rest on the flight deck. He turned to see what was going on and ruefully laughed as he saw John Mack standing by one of the port window waving frantically one of Steers' maps. As if a fighter pilot whizzing by could see that or even understand it.

"What's happening back there, John?" Ford asked Steer

"They are forming up again, Captain. Here they come! NO! NO! Wait. Just one is coming in and the other three are spreading out behind him. Now he's coming under us!" Steers reported.

VanderKellen had watched as his pilots peeled off and dove at the big plane. They did it beautifully, coming out of the sun one by one to flash over the top of the enemy plane, shaking her. He looked for gunfire from the plane at his fighters but there was none! His three returned and began their second run, trying to again draw fire from the bomber and keep them busy as he prepared to come underneath the target and shoot her down. Again, his men made the textbook pass over the target and as before, there was no return of fire from the enemy. VanderKellen could tell that the plane had no nose or tail guns or any on the top. If this was an enemy fighting ship, it was the weirdest he'd ever seen. Now it was his turn. He had the honor of shooting down the first Japanese plane to attempt to bomb Surabaja!

Dropping down about 500 feet lower than the plane he was attacking, Captain VanderKellen began his run. Pulling on the throttle to give her more speed, he began to climb towards the target, then rolled the Brewster to the left and then to the right, always giving the gunners on the enemy ship his most protected area. But there still wasn't any fire from them! "Naked as a baby" he thought. Now he could easily make out the grey/green camouflage paint that had been randomly splashed on her body. His finger closed on the trigger. And suddenly, without knowing why, he shouted "Southerland" and pulled hard to the left, spinning away from the enemy plane. He rolled the Brewster over twice to signal to the others to break off the attack. As he leveled off and turned back behind the huge plane, he picked his microphone.

"Base. Base. This is Captain VanderKellen. I'm breaking off the attack. As I closed to shoot, I spotted some paint underneath her stabilizer. It looks like an American flag. And this is not, I repeat not, a Japanese bomber. It looks like a British Sutherland but it isn't," VanderKellen spoke into his mike as his analysis went back to VanGelder at Base Operations.

"Captain, this is Base Ops. Are you sure it is an American plane? Anyone can paint a flag on the body. Do not break off. Be ready to shoot her down unless she can give you definite identification. If they do not radio who they are, shoot them down. I repeat, shoot them down in ten seconds," Colonel VanGelder ordered.

Steers, listening to the byplay between his attackers and their boss, began yelling at the speakers, "Yes! Yes! We're Americans! Americans! You can't shoot us down!" The whole crew listened as the Dutch pilot and his commander discussed their fate and heard Steers yelling and joined in, as if ten voices inside a sealed airplane could be heard! Then they stopped as they listened to the fighter pilot call them, knowing they couldn't answer!

"Enemy plane. This is Captain VanderKellen of the Royal Dutch Air Force calling you. You are in Dutch territorial air space. We will shoot you down in ten seconds unless you identify yourselves. I repeat, identify yourselves or be blown from the sky. Tell us who you are. Come in," VanderKellen radioed in clear air transmission so there would be no misunderstanding who he was and what he wanted.

Silence.

"Identify yourselves, please. Who are you? Come in," VanderKellen repeated.

Silence.

Ford listened, awaited and suffered. He could not break radio silence and there was no way to identify themselves. What had happened to the code telling Surabaja they were coming? Too late to worry about that now. How could he let the Dutch fighter planes know they were friends? How?! "Captain VanderKellen, this is Colonel VanGelder. If they have not identified themselves to you, commence their destruction. That is an order," the Dutch commander spoke.

"Base, give them more time. They may have a radio malfunction but this plane is not a bomber. I repeat. It is not a Japanese bomber. In fact, it is a commercial amphibian plane, like the British Sutherland. Sir, this is not a warplane," VanderKellen pleaded with his commander.

Ford and the rest of the crew of the Pacific Clipper were nodding with some yelling "Yes, Yes" at the speakers as Mack and Kathleen were waiving white sheets at the Dutch planes from the portholes, knowing even an eagle couldn't see their pleas.

Suddenly the radio jumped to life as one of the Dutch pilots yelled, "Madeline Carroll! That's it. Madeline Carroll! The plane is an American Clipper ship!" exclaimed Lt. Eric Heyden over the radio. "I saw this plane, or one like it in one of those newsreels... you know the one... where the camera zooms right at you... Movietone News! That's it. They showed Madeline Carroll getting on a plane in New York and it is the same as this one. This isn't a Jap bomber! It's a Pan American plane! We can't shoot her down," the young pilot illuminated and pleaded.

"I don't care if King Olaf himself flew on that plane. She could be loaded with high explosives, planning to crash in the harbor. Unless they radio you some identification, shoot her down!" VanGelder ordered.

"Sir, please. They must have a good reason for not breaking silence. We can fly right on her tail into the harbor. If she does anything suspicious, we'll take her down. We'll drop her long before the plane can do any damage," VanderKellen stated.

The silence from Surabaja was deafening, especially to the crew of the Clipper. Ford kept the plane on an even course and ahead he could see the port turn towards the harbor at Surabaja. But without approval for that bastard commanding the base, he dare not move off course. As for the Dutch pilots, Captain VanderKellen had made their case. Now all they could do was sit and wait. Closer the Clipper flew to the turn Ford had to make to start his run into the harbor at Surabaja. Silence from Surabaja. Nothing from Colonel VanGelder. Then the Clipper heard the orders from Base Operations.

"Captain VanderKellen," Colonel VanGelder began. "Escort the unidentified aircraft to our harbor. If she so much as moves ten feet from her course, shoot her down. She is to land five miles from the docks and a gunboat will be waiting to board her before she can enter the harbor. Remember, Captain VanderKellen, ten feet. If she strays, I don't give a damn why, blow her to hell. I hope you're right on this Rolph. Otherwise, you'll be standing next to me as we face the firing squad,"

The Pacific Clipper landed at Surabaja, Java at 1535, 18 December, 1941.

Chapter 6

No Gas For The Clipper

Tanaka's fist smashed into the small metal desk and the force of his blow ripped the tiny writing platform from its metal moorings in the bulkhead. The papers that were laying there went flying as the nephew of the architect of Japan's conquest of the world reacted to the words he had just read.

"DUTCH FIGHTERS ATTACKING PACIFIC CLIPPER," THU

He had crumpled the message in his left hand as the powerful right delivered the death blow to the innocent desk. Now, trying to compose himself, he opened the wrinkled paper and read it again. And again.

"Dutch planes attacking Pacific Clipper! Thu is an experienced combat officer. He wouldn't panic. The message is accurate but it is incomplete. What happened?" the tall man thought as he paced Nagoma's cabin. And in the back of his mind, like the beginning of a painful toothache, Tanaka knew that if the Dutch were indeed shooting down his prize, he'd soon be kneeling on a ceremonial rug at an altar that held the ashes of his illustrious ancestors, about to join them when he had administered his own execution by Hari Kari.

"Damn it. Thu should have been more precise. The Dutch are ready to shoot down anything that they think is Japanese. Ford knows that and would never fly unannounced to a place like Java. He'd have radioed that he was coming," Tanaka thought. "But there hasn't been any transmissions from the Clipper since he found out about Pearl Harbor!" Tanaka suddenly remembered! "That's it! Ford won't break radio silence and the Dutch don't know who he is! By Buddha's balls. No wonder they are attacking him," But it didn't make any sense. Tanaka knew Ford wouldn't leave Darwin for Java unless he knew they were expecting him. And as he thought about it, his suddenly realized that their only knowledge of Ford's movements came from his own people, their submarines and spies.

"Think, man. Ford is a logical man. Yet Thu is telling me that he flew his plane into Surabaja, a city about to be bombed, to a country about to be invaded, without alerting them that he is coming! No. Something is missing," Tanaka had too much respect for his enemy to think Ford would fly blindly into the teeth of a country ready for war.

"He leaves Darwin for Surabaja. He has to alert the Dutch he is coming. But he is attacked by their planes with orders to shoot him down. So, if I'm Ford and can't or won't break radio silence, I have Darwin send a coded message to expect me. But Thu says the Dutch attacked him. Ergo, either the message wasn't sent to Surabaja or if it was, someone on the ground fucked up. Granted that happened. But all Ford has to do is tell the Dutch fighters who he is and they'll break off the attack. Ford must know that thousands will see the Clipper land in the harbor. Why risk your plane and the lives of your crew to keep radio silence when you've already been spotted?"

Tanaka sits on the edge of the bed, the message from Thu still in his hand as he tries to figure out Ford's rationale, risking getting shot down just to keep radio silence. Why? Why?

Suddenly, Tanaka jumps off the bed and bangs his head on the ceiling. He doesn't even feel it. "Ford knows. That son-of-a-bitch knows I'm after him. And he'll not give me a chance of finding him by breaking his precious radio silence. Good show Robert Ford. But I've been with you since you left Seattle. Every mile of the flight I've known where you are and my guts tell me the Dutch didn't shoot you down. The gods didn't send me to capture the Clipper just to have some fat ass Hollander blow you out of the sky. No, somehow you made it Bob Ford and you're sitting in Surabaja planning your next move. I feel it in my heart. But I have to know for sure. If you're dead and my plane is sunk in the harbor there, I have to know. Thu, you bastard. Where is your message that the Clipper landed and the plan is still on!"

Spinning on his heels, Tanaka flings open the cabin door and races along the narrow corridor towards the bridge and command center of the Arista. After his feet hit the control deck, two steps have him across the room and he grabs the radioman to find out if there has been a message from Major Thu at Surabaja.

1330 hours 18 Dec. 1941-Australian Embassy, Surabaja, Java.

"You goddamn got us killed!" Bob Ford shouts as his fist pounds on the desk of the Australian attache, sitting, ashen faced and mouth open, knowing full well that if he as much tries to speak, this madman would reach over and try to strangle him. The veins in the man's neck bulge and his eyes are black with anger. And the poor man has no idea of what this nut was raving about except he had brought in his wake the ranking members of the Dutch military and their government in Surabaja. Whatever had happened he was suppose to have done something so it didn't happen and he hadn't the foggiest idea of what was going on. And there was no mistaking that the man threatening to draw and quarter him was an American... a very angry one. The attache had no earthly idea of who this man, obviously a pilot of some kind was or why he was carrying on in such a fashion. But he knew better than to interrupt!

Ford took a deep breath and was about to continue but as he looked into the poor bastard's eyes, he could see only total bafflement and confusion. Suddenly, Ford felt sorry for him. He knew he was wasting his breath and beating on the bones of someone that didn't have a clue about what had happened didn't help. Well, it did. It allowed him to blow off steam and that felt good. But it wasn't this guy's fault that the message from Darwin hadn't been delivered. "Shit, I don't know if Jocko ever sent it!" Ford thought.

Ford took his hands off the man's desk, straightened up and turned. The room was still. He looked at Colonel VanGelder standing with other Dutch officials that included a distinguished gentleman that Ford guessed was British, Kathleen Elmes, John Mack and Captain Rolph Vanderkellen of the Royal Dutch Air Force.

Sighing, he looked at Kathleen and John then walked over to Captain VanderKellen. He put his hand out and the Dutch pilot took it. They looked at each other and Ford smiled ruefully. Neither spoke. Ford turned and walked towards the door and the corridor that led to the outside of the Australian embassy. Kathleen and John Mack turned to join him, pausing to nod at the Dutch pilot. He smiled at them and just as they were about to cross over the doorjamb, Kathleen stopped and walked over to Colonel VanGelder. Putting her hand out, she smiled at him. He took her hand, bent over it to kiss it, raised himself, smiled and shrugged. She nodded in understanding, turned and hurried to catch up with the Captain.

Sitting in shock behind his desk, the young Australian, his eyes still glazed looked at the others in the room and asked, "What in the name of Botany Bay was that all about?" His query went unanswered as the rest filed out of the room.

Mack was standing just outside as Kathleen came out, hurrying to catch up with Bob Ford. He put his hand on her arm and shook his head. Ahead she saw Ford going through the wrought iron gate that led onto the Jalan Tunjungan, the main thoroughfare of Surabaja and she wanted to catch up with him. But Mack's slowing her down made her realize that Mack wanted his Captain to have some time to himself. So the two of them walked slowly down this most European street in all of Asia, keeping their eye on Ford as he strode swiftly down the avenue. They knew they'd have little trouble spotting him, even on the crowded street. After all, how many six foot Americans in a white uniform were there in Surabaja?

The two moved slowly and easily with the crowd. They knew the natives were close to panic with what was coming their way but even though the street was crowded, the people were very cordial. Both Americans could see they were being eyed by the people out of the corner of their eyes but there never was any overt display of curiosity by the Javians. In a few days it would be Christmas but with the threat of the invasion by the Japanese, most were concerned with getting away from Surabaja and into the hills or trying to escape across the seas. But for thousands of others across Java and the rest of Indochina, the imminent invasion by the Japanese was their moment. The 400 years of Dutch and British domination was about to end. What would happen to them when the Japanese arrived wasn't clear but one thing was, the foreigners would be gone. And that was all they cared about.

To John Mack and Kathleen Elmes walking casually down the avenue, the past and future of Java failed to enter their thinking. To both, after what had happened just a few hours ago a stroll down the Jalan Tunjugan was the perfect therapy. The normal diffidence of the locals was severely tested by the sight of a beautiful woman in a military uniform and a handsome man in white shorts walking so confidently along their streets. The only conclusion they came to was that the two were Americans. Who else but Americans would seem so at ease strolling down the street in a foreign country about to be invaded!

The small talk the two made filled them with laughter. Both had taken courses in college in Anthropology, Mack at Stanford and Kathleen at Georgetown and had studied about the Java Man and the Peking Man. And although both had terrific teachers, all they could remember was that the two fossils were called "homo erectus" and were a major connection to the "missing link," Other than that, both understood that their field of endeavor was not digging in rubble looking for artifacts.

They were comfortable with each other, walking along in silence thoroughly enjoying the few minutes of conversation and being able to relax. Kathleen knew she was a very attractive woman and that John Mack was quite handsome. To the casual observer, they made an ideal couple. But the two of them understood from the first time they met in the Officer's Club at Pearl Harbor, good friends would be all they would become. A few minutes passed as both enjoyed the warm afternoon sun and Mack turned to say something to Kathleen when it dawned on him that he could no longer see the Captain. He spun around and searched frantically for Ford but couldn't see him. Kathleen immediately knew what Mack was doing and without asking she walked back quickly about fifty yards while Mack went ahead. The two raced back to where they had lost Ford and looked at each other. Then they heard laughter, and turning, sitting on the edge of a huge concrete flower box, filled with bougainvillea, was Bob Ford, grinning.

1345 hours-18 December 1941-Aboard the Arista, Java Sea

The sudden appearance of the huge form of Commodore Tanaka at his elbow cause the poor radioman's heart to stop as the tall man placed his huge hand on his shoulder.

"Any transmissions from Major Thu?" the Commodore asked, his powerful hands squeezing the sailor's shoulder. Before the terrified seaman could respond, another hand was placed on top of the Commodore's. It was his Captain's and the poor man closed his eyes and begged Buddha to make him disappear!

"Commodore Tanaka. May I be of help?" Captain Nagoma asked, his voice almost a whisper but so filled with anger that Tanaka's response was immediate indignation and fury. He threw Nagoma's hand off his and spun to berate the Captain and suddenly realized he had lost face in front of the crew! He had allowed his own frustration to shame him! Taking a deep breath to regain his composure, Tanaka rose to his full height hoping to intimidate Nagoma and nodded to the sub's commander.

"Indeed you may, Captain. Have there been any transmissions from Major Thu?" he asked in his most imperial tone.

Not bowing or even nodding, Captain Nagoma answered. "Commodore, had there been, the message would have been brought to you immediately. Sir, from now on, if you have a question of a member of my crew, please ask me or another of our officers to accommodate your request."

Tanaka's green eyes burned with anger that this toad would correct in him in front of his crew! As the bile rose in his throat, Tanaka had to almost bite his tongue to keep from responding physically to Nagamo. But he hadn't climbed through the labyrinth of intrigue within Japan by fighting with inferiors in front of underlings. And Tanaka knew very well that this was one of those times when his stature, reputation and rank didn't do him one goddamn bit of good. He had been humiliated by Nagoma and within seconds, after he left the bridge, the whole crew would know. And there was nothing he could do about it. But he would get even someday and as he looked at Nagoma, he smiled to himself as he pictured the Captain commanding a garbage scow in Tokyo harbor!

"Ah, my good Nagoma. In my zeal to make sure our objective was still within our grasp and not wanting to interfere with your many duties, I simply asked this fine young man had there been any message from our commandos on Java. In hindsight, remembering the importance of the chain of command on the Emperor's fighting ships, I should have contacted you to relay my request," Tanaka lamely tried to explain.

Nagoma listened to this non-apology apology from Tanaka and wished himself far removed from where he was standing. He had humiliated a person of such power that he knew he had no future in the Imperial Navy. But he was still the Captain of His Emperor's Arista and its final authority. Nagoma's position was the same of any captain of any ship in any navy around the world. Nagoma knew he was right but he also knew that the big man had the might. The first round was his and his men would applaud. But Nagoma was also realistic enough to know that although the men would be proud of him, when Tanaka got finished with him, he'd be lucky to command a scow in Tokyo harbor. Nodding to the imperious bastard, he tried to relax things.

"Commodore, in a few minutes, we will be in position to receive Major Thu's signal from Java. Would you prefer to stay with us on the bridge or your cabin?" the Captain asked, knowing nothing he could do would ever offset what had just happened.

"Captain Nagoma. Thank you for your kind invitation. Yes, I will stay here with you and your men and enjoy watching the Emperor's subjects doing their duty. But, of course, I don't want to be in the way," Tanaka answered in a most pleasant manner.

Noagoma nodded and signaled to another officer to bring the Commodore a stool and placed it by the Navigator's table. Then he went back to commanding his ship. His honored guest sat and for the first time noticed that the Arista stunk! The combination of the fumes from the diesel fuel, the body sweat of the crew, the oil that was on everything and the dampness that comes with being at sea, especially underwater, made him almost ill.

Suddenly, the whole tenor of the Arista changed. The men seemed to move more quickly, and Tanaka knew what was happening. They were about to come to the surface. He and the crew knew that there was nothing that could threaten them in the Sea of Java but whenever a sub rose for the depths, no matter where they were, Tokyo Bay or off the coast of San Diego, the tension rose and hearts beat faster and the toes gripped harder through their tennis shoes to grip the deck. Without looking directly, the men of the Arista watched their Captain. For although a submarine was a collection of steel, wires, torpedoes and mechanical things, what held it together was not welds but the sinew that was the Captain. In Nagoma, the crew of the Arista had the best in the Japanese submarine fleet. And those on the bridge that witnessed his stand against the formidable Commodore were drawn even closer to their Captain. As the sub leveled off just two fathoms below the surface of the Java Sea, Nagoma ordered the periscope to rise.

As he quickly scanned the skies and the surface, he knew that there was nothing out there to endanger them and ordered the "periscope down" and as it slide back into its cylinder, the radio antenna rose. Thu's transmission was due at 1415 hours. It came on the second. Nagoma watched from across the bridge as his radioman transcribed the message. He knew he could have walked over, taken it and personally brought it to Tanaka.

"Fuck him," Nagoma thought. "I know he'll bury me for what happened but I don't care. His balls are on the line with this nutty scheme. I almost hope the Dutch shot down the Americans. Then I can spend a slow day watching him suffer as I bring that bastard back to Koto Bhara and the shame of arriving with no Clipper ship waiting!"

The radio officer brought over the message and Nagoma delighted in furthering the torment of Tanaka. He couldn't read the code but he held the message long enough for him to watch the Commodore's twitching in anticipation. But Nagoma wouldn't bring it just yet. Then, he capitulated. "Enough of this pettiness. He's an asshole and now he has me acting like one. I'll bring him his precious message," Walking the few steps across the bridge, he handed the Commodore the message.

The big man, knowing full well what Nagoma was doing, took the message from the Arista's Captain's hand and opening the paper, he read: CLIPPER LANDED. AGENTS REPORT DEPARTURE DELAYED.

1500 hours, 18 December, 1941-The Black Swan-Surabaja

"You both looked so funny... I just couldn't tell you I was sitting a few feet away," Bob Ford laughingly explained as the two moved closer to him. Kathleen was amazed as how relaxed Ford looked after that tirade at the Australian embassy. She was glad he was laughing.

"Let's get a drink," Ford said rising. "Jocko MacDonald said the best bar in all of the South China Sea was the Black Swan in Surabaja and if you'll turn around and look down the street, you'll see her sign hanging over the street down the way. Looks like it is right on the harbor. Lets go," the Captain stated and started down another crowded street as narrow as the Jalen Tunjugan was wide. Weaving their way through the people, they arrived at the hinged Rattan doors, pushed them open and stepped in. Allowing their eyes to adjust to the dimness of the interior of the tavern, they stood on a small step before walking in. When their vision had adjusted, they were impressed. If the drinks were as good as the ambience of the Black Swan, Jocko had steered them to the right spot. Directly ahead, about forty yards from the entrance was a deck that wrapped itself around the front and side of the Black Swan. The cafe was perched above the mouth of the river that opened up into the harbor. On the deck sat a number of circular tables with colorful umbrellas for shade and four small bamboo chairs at each. All but one table, the one in the center were filled with people, mostly Occidentals, quietly enjoying a drink and the lovely weather of this day in Surabaja. To their right was a bar that stretched the length of the room, about 80 feet plus and even from where they stood, they could see that this bar was something special. It was made of mahogany and from one end to another, seven clipper ships were carved in the lower part of the bar. Each panel was about 10 feet in length and about five feet in height. And unlike almost all bars, there was no brass foot rail running its length, as if the craftsman that made it and the owner that paid for it didn't want customers bellying up to it and spoiling the view for the other customers.

As they were about to step into the room a door opened behind the right end of the bar and a man entered, walking towards them, smiling. He was dressed in the traditional long silk jacket worn by merchants throughout Asia with Western trousers and shoes. He was tall for an Asian and upon closer inspection, he wasn't an Oriental but Occidental!

"Captain Ford. Welcome to the Black Swan. And, Miss Elmes. You are far more lovely that I was told. And Mr. Mack. We are honored. Please allow me to introduce myself to you. I am Shamus Ginsberg, your humble servant and host at the Black Swan. I insist that you be my guests and join me at my table on the deck so that I can properly introduce you to the finest harbor in the South China Sea.

Motioning towards the deck, Shamus Ginsberg led the three Americans to his table. As he held the chair for Kathleen Elmes, he had a good look at the expression on the two flyers. He knew Lt. Elmes's was the same. For in front of them lay the harbor at Surabaja and what they saw boggled their minds, as Ginsberg knew it would. As far as they could see across the harbor and out towards the beginning of the Sea of Java, boats of every size and shape were in a headlong race to escape the city. From triple decked steamers to huge sampans to outriggers and even motor boats, the waters churned as this motley collection of boats tried to reach for the freedom of the open sea. The only thing they all had in common was that each one was filled to the very limits of capacity with human beings.

Ford sat and looked and was stunned. "This is the real face of war. People trying to escape other people that want what they have. God, these poor bastards have nothing to say about it and nothing to stop the other guys. This is what war really is. Not the newsreels where we see old farts in uniform on the reviewing stand looking at clean, young enthusiastic men marching in parades. No, it is people fleeing in anything they can, carrying what they can take with them and running. And they are running to nowhere. Out on that sea is death. And here on their land will come death. Christ!"

"Do you think they will find safety, Captain Ford?" the innkeeper asked. As Ford looked at their host, Ginsberg just shook his head in understanding that there was no way Ford could answer. So he answered, summing up the futility of what was happening here in Surabaja and across the world. "Where will they go? How will they live if they ever get there? Will the locals welcome them or push them back into the sea? Will they even have the chance to land somewhere or will the captains of the boats just dump them on some deserted island or at sea and then come back for another load, filling their pockets with money before they also run from the Japanese?" His attitude shocked Kathleen Elmes.

"Mr. Ginsberg," she began, her voice already an octave higher than normal. "There must be some place where these people can go and save their lives. You just can't write them off. You have to hope for them!"

"Forgive me, Lt. You are right and I do wish for their safety. But the hard truth is that they died when they decided to take to the water. These are farmers, merchants, peasants. They know nothing of survival on deserted islands or in the mountains if they are lucky enough to get to land. The men that run those ships you see headed towards the sea will come back empty in a day or so. Where they left their human cargo... well, Lt., this is Asia and life is cheap... very, very cheap," their host stated.

Ginsberg's matter-of-fact attitude shocked her, and in some ways, the other two. He had intended it to do. And as he sat back and looked at the three, the waiter arrived with one of the Black Swan's specialties, Mimosas. They sipped on the drinks and the taste was superb. The two men began to relax and the scene they were watching in the harbor seemed to be accepted, knowing there was nothing they could do about it. But Kathleen wasn't finished. As she began to question Ginsberg again, a look from Ford silenced her.

"Jocko MacDonnald in Darwin told us of the Black Swan, Mr. Ginsberg." Ford stated. " And these Mimosas are special. Jocko was right on," Ford stated as Kathleen looked daggers at him. But both John Mack and Ginsberg were appreciative of his cutting her off.

"The wooden reliefs on the bar," John Mack interjected. "They are superb. Who did them, may I ask."

Ginsberg nodded to Mack and shot a swift glance at Ford, showing his gratitude for getting the Lt. off her "these poor people and why" diatribe.

"To appreciate the carvings and the story behind them, let me give you a brief history of the Black Swan. I'm sure you'll enjoy it. Legend has it that about one hundred years ago, a Dutch ship docked here filled with settlers from Europe. The captain fell in love with a beautiful Balinese girl, sold his ship and built the Swan. The girl dumped the captain later and he sold the Swan and returned to Europe. Over the years, the place was owned by any number of men and became one of the worst dives on the South China Sea. And that is saying a lot. But in the early 1920's, a woman became the owner," Ginsberg paused and took a sip from his Mimosa, as the deck became quiet, the other guests listening to the host.

"She was Eurasian and many say she was of Russian nobility, escaping from the Bolsheviks. Others say she was the spawn of one of the I Ho Ch"Tian leaders and the captured wife of the British Counsel General. The lady had been captured by the Chinese during the Boxer Rebellion. In any case, she never told anyone anything about her background. She let them articulate who she was and where she came from and as the fame of the woman that owned the Black Swan circulated through the joints of the Far East, more and more captains and their crews came here to see her. Over the years, the stories of her beauty and the aura of mystery that surrounded her became the stuff balladeers make up. I can't verify this but part of the fable is that your comic strip writer, Milton Caniff came here, met her and modeled his enchanting and delectable Dragon Lady after her for his "Terry and the Pirates" stories. The woman that owned the Black Swan was Surabaja Sue."

Their host paused, took another sip of his drink and looked at his guests. They were thoroughly caught up in his story, as were all of his other patrons. How much was truth and how much fiction, no one really cared.

"Now, Mr. Mack, as to the origins of those seven Clipper ships carved into the bar. About a decade after the Great War, a British Man of War sailed into Surabaja. That night, some of her crew came into the Swan and as men being men, having been at sea for quite some time, they quickly got into their cups and soon a ruckus broke out and the police were called to break up the fight. The British sailors were thrown in jail. The next morning, a British officer arrived from the battleship and demanded the release of his men. When the local officials insist on payment for the damages to the Black Swan plus the fines for the breaking of their laws, the British reacted in typical fashion, blaming the locals and demanding release and an apology from the Dutch. Finally, the Dutch cave in, probably more frightened by the guns of the British battleship in the harbor. The British sailors are released and the ship leaves. But one of the sailors was so beat up in the fight that they took him to the hospital. When the British ship out, this one is left in the hospital," Ginsberg pauses again and signals for one of the waiters to bring another round.

"So here we have this British seaman in a Dutch hospital, his ship gone and without his knowing, that same officer that harangued the Dutch also hated the man left in the hospital. The seaman's name was Colin McCarthy. He was Irish. The British officer, who left him in the hospital, reports McCarthy for desertion. When McCarthy leaves the hospital, he goes to the British consulate to get passage to rejoin his ship. But they throw him in jail as a deserter. Somehow, McCarthy got released. No one knows who puts up the bail money but most think it was Surabaja Sue. But whomever was Colin's benefactor, when he is released, he is a pariah. No one would give him work. The British regarded him as a deserter, the Dutch merchants wanted no part of him, fearing reprisals from the British and the Javanese took positive delight in seeing an Occidental being humiliated by other whites. So the Irishman hung around the docks, where all the bums go, looking for work and a ship to take him away."

The next round of Mimosa's arrive and as the three Americans enjoy these wonderfully refreshing drinks, they notice that the people on the deck have moved very close to them. Ginsberg is a marvelous story teller. He can easily shift from one dialect to another; the lilting Irish brogue, a crisp British accent or the guttural sounds of the Dutch.

"But none of the merchant ships landing here want to take on the Irishman," he continues."They all know of the mark of Cain that the British have put on him. But the plight of Colin McCarthy comes to the attention of Surabaja Sue and she takes pity on the Irishman. She hires him as a swabbie and gives him a cot in the basement. It is poor at best but Colin is happy to have it. Now, as I said earlier, no one knew where Surabaja Sue came from but when she brought the Swan, she paid cash!" Ginsberg continued. "She wanted to change the image of the Swan and appeal to a higher cliental. Within a year, the riff-raft are gone and the Black Swan is the oasis for the wealthy merchants in Surabaja and the shippers and ship captains that did business in Surabaja. Now, in this business, a good bar makes a good tavern and a great bar makes a great watering hole. Sue wanted the bar at the Black Swan to be the best in this part of the world but she wanted a bar that people would come in just to see it. But only people with money."

The innkeeper pauses and the three Americans look into the bar room to see what Surabaja Sue had built. Now Ginsberg continued. "Sue was looking for something to make the Black Swan special. The sea captains that came to the Swan all had different opinions on who ran the best bar in the South China Sea but without exception, when it came to the wood for the bar itself, they recommended mahogany and told her that the finest mahogany trees growing in the world were on a little island in the Caribbean, the island of St. Lucia. So she commissioned a captain she knew that sailed to the Caribbean to bring her back a tree so she could build her the bar that would be the envy of every tavern in the Pacific. Six months later, the captain returned and in the hold of his ship, he had Sue's one hundred foot tree. Now, it was just a few weeks after she'd taken pity on Colin that the tree arrived. Colin had told his boss that he had been a Master carpenter in the British Navy and when the tree arrived, the swamper went to Sue and told her of the Irishman talents," Ginsberg concluded.

Now he rose and escorted the three into the bar, the rest of the deck following a respectful distance behind. Looking at the pride of the Black Swan, Ginsberg continued. "You'll notice that the bar is one unit, not cut up into three or four sections. This was Colin's idea. He convinced Sue to let him trim the tree so that when it was placed inside the Swan, it would run from one end of the room to the other. She agreed but wanted something other than a long bar. That was where Colin came up with the idea of having the seven most famous clipper ships that sailed the Seven Seas etched into the mahogany. Sue had the captains of the different ships name their seven best and when she had about fifteen, they took the seven that were on everyone's list. And here they are!" Ginsberg summed as he waved his hand at the bar and the seven ships sculpted into the wood. Ford, Kathleen and Mack moved closer. "If you'll look closely, you'll see that the ship in the center is not a four masted clipper. Rather it is the Black Swan, the ship that most historians say was captained by Bluebeard himself. The other six are all merchant ships, carrying cargo and passengers to all parts of the world. Like your plane, Captain Ford, these great sailing ships traveled from continent to continent, criss-crossing the great oceans and seas."

Now Ginsberg really warmed to his story. "These carving brought back a time when men pitted their courage and strength plus their technology to conquer the seas. Faster and faster were the demands of the merchants that owned the ships, for speed would get their goods to the different parts of the world ahead of their competitors," And looking at these magnificent replicas carved in the deep brown of the mahogany bar, Ford could easily relate to the demands of those merchants just one hundred years ago. Now he looked at Ginsberg, anxious for more.

"On the far left is the Flying Cloud. Built in Boston in 1851, she set speed records sailing prospectors to California during the famed Gold Rush that began in 1849. Next to her is the Ariel. Among sailing men, especially the Americans, she is a special favorite. A British ship, the Taeping, was then considered the fastest sailing ship in the world. It seems that the crews of both ships met in a bar in Singapore, the Lotus Blossom, I believe. Well, when two crews of the great sailing ships meet in the same bar, bragging and "we're faster than you" are bound to lead to "friendly disagreements"--in this case, a hell of a fight, leaving the Lotus Blossom a pile of glass, broken bamboo tables and rice shades. The two captains decided to settle the argument themselves. They would race to Portsmouth, England and the winner would get 1000 pounds, the loser nothing. The purse was put up by Lloyds of London who also handled the betting. Across the world, over 100,000 pounds was wagered. Lloyds did very well, thank you. The great ships left Singapore, all sails full and they raced down the South China Sea, across the Indian Ocean, around the Cape of Good Hope into the South

Atlantic, then on to the English Channel into Portsmouth. It was almost too close to call but the British judges at the mouth of the harbor called it for the Ariel. After sailing over 10,000 leagues, through some of the most brutal seas and weather on this earth, the Ariel and Taeping entered the harbor at Portsmouth almost bow to bow. The captain of the Ariel refused the 1,000 pounds, declaring it was a tie! The Captain of the Taeping would have none of that and before another fight could break out, another contest was agreed upon. Not sailing but drinking. The owner of a bar in Portsmouth, the Ship and Turtle became a rich man as the two crews blew the 1.000 pounds there," Ginsberg finished to the applause of everyone.

Bowing to the applause, Ginsberg walked up to the bar and pointed to the third ship. "This is my favorite... the Cutty Sark!" and laughter cascaded across the room as all the locals knew that the only Scotch served in the Black Swan was Cutty Sark. After passing the Cutty Sark and the Black Swan, Ginsberg quickly summed up. "This is the Sea Witch, the Champion of the West and the famed Yankee Clipper. This will probably upset our British friends but all of these ships, except for the Black Swan, were built in America!

As Ginsberg escorted the Americans back to his table, the other guests moved closer to the bar to enjoy the exquisite details of the work of the swamper that Surabaja Sue took pity on. Fresh Mimosas were waiting for them and as they sat, Ford looked at his watch. He knew they should be getting back to the plane but he was enjoying himself.

"Shamus, I don't know how to thank you for your hospitality and a most entertaining and enjoyable hour," the pilot began. But before he could continue, their host held up his hand.

"Please, Captain Ford. It is you and your crew I wish to thank. Your arrival in Surabaja has given all of us a thrill. Imagine... a Pan American Clipper ship landing in Surabaja. It is I that on behalf of all of Surabaja that should thank you for such a memorable event," Ginsberg stated as he raised his glass in salute to the Americans. But before Ford can respond, Kathleen Elmes cuts in. She wants to know more about Surabaja Sue.

"Shamus, you've thrilled us with the story of the sailing ships and the carvings on the bar but what about Surabaja Sue. How did a woman in this part of the world were women, at best are second class citizens, become so successful? Was she as beautiful as the Dragon Lady? I'm dying to know more about her," the Naval Intelligence officer asked.

The Irish Jew sat back and looked at the lovely young woman. Ford and Mack wait to see which story Ginsberg will tell Kathleen. In his best Irish brogue, he answers. "Beauty is in the eye of the beholder, Kathleen and there was a great deal of Surabaja Sue to behold," As the three laughed, Ginsberg continued. "To answer why Sue was so successful in a man's business," Ginsberg switched to a guttural Dutch dialect. "Da voman give da men vat de vant... Ya... vat da men vant. Ya!"

The look of puzzlement on Kathleen's face cause Ford and Mack to break up laughing. Frowning at the two of them, Kathleen looks at her host for more details. "What do you mean... she gave them what.," and her voice trailed off as she suddenly understood why Surabaja Sue was so successful! She quickly looked away as she could feel the blood rush to her face. She wanted to sink into the waters of the harbor and be gone from sight!" John Mack stepped forward and changed the conversation.

"Shamus, I'm sure I have seen you some place other that the Black Swan. I don't know where but when you were regaling us with the story of Colin, Surabaja Sue and the Clipper ships, I suddenly felt that I had seen you somewhere or at least heard your voice before. Is that possible?" the First Officer asked.

"Yes, Mr. Mack. It is possible. Although I have never flown on a Pan Am Clipper ship, I have been in places where your planes land, like Hong Kong, Singapore or even Manila. You may have seen me in a hotel where you were staying between flights. As I said I've never been a passenger on a Pan Am flight but I'd love to be going with you to Trincomalee," Ginsberg quietly remarked as Ford almost choked on the Mimosa he had in his mouth. Ford thought his flight plans a secret!

"Don't look so surprised, Captain Ford. When word reached me that you were coming into Surabaja, albeit escorted by Dutch fighters, I immediately got out my atlas of the world to see where you would go from here. Now it doesn't take a Marco Polo to figure the only way a flying boat can return to the United States is to fly across the underbelly of the world. With all your landing sites destroyed by the Japanese, your only way home was this way. After Surabaja, where would you find aviation fuel? The British have a Naval base at Trincomalee in Ceylon and that would be the logical next step for you after you leave us here. And if I were a betting man, I'd guess you'd head for India, maybe Karachi and then try to reach Arabia. I don't know the range of the Pacific Clipper but it must be great if you can go from here to Ceylon in one shot. Then after you find some place to land in Africa,

I'd guess you'd try for South America and then home. How's that for dead reckoning, Captain Ford?" the innkeeper asked.

Ford tried to keep his poker face on but he was shaken! Jocko's warning about the Japanese message popped into his head. If this tavern owner could guess his planned route, and he was right on target, what if someone was trying to capture the Clipper? But who would want a commercial plane that could only land on water! And why?"

Nodding to their host and looking at his watch, Ford rose and the others did as well. Shamus escorted them towards the front of the Black Swan. As John Mack pushed open one of the Rattan doors and held it for Kathleen Elmes, the bright sunlight hit their eyes and they walked into the street with one hand over their forehead, shading their eyes. Ford and the innkeeper followed. On the street, in front of the entrance, a car waited with the passenger doors open. A driver stood by ready to assist the Americans. As Ford turned to Shamus Ginsberg to protest, the Irish/Jew shook his head and smiled.

"Just how did you think you were going to get back to the Pacific Clipper, Captain Ford? You could walk up to the main drag and try to get a cab but this isn't Los Angeles or New York. My man will take the three of you back to your plane," Ford nodded his approval and walked over to the car. Both John Mack and Kathleen Elmes stood by the rear seat door, to say goodby to Shamus Ginsberg.

Putting his hand on Ford's arm, he delayed the Clipper's Captain from joining the other two.

"Captain, I know that the odds are against you making it from here back to America. And I'm sure everyone has told you that you can't make it. I think you can... at least as far as India!"

They had reached the car and the four stood and before they could make their goodbys, Ginsberg took Kathleen Elmes's hand in his.

"Lt. Elmes, I know your dying to find out what happened to Surabaja Sue and Colin McCarthy. Would you like the movie scenario, the truth or an old Irishman's version. For someone as beautiful as you and an obvious romantic, my recollections will be the truth. The two had fallen in love. Sue and Colin decided to leave Java and they sold the Black Swan to a group of local Dutch investors. They were married at a small church of no particular domination and the wedding was attended by all who were anyone in Surabaja. The next day, a very expensive sloop was docked over there at the landing and Colin and Sue boarded her, looked back at the crowd and their friends, waived as Colin started the engines. He took her out into the harbor and amid the blasting of horns from all the freighters and other boats, they slowly motored out to the opening into the bay. As they cleared the harbor, Colin hoisted the mainsail and they were off to who knows where. Sometimes someone will come into the Swan saying they saw Sue and Colin living like royalty on some island in the South Pacific. In truth, no one knows where they are and that was the way they wanted it. Oh, by the way, they named the sloop the Black Swan II," Shamus Ginsberg finished his tale of Surabaja Sue and her Irish lover.

Kathleen Elmes leaned over and kissed Shamus Ginsberg on the cheek and she had tears in her eyes. As she got in the front seat and John Mack the back, Ford and Ginsberg walked around to the other side. Ford shook hands with the innkeeper and as he tried to thank him for the afternoon, Ginsberg leaned close to Ford and whispered in his ear. "Watch your back. Don't trust anyone. The Pacific Clipper is a major prize. Be very careful."

The three were silent as the car pulled away. Ford turned to wave goodby to the tavern owner and it suddenly dawned on him that he hadn't paid for the drinks and silently chalked up another small debt he owed Shamus Ginsberg. He was about to tell the driver where to go when it dawned on him that he didn't know where to tell him to go, or how to say it in the local jargon. And most importantly, he knew he had no money to pay for the cab ride! As he was about to ask Mack if he had any money, the driver spoke and his English was exceptional!

"Good afternoon, Captain Ford, Mr. Mack and Lt. Elmes. My name is Tacki. I have been assigned by Mr. Ginsberg to chauffeur you about Surabaja until you leave us. Mr. Ginsberg has also assigned two other cars for use by the other members of your crew should they wish to see Surabaja," Tacki said, introducing himself and setting any concern aside that Ford might have had.

The car was slowly weaving it way through the crowded street and ahead Ford could finally see the high three fins of the rear assembly of the Pacific Clipper. "Captain, you, Mr. Mack and Lt. Elmes are invited to the VanGelder's plantation for cocktails and dinner. You are expected at 7PM. For your information, all important government officials and leading members of Surabaja society will be there in your honor. Mr. Ginsberg has instructed me to take you to the VanGelders. The other members of the crew have been invited to be Mr. Ginsberg's guests at the Black Swan."

"Thank you Tacki. We'll pass on the dinner invitation. We have far too much to do getting ready for tomorrow," Bob Ford responded.

"Beg your pardon, Captain. Mr. Ginsberg told me to tell you to go; said it important if you wanted to get out of Surabaja!" Tacki stated.

Ford was about to respond when he remembered Shamus' warning a few minutes earlier. Ford felt that Ginsberg was not the kind of man to throw out warnings easily unless there was a real threat to the Clipper and the crew. They were strangers in a foreign land and knew nothing of the local politics.

"Tacki, tell Mr. Ginsberg we'll be delighted to attend. But unless the dress is very informal, what you see is what we'll be wearing. I can't speak for Lt. Elmes but unless Mr. Mack has a tux hidden in his wardrobe, he and I will appear as we are."

"Don't worry Captain. The old Dutchman will be telling his grandchildren how he entertained the famous Captain Ford of the Pacific Clipper. And if you wear those uniforms, he'll be so much the happier! But Captain, the Dutch may seem slow but they have a price for everything and they are great traders. Count your fingers after shaking hands," Tacki warned. This was the second warning Ford had received about the Dutch and now he was going to a party he didn't want to attend because Ginsberg had warned him he had to. Why remained a mystery but he suspected he'd find out tonight at Colonel VanGelder's estate. Ford shook his head as he remembered that just a few hours ago, he'd almost had his plane blown out of the sky by the same VanGelder that was now throwing a party in their honor!

As they approached the gate leading to the dock, the crowd parted to allow the car to go through the gate. Getting out, the three moved quickly to the Clipper and their shipmates. Norm Brown was at the gangplank to greet Ford. "Ok, Norm, what is the situation here?" Ford's attitude told Brown he wasn't ready for any of that "If you had listened to me, Sir" crap so he made his report succinctly.

"No 100 octane. Mr. Henricksen and Swede Rothe went over to the Dutch airdrome after you left for the Australian Embassy. For whatever reason, as of now, there is no aviation fuel for us," the Second Officer reported.

Ford looked at Brown and knew he had another opinion as to why and asked for it. "Norm, have you any idea of why they would not give us the fuel?"

"Captain. There is aviation gas here and the Dutch as much as told Jim and the Swede that. But for some reason, we can't have any of it. Why? None of us could figure out any rationale answer. While you were in town, maybe someone explained all of this to you," he asked.

"Wish they had Norm but the subject never came up. However, maybe this evening we'll get to the bottom of things. The three of us are invited to a party at Colonel VanGelders, the man who ordered us blown out of the sky! I rather suspect that there we'll find out why one of the richest oil countries in the world has no aviation fuel for us. Oh, by the way, does any one have any money?" Ford asked his crew.

They looked at him in wonder. Never had any of them ever needed money on any flight for Pan Am. Wherever they landed, they would just sign Pan Am's name for their bills and Pan Am would pay them. Across the world, a Pan Am signature was always honored. So why the need for anything more than pocket money? The crew looked at their Captain, shrugged their shoulders and that told him they didn't have any cash either.

"What a mess. Here I am, Captain of the flagship of the greatest airline in the world and we probably don't have twenty buck between us. And Mr. Juan Trippe, since you won't let me break radio silence so I can call and ask, just what am I to do when I must pay in cash for the gas we need? Do you really think some towelhead in Arabia is going to fill the Clipper's tanks and take a Pan Am marker!" Ford thought as he realized his humor was becoming quite black. "But what in hell am I going to do for money?"

Before he could continue in his self pity, John Poindexter came down the stairs from the flight deck, a piece of paper in his hand, looking at Ford and Kathleen.

"Yes, John. What is it?" Ford asked.

"Not sure Captain. I picked up the first one as we were landing but you were too busy to bother. Anyway it was in code as is the second. That was sent almost immediately after we landed. Both were outgoing and both sent from somewhere near Surabaja and by the same person. I recognized his touch the second time he transmitted," the shanghaied radioman explained.

Poindexter passed the coded messages to Ford who looked at the gibberish and passed them on to Lt. Elmes. She studied them for a few seconds, looked at the two and shrugged.

"Sorry. However, an educated guess is that someone is very interested in our movements and is tracking us. John told me that he had picked up a transmission from Darwin after we landed. Like these, it was outgoing with no return," She summarized.

"Ok, lets not start worrying about mysterious transmissions. There is a war going on and we know the Japanese are coming this way so there is bound to be a great deal of coded messages being sent to and from these areas. Thank you John, and you Lt," he concluded as he looked at his watch and swore. "Damn. As I said, John, Lt. Elmes and myself have to go to this stupid party. However, Mr. Ginsberg has been kind enough to have two cars with drivers available to the rest of you to come to the Black Swan as his guests. Norm, you and Jim decide who'll stand the first watch. Any questions?" Ford asked, knowing his men were all professionals and would keep the "what-if" questions to themselves. So with no one saying anything, Ford and Mack went up to the flight deck and their little rooms to get ready for the evening. Kathleen Elmes turned and headed for the Master Suite.

Australian Embassy in Surabaja

While Bob Ford was having his explosion in the office of the Australian attache, a distinguished looking gentleman was standing in the rear of the room observing. He was Sir Reginald Leach, the British Ambassador to all of Indonesia and based in Batavia. He was in Surabaja to make sure of the arrangements to evacuate British diplomatic personnel. With him was his aide, Edward Finch. After the Americans left, the Ambassador turned to his host, Otto Brock, the Mayor of Surabaja and asked him what in the world could have cause the ruckus. The Mayor explained that the American Clipper ship had almost been shot down by accident, that the Australian Embassy was to have been told of their coming from Darwin and alerted the Dutch Air Defenses. The American captain was understandably upset, the Mayor explained. Leach nodded his thanks and went over to offer his commiserations to the Aussie, a Mr. Armstrong. Flattered that someone so important as Sir Reginald felt sympathy for him, he invited the Ambassador back to his office for a drink. When Sir Reginald accepted, the Aussie was quite surprised, knowing the Englishman's low opinion of Australians. But there was something that Sir Reginald sensed about what he had just witnessed that intrigued him. He felt there was more to this and there might be something in it for him. So paying his respect to the underling from Australia was not out of sympathy but opportunism. He was very curious about the American plane. He'd heard about the new Pan Am planes, the Boeings and now one had landed in Java, part of his domain. There could be an opportunity here.

As he entered the office of the attache, the Ambassador immediately walked over to the chair behind the desk and sat. His aide and the Aussie stood for a second, when the side door opened and the secretary entered with a tray carrying a filled ice bucket, three highball glasses and an unopened bottle of whiskey. The Ambassador abhorred the American habit of putting ice in a glass of whiskey and when he looked at the bottle, he recognized that it was Haig & Haig, what the Americans called "pinch." He also knew that the company that made the whiskey was controlled by the former American Ambassador to the Court of St. James, that Irish bastard Joe Kennedy. Sir Reginald could never fantom why Whitehall didn't understand that Roosevelt was tweaking England's nose by naming an Irish Catholic that was having affairs with movie stars to the most important diplomatic post in the world. He knew Queen Victoria would never have accepted the credentials of Joe Kennedy. But he took the whiskey when it was offered, along with the ice.

As the other two fixed their drinks, Sir Reginald sipped and thought about his favorite subject, himself. He was playing second banana to Mountbatten in this smelly, sweaty, steamy asshole of the world. He should be in London, lending his expertise to Churchill and General Staff, helping where the real war was being fought, against the Germans. But he was stuck in the backwaters of Asia with the flies, the filth and the unwashed millions of aliens. Leach thought of all Asians as subhumans and as he tromped from capital to capital, it took all the cunning and tact of his staff to keep the Ambassador from causing a major diplomatic flap. He looked like a British Ambassador right out of central casting. He was tall, quite handsome with a thin, grey mustache and his whole demeanor bespoke of the centuries of proper breeding. His obvious disdain for the people of the Commonwealth, including Wales, Scotland and especially Ireland, made it very difficult for the Foreign office to keep him in the diplomatic corps. So Whitehall sent him to Indonesia, never dreaming that one day the Japanese would strike and Sir Reginald would be in the midst of it all. But the war was going so badly that any problems Ambassador Leach caused were ignored.

And Sir Reginald knew exactly what Churchill, Whitehall and the rest thought of him. To him, they were the ones that didn't know what was happening out here. They treated the colonies with kid gloves. England had conquered India, much of the Middle East, Australia, Ceylon, Australia, Canada and most of Indochina, with the exception of a few countries the Dutch and French had taken. So what was all this drivel about freedom. He had strongly approved the Japanese move into China to claim Manchuria as part of the Japanese Empire. After all, wasn't that the way England became the greatest colonial empire in the history of the world? You just walk in and take it. But do it under the guise of "protecting the little man against war lords, despots and dictators," or whatever.

Now he sat in the chair of a second level official from one of the colonies, sipping a whiskey. He wasn't certain why he felt that the miserable exhibition he'd just witnessed held promise for him but he knew that the Boeing plane was at the heart of the matter. Maybe the man from downunder could tell him why.

"Mr... ah, my apologies but I'm not certain of the pronunciation of your name, my good man. How do you say it," the Ambassador asked, hiding the fact that he hadn't the foggiest idea of the Aussies name.

"Armstrong, Sir. Lawrence Armstrong," the attache replied knowing full well the Ambassador didn't have a clue when he walked in here who was his host.

"Right. Armstrong. Yes. Well, my colleague and I certainly sympathize with the way that lout of an American treated you. The man should be horsewhipped!" the Ambassador commented. "Please enlighten us on why the Americans are here in Java and why the fuss over a plane."

Armstrong looked at the Ambassador, whose mein was one of calm and conviviality He could see his aide, Finch standing nearby. Finch was a dolt, a loser but from a family born to the purple. Finch couldn't make it as a goat herder but his family put him in the Foreign Service after pulling him through Oxford. Whitehall stuck Leach with him, feeling they were kindred souls. Armstrong had heard the stories about the Ambassador. They called him 'Sir Reggie the Ridiculous' in the stripped pants circuit. But his question raised a warning flag in the Aussies mind. "Careful, ole sot. He may look like a mannequin but he is a peer of the Empire. Protect thy ass," Armstrong thought before answering and he wondered what answer he should give.

"I'm afraid I don't follow you, Sir," he replied.

"Ah, he is not as dumb as he looks! This could be fun," the Ambassador mused as he formed his answer.

"It is a simple question, Mr. Armstrong. Why is this particular plane so important? I mean, with all the hollering and pounding in the other room, one would have assumed that the plane was made of gold," Leach replied.

The Aussie answered. "Sir, the Sutherland is the jewel of the British commercial air fleet. The plane that landed here this afternoon, the Pacific Clipper is the jewel of Pan American Airways. And quite simply, Mr. Ambassador, the Sutherland is paste when compared to the Pacific Clipper."

The Ambassador coughed as Ambassadors do when stalling, not wanting to show his hand. "Ah, my young aborigine, you have given me the key. The Pacific Clipper. But easy here. Don't seem too excited," Leach thought to himself.

"I'm afraid that you overrate the American plane. Our engineers assure us that the Sutherland is the best commercial plane flying. You disagree?" the Ambassador asked, leading the young man on.

"Sir Reginald, quite frankly, comparing the Sutherland to the Pacific Clipper is like comparing the Golden Hind to the Queen Mary," Lawrence Armstrong answered. The Ambassador reacted as if the Aussie had flipped a wet haddock into his lap!

"By Jove, young man. The Sutherland is the pride of England, the finest commercial plane built in the world. And I resent your comparison of Queen of the Seas to a ship built three hundred years ago. I say, have you no pride in the Empire!" Sir Reginald responded.

"What a crock of roo dung! But why do I have the feeling that you're baiting me, overreacting so I'll tell you more. And why are you so interested in the American plane? There is something else here and I better watch out. You may look like a character from a Dickens novel Mr. Ambassador but you are up to something. What?"

"Mr. Ambassador, the Southerland is a fine plane. The Pacific Clipper is the best. And why she is so much better than anything flying today is right there in the magazines about aviation that sit on my shelf. To answer another part of your initial question, Sir, the Americans are just trying to get home!"

And Sir Reginald Leach almost jumped out of his chair. The Aussie had hit it, the thing he was looking for, the reason he had felt there was much more than the spat between the pilot and this poor soul. "Home! Going home. The Americans are here, trying to get back to America; as their ally, I should help them. And I will. Ha!"

"Mr. Armstrong, please illuminate me. Why is this particular plane so valuable," the Ambassador asked.

"Sir Reginald, on the shelf behind you is an issue of an American magazine called Air Age. Everything you want to know about the Boeing 314A is there in that article," the attache stated.

"Mr. Armstrong, I know the Americans are somewhat backwards when it comes to protecting their secrets but every nation in the world would know the Boeing's secrets," the Ambassador prodded.

And Armstrong bit. Walking over to the shelf behind Sir Reginald, he picked up one magazine and opened it to the article about the Boeing 314A. Placing it on the desk in front of the Ambassador, he stood back while Leach read.

"Plane has the greatest range and can carry the heaviest payload in aviation... fly non-stop over 5000 miles... each of the four Wright

Cyclones generates 1600 horsepower... the young man was not exaggerating," the Ambassador thought.

"With that range, she could bomb Berlin, land on water somewhere in Russia, like the Aral Sea, reload and bomb the Germans again on the return trip home!" the Ambassador mused, this time out loud so both the Armstrong and Finch could hear him.

"I'm sorry, Sir. The Boeing could reach Germany, that is true but even she doesn't have the range to fly from New York to Russia and back to America," Finch injected, finally getting the chance to contribute. The withering look he received from Sir Reginald made Armstrong feel sorry for the poor slob.

"Mr. Armstrong, it is obvious that you think this American plane will leave Java. But where can it go? I mean, it needs petrol and I assume someplace where the plane's engines can be tended to. Right? Where would you go?" Sir Reginald asked and the Aussie jumped right in, being flattered to offer his opinion, forgetting his own cautions of a few minutes ago.

"Ceylon, Sir. Probably Trincomalee. There is a British Naval installation there and aviation gasoline available. If I were her captain, that is my next stop," As he was about to continue, there was a knock at the door and his secretary looked in and spoke.

"Pardon me, Mr. Armstrong. An invitation from Colonel Van-Gelder has arrived for Ambassador Leach, Mr. Finch and you to attend a party at the Colonel's estate. Cocktails are at 7PM. Oh yes, the American Captain has been invited," she nodding, closed the door.

"Well. Mr. Finch and I were planning to return to Batavia today but this will give us more time to talk with our Dutch allies about evacuating our subjects. And with the American captain there, I'm sure you'll have something to say to him, right, Mr. Armstrong," the Ambassador said as he arose from his chair and walked towards the door, being held open by Finch and the two departed. The Aussie walked over to his desk, put more ice in his glass and filled it with "pinch," He picked up the magazine and began reading about the Boeing, but his mind wandered back to the conversation with the Ambassador. "Why the interest in the American plane? Why should it matter to him where they went from here. Leach doesn't give a damn about the Americans. Why? A British Ambassador spending 15 minutes with a low level Australian attache, drinking his whiskey. Unheard of. And although I've made fun of him, now meeting him for the first time, Leach is a much more formidable man than most think. Well, I better finish this drink and get my ass in gear if I'm going to be at the

VanGelders on time. And I'll have my shot at that arrogant bastard Captain Ford. He shamed me. I'll get even tonight."

The Jungle above Surabaja

As interested in the Pacific Clipper as the Ambassador to Indonesia was, there was another even more concerned. A few hours earlier, he stood in the verdant woods above Surabaja and watched as the Dutch Air Force attacked his prey. His mission in Java was about to go down in flames. Then Buddha took mercy on him and the Dutch allowed the Pacific Clipper to land in the harbor. So now, Major Seishu Thu's mission was still a go. When the word came that the Americans could land, Thu silently thanked the gods. Now a few hours later, the Major was deep into the plans of fulfilling his mission, capturing the American plane and bringing her to Kota Bharu and Commodore Tanaka. Suddenly, there was activity down the trail leading to his camp. Thu looked as one of his soldiers escorted a visitor... Mr. Jalara, a respected businessman from Surabaja. He owned a tailor shop along the Jalan Tunjugan that was often frequented by the leaders of Dutch society. They considered him an ideal Javanese, making a success in his business while completely happy with the Dutch rulership. Mr. Jalara was also the clandestine leader of the Sarkari, Java's strong insurrectionist movement! Jalara welcomed the coming invasion, knowing that the Japanese would help rid the Javanese of the foreigners, the Dutch. Thu, watching his ally walk towards him, smiled about Jalara's future.

"Too bad, my friend. Soon, you will be standing in front of a firing squad. As you would turn over the Dutch to us to get rid of them, so you would lead your people against us after living under our rule," the Japanese officer mulled as Jalara neared.

Bowing, Jalara took the extended hand of Major Thu, and nodding to Lt. Auho, began his report. "Major Thu, there is no fuel for the American plane! Two members of their crew went to the airdrome and requested fuel and were told that there was only enough for the Dutch fighter planes. Does this mean that they will stay here and be captured by your troops when the invasion comes?" Jalara reported and asked.

"Where else could the Americans get their aviation fuel" Thu asked, knowing that his whole scheme depended on capturing the Americans while they were in the air and then flying them Kota Bharu. Where would they Americans go for fuel?

'"There are the great oil refineries of the Royal Dutch Shell Oil Company, about 100 miles up the coast at Rembang," the tailor reported. "The gas that is at the airdrome is for the Brewsters even though the Dutch do not expect those planes to last more than one attack. So the Americans are stuck here unless there is enough gas left in their tanks to go to another place."

Thu sat back and looked at his pilot and then at the tailor. He didn't want to discuss anything about his plans for the American plane and all the tailor knew was that he was just to report on the gasoline needs of the Americans. Rising, Thu stood and shook hands with Jalara. Bowing, the tailor walked out of the tent as the same soldier escorted him down the path away from their camp. Suddenly, the tailor stopped and walked back towards Thu.

"One other thing of some importance. The British Ambassador is here. He met this afternoon with the Australians. One of my people heard that he had been invited to a party being given at the VanGelders tonight and delayed his flight back to Batavia just to attend. I do not know what this means or if it is of any import to you but since it does involve the British Ambassador, I thought you should know."

Jalara turned and began to walk away. Thu called to him and nodded back towards the tent. He needed more information. Once inside and the soldier gone, he looked at the tailor and told him to repeat everything his people in the Australian Embassy had heard. Jalara then told of the shouting match between the American captain and the attache, the visit of the three to the Black Swan, their return to the plane and the conversation between the young Australian and the Ambassador. He concluded that six of his people would be working at the VanGelder party and would report to him when it was over. If he thought some of the information was important, he'd bring it to Major Thu the next morning.

"My good Jalara, you will report to me tonight after the party. We will move the camp after you leave so go to the third station and my men will escort you to the new camp," Thu ordered.

Thu stood and again shook the tailor's hand. "Remember, tell your people to report everything they see and hear at the party tonight, especially any information about when the American plan to leave, if they can," Jalara nodded and as he again began down the path, he could see some of the commandos beginning to pack for their move. He found that amusing and a waste of energy. The Dutch were not looking for Japanese soldiers. They were afraid they might find some!

Chapter 7

What Price Gas?

1815 hours aboard the Pacific Clipper

As Ford, Mack and Kathleen Elmes left the rest of the crew on the passenger level to get ready for the evening, some of the Clipper's crew began to speculate what their special code breaker would wear tonight.

"She had only that little suitcase when she came aboard in LA and unless she shopped in Auckland, all she's had to wear is that Navy uniform," Barney Swacki stated.

"You're right Barney but we are dealing with a woman. My bet is that she'll come up with something better than her uniform to wear tonight," Norm Brown offered.

"I'm with you, Mr. Brown," Swede Rothe added. "She'll have something on that is a knockout."

"She could wear a sack cloth and hunting boots and she'd still be the best looking thing the Dutchmen have ever seen," John Steers chipped in," To a chorus of "Amen and you said it" the rest of the men began to ready themselves for the evening.

The object of their interest was standing inside the door to the Master Suite, looking at her closet, knowing what was hanging in there and not anxious to open it. She thought of her closets at home, stuffed with clothes. She would often change her outfit two, three or even four times before her date arrived. With the exception of the day that Pearl Harbor was bombed, she had worn her Navy uniforms. Resignedly, she walked over to the closet and opened the door, quietly saying a prayer that something was hanging there that she'd forgotten about. There wasn't. As she looked she could almost hear her Dad hooting at she and her mother when they came home from a shopping spree, something about needing another dress like a fifth thumb. What she wouldn't give to have just one of those closets to choose from. Now, looking at the disaster that was her wardrobe, she took out all the clothes and lay them on her bed. Looking at them she saw another uniform, a pair of white bell-bottom slacks, a cream colored skirt, two blouses, white and blue, and a blazer, Navy blue, of course. And the green and white summer dress she'd worn that horrible morning. Her shoe selection was just as limited. Another pair of ugly Navy shoes, a pair of penny loafers, spectator pumps and wonder of wonders, white heels, patten leather, perfect for this weather and tonight. The surprise lifted her spirits. Now she studied the clothes on the bed and critically looked at them, trying to visualize different combinations, something that would knock the Dutch on their collective heels, as well as impressing her fellow crew members, including that stiff, Captain Robert Ford.

Looking at the meager selection in front of her, Kathleen felt almost resigned to wearing the blue blazer with the white slacks. If she had a Captain's cap, she could pretend she was Marlene Dietrich in "South Sea Woman," have a cigarette dangling from her lips and give the eye to all the men in uniform! Staring at the clothes, she racked her brain for some combination that would let her look like a woman. She couldn't bring herself to put on that Navy uniform this night. "Kathleen, you need an inspiration, a Coco Chanel to fly in from the night and create a night! That's it, night. Mom's going away present. The thing she bought at Saks, the robe, the caftan!" Spinning on her heels, she threw open the door of the closet and there on the floor was her little suitcase. Quickly, she brought it out and putting it on the bed, she reached in and searching with her right hand, she could feel in the corner, pushed against the side of the case a package. Taking it out, she slipped off the Saks' wrapper and there was her evening gown, a crimson polished cotton caftan, with gold braid around the voluminous sleeves, the hem and the plunging neckline.

"Whee, I've got it! Thank you Mother for making me take this robe on the trip. I hope someday to tell you how it saved the haute couture reputation of American women in Java! Look out VanGelders, here comes plain Jane of the United States Navy, soon to be our great Cinderella!"

Laying the robe on the bed, she planned her accessories. The robe itself was long, coming just to her ankles. Her Mother had included a pair of gold mules to go with the caftan and the heels were high enough to let her wear silk stockings. The hem was designed to give maximum freedom of movement, in a bedroom or alone in the house. But the slit up the side would surely expose her legs up to and above the knees. She quickly dismissed any modest concerns since the women of Asia had worn long silk dresses slit up the side for centuries. As for the plunging neckline, let them think it was decadent America on display. She'd seen many a ball gown that left very little to the imagination. But the caftan was a smock, draping from neck to foot with no flattering curves. And she wanted to show her figure. Looking around at her selection of belts, just two, the heavy Navy issue and the thin green one she wore with the summer dress, she knew neither would do. Something triggered her mind and she remembered in the Master Suite, the small drapes pulled aside of the portholes were tied back with golden sashes. Quickly walking over to one, she undid it and wrapping it around her waist it seemed to be a little loose but with the caftan on, the sash would bring the robe tight and show off her figure. And grinning from ear to ear, she remembered that on one of the few afternoons she had free in Auckland, she joined a couple of the other women at the Embassy and went shopping. In a charming boutique, she bought herself a pair of earrings, telling one of the other girls that no woman should be without a pair of hooped golden earrings. Taking them out of her little jewelry case, putting them next to the gold braid from the porthole, the match was close enough that even some Dutch dowager looking down her lorgnette would not notice they were not a perfect match.

Quickly checking off what she had before her, looking to see if her eclectic grouping was complete enough to be the belle of the ball, Kathleen Elmes stood back and surveyed her finery, a bathrobe, bedroom slippers, a sash that held back a small drape next to a port hole, silk stockings and a pair of earrings from Auckland. How could a girl go wrong with such a wardrobe! And then there was her hair. For this evening, she decided that she would wear it in a chignon, the braid not quite complete, leaving some of her blond hair flowing loosely down her neck to the collar of the caftan.

"I know there is a war on and I'm not suppose to be having fun," the Naval Intelligence officer thought, "but, wow! I'm going to a party in Java with the Japs just days away and no way is anyone there going to be more beautiful than Cliff and Jill's daughter, of course, all this is in the line of duty for the United States Navy, and the great Pacific Clipper!

When Kathleen emerged from the Master Suite to leave for the party, the whole crew was sitting around in the lounge, waiting to see their three representatives off to the big bash, but especially to ogle the

Navy's compliment to the group. As she walked down the aisle towards them, they stood and began clapping and Barney let out a wolf's whistle. Kathleen stopped and with a low curtsey, acknowledged the applause and warm affection. Rising, with a huge smile on her face. she swept out the door on the arm of John Mack, Captain Robert Ford trailing but smiling.

The Party at the Van Gelders

The road they traveled on was almost empty of automobiles but jammed with people walking towards the hills, most carrying everything they owned on their heads or in baskets on their bikes. It was a grim scene and the elation the Americans felt when they swept out of the Clipper to go to the party was quickly blunted by what was in front and around them. And while Bob Ford saw the same things that John Mack and Kathleen Elmes did, his mind was focused on only one thing, getting gas for the Clipper. No gas and no go. He knew the tanks were a little more than half full of 100 octane. He needed them filled if they hoped to reach Ceylon in one shot. Worse case scenerio would be to fill the tanks with 87 octane but the thought of putting automobile gasoline in those beauties made his skin crawl.

The thoughts about fuel brought Ford back to the warning from Shamus Ginsberg to "be careful," Ford had flown often enough to the Far East to understand how swiftly news could circulate and it was probably that Ginsberg already knew that the Dutch were going to give them a hard time about the gasoline when they entered the Black Swan. But why would the Dutch want to obstruct their flight home, why keep them here? The plane itself had no military usefulness. So keeping them here wouldn't help the Dutch. Ford did not for one moment believe, no matter what Norm Brown reported, that there wasn't aviation fuel available, not with one of the world's great refineries just an hour away. That and the rubber were the reasons the Japanese were on their way to Java.

He knew he wouldn't solve the problem in the back seat of the car and so he forced himself to put the gas question behind him and find something to focus on. He found it in the right hand driver's seat. Looking at Kathleen Elmes, he was amazed how she was able to make an outfit so stunning out of a robe and a rope! She was a knockout and he felt himself beginning to think of her other than the bearer of bad tidings.

The crowds along the road had thinned considerably and now the three Americans could appreciate the land they were driving through.

The road to the Van Gelders wound along the waters of Machain Bay above Surabaja and to Kathleen Elmes, the sandy banks recalled her days as a child playing along the shores of Chesapeake Bay. Looking off to the left at a grove of trees hugging the hugging the ground, the land reminded John Mack of the Napa Valley and the vineyards of Central California. Ford saw in the rich, loamy black soil of the rolling hills something that reminded him of the farms of Southern Wisconsin, some of the richest farmlands in the world. This was beautiful country and it was no wonder the Dutch wanted to keep it, the Japanese needed it and the natives wanted it back. The American's sympathies were with the losers in the coming struggle, the natives who were, for the most part, un-armed.

Up ahead they could see white railed fences that stretched for at least half mile. Tacki, their driver, told them the fences marked the beginning of the VanGelder estate. The Americans were quite impressed. No one had bother to alert them that the Colonel and his lady lived on an estate of such beauty. Resting on a small knoll in the lush Surabajan lowlands, the three could see that the house commanded a beautiful view of the hills to the rear and the bay to their front. As they swung into the driveway and headed for the house, the three began to compare the VanGelder home to ones they knew. Leaning forward from the back seat, John Mack said, "Tara. But missing that beautiful winding staircase."

"Mount Vernon," Kathleen Elmes countered.

"No. Not Mount Vernon. That's George Washington's place," Ford chided.

"No kidding, Captain. Thanks for the history lesson," she said.

"You're both wrong," John Mack said.

Before they could continue with their little game, the car stopped and a liveried footman dressed in the traditional Dutch Liederhosen and vests, skillfully colored in the Netherlands's red, white and blue, opened the doors and helped them from the car. As they got out, Kathleen took the extended arm of one of the servants, and, as she began up the steps, she shot back over her shoulder, "Mount Vernon."

Reaching the top of the stairs, Ford stopped and moved over to the side. The other two came over and he spoke. "Look, I'm very nervous about this. Why anyone would want to throw a party with the Japanese steaming here at flank speed is beyond me. I've got a gut feeling that this little shindig directly affects us. Let's keep our ears open and hopefully, we'll find out how we can get 100 plus fuel," Then he laughed. "And maybe someone will tell us how to pay for it!"

Finished, he stood aside as John Mack offered his arm to Kathleen and they entered ahead of the Captain. Inside, they could see a crowd of maybe fifty to sixty people mixing easily, enjoying the hors d'oeuvres and champagne offered by the waiters circulating among them. The room was wide and long, stretching about halfway across the length of the house. Thirty feet ahead, a wide portal led to another room where they could see buffet tables set up on either side of the room and at the rear, a small eight piece band playing softly. On either side of the entryway to the dining area two bars were being attended by three men at each, serving drinks other than champagne. And standing just to their right, greeting his guests was their host, Colonel Alphonse VanGelder and his wife. Just as the three moved forward, the Colonel spotted them and began to stride briskly towards them. He was resplendent in his full dress uniform of the Royal Dutch Army, the waist jacket a deep blue with gold stripes embroidered along the sleeves, from the cuff to the elbow. The front of the jacket was buttoned from the waist up to the neck with large, silver dollar in size buttons, the collar was bright red velvet, matching the trowsers he wore. A large gold sash encircled his girth and he wore black evening pumps on his feet. The Colonel looked magnificent and equally uncomfortable.

Extending both hands, he beamed as he greeted Kathleen. "Ah, Miss Elmes. Your beauty does wonders for this old house. Captain Ford and Mr. Mack, welcome to our humble home. If you don't mind, I'll monopolize Miss Elmes for a few minutes. I want to introduce her to Mrs. Van Gelder and the other ladies," the jocular Colonel stated as he placed Kathleen's left hand on his right arm and began moving towards their hostess. Ford and Mack just stood there until the waiter came by and rescued them with a glass of champagne. Sipping and looking around the room, they both spotted what appeared to be the Grand Marshall of the St. Patrick's Day parade, Shamus Ginsberg, dressed in the tartans of his ancestors from the 'ole sod.' The innkeeper put out both hands to greet the Americans and Mack and Ford each took one.

"Ah, the honored guests. I assume both of you know this spur of the moment wing ding is strictly to exhibit you three. But come, let us repair to the bar for some sterner stuff than the bubbly," the Irish man invited.

As the three turned to go over to one of the bars, Ford's eyes picked up the form of the Australian attache leaning against the bar, his right elbow resting on the wooden top while in his left hand was a drink. The Aussie was looking at him and Ford didn't need anyone to tell him what thoughts were racing through the mind of the man from Downunder. Suddenly, the Aussie pushed himself away from the bar and began lurching towards them. Ginsberg had caught the exchange of glances between the two, being well aware of Ford's verbal lambasting of Armstrong earlier. He turned to warn Ford but before he could say anything, the American pilot strode directly at the man. Putting out his hand in greeting, the American took the suddenly startled Aussie's in his.

"Mr. Armstrong, let me apologize for my rude behavior this afternoon. I was completely off-base, blaming you for the mix-up on the message about our arrival. I hope you will forgive me and join me and my friends at the bar for a drink," Ford announced, completely catching the young man by surprise. As Armstrong groped for a response, Sir Reginald Leach appeared at his side, looking at Ford.

"Captain Ford. I am impressed with your understanding of the delicate nature of Mr. Armstrong's psyche. Your confrontation this afternoon was most disruptive to my friend. Fortunately, I was in the room when it happened and later was able to explain to him that your reaction was quite natural considering the circumstances. And I'm sure that if Mr. Armstrong would close his mouth and remember his manners, he could introduce us. However, let me do that. I am Sir Reginald Leach, His Majesty's Ambassador to Indonesia. And if you have a few minutes, may we get together for a brief chat. Is now a good time, before we are called to dinner?" the Ambassador asked, putting out his right hand to shake Ford's.

Ford automatically took the Ambassador's hand and as he shook it, the first thing that popped into his mind was "My God, its a young C. Aubury Smith. Of course, he has to be the British Ambassador!"

"Mr. Ambassador, I'm pleased to meet you," Ford responded, releasing his grip on the Ambassador's hand and turning slightly to his right. " May I introduce my First Officer, Mr. John Henry Mack and our host this afternoon at his wonderful establishment, the Black Swan, Mr. Shamus Ginsberg."

Both men moved forward to shake the Ambassador's hand and Ginsberg, after greeting the Ambassador, stood off to the side, looked at Ford and rolled his eyes, a clear warning to avoid a meeting with Sir Reginald. The Ambassador finished his greeting with John Mack and turned to the owner of the Black Swan.

"Mr. Ginsberg. I wish my schedule permitted me time to visit your famed establishment. Of course, we in Batavia and even in India have heard of the fabulous carvings of the Clipper ships at your pub. They were done by an Englishman, I believe. The same man that legend has it lives like a maharajah with the enchantress, Surabaja Sue. Ah, the stories we hear out here in the East, Captain Ford. Scheherazade would need another thousand nights to tell those. But to more mundane things. I think we could find mutual benefit if you and I could take a few minutes and chat," the Ambassador almost commanded.

"Sir Reginald, I would be delighted to visit with you but I'm sure that with what is coming down from Singapore, the British Ambassador must have time only for people far more important than me to see here tonight," Ford responded.

"By Victoria's balls! Another diplomat," the Ambassador thought as he nodded at Ford's answer. "Why is he suspicious, already on the alert? I thought all Americans were easy to read. This Captain may prove to be a little more difficult but he is the product of an inferior system so I should not worry."

"Captain, I appreciate your concern over my schedule with, as you so aptly put it, 'what's going on out here.' And that is precisely why I wish to speak with you. Our host has made his study available for our get together and shall we adjourn to it?" Sir Reginald instructed as he slowly began walking towards a door adjacent to the anteroom. Ford had no choice but to follow and as they entered the library, John Mack and Shamus Ginsberg looked at each other and Mack shrugged. Forgotten in the brief encounter was the Australian attache, who turned, walked over to the bar, and ordered another Haig & Haig.

The room the Ambassador and Bob Ford entered was quite luxurious. From ceiling to floor, bookcases dominated the room. Lined with red, black and green leather volumes were literary classics, encyclopedias, atlases and other works. It was apparent that the VanGelders' prided themselves on their collection of fine books and as he admired the gathered titles, Ford wondered just how many had ever had their gold leafing cracked. Against the back wall of the library was the fireplace, crackling with a very comfortable blaze. To the left, another door leading to what he thought was probably a small pantry. Over the mantle above the fireplace was a magnificent painting, a Rembrandt, with frame, almost six feet across and four feet high. Ford didn't know the name of the painting or if it was an original but he felt it was.

In front of the fireplace were four, high backed red leather chairs spaced in a semi-circle around a low coffee table, maybe six feet in length and about two feet high off the Persian rug. In the center of the table sat a silver service with an ice bucket instead of a coffee urn. The bucket was filled with ice and there were two bottles of champagne and two tall crystal goblets in it being chilled for the two guests.

They sat, one at each end of the coffee table. The Ambassador leaned forward to inspect the vintage and make of the champagne from the Colonel's cellar. "Well, the good Colonel must have an excellent cellar and knows his champagne. It is Tattingers, 1927. I say, that was a very fine year. Have some myself at the castle in Essex. Shall I do the honors, Captain Ford?" Sir Reginald asked as he deftly placed his two thumbs below the imprisoned cork and pushed up. The cork came loose and just as it was about to fly off the bottle's neck, the Ambassador, with his left hand took the cork slowly out and a soft 'whoosh' was heard as the air escaped from the green bottle. Taking the two goblets, Sir Reginald poured the golden liquid into each glass, about two thirds full and finished, placed the bottle back into the ice bucket and slid one glass over to Ford and raised his glass.

"Usually, I thrust my glass out and say, in as serious a manner as I can, 'to the King!' but with you, Captain Ford, such formalities are quite unnecessary. Instead, let's toast to our eventual victory over these bastards," Raising his glass, the Englishman sipped on the delicious wine. Ford did the same, remembering it was only two days ago he was doing the same thing with the American Ambassador in Auckland. "Ok, Mr. Ambassador, you have me to yourself. What do you want?" Ford thought to himself.

Almost reading Ford's mind, the Ambassador smiled and looked at Ford, trying to read the American but saw only a strong face that seemed perfectly calm and in total control of himself. "He isn't the least bit impressed by me or my title," Sir Reginald thought.

"Captain Ford," the Ambassador began, leaning forward in a conspiratorial manner, hoping Ford would look on him as an ally. "I'll get right to the point. You need aviation gasoline to continue your journey. And I know that as of now, the Dutch are not going to release any of their stock of high octane for your use. There is only automobile gasoline available and I'm certain you don't want to try that."

The Crown's representative picked up his champagne glass and sipped, looking over the lip of the glass to assess the opening of his first move. The American didn't react nor did the Ambassador expect any. After stating the obvious, he began again with another easily understood fact, but one that carried great implications for the pilot and his plane.

"And I know that your planned route back to America will take you over the subcontinent, probably across the Levant and into Arabia. From there, you'll probably try to cross Africa to reach the South

Atlantic. Don't look surprised, Captain Ford. I know the great range the Pacific Clipper has and how much petrol you can carry. You'll be flying across oceans and landing on lands and waters that are part of the British Empire," Finished with his opening lead, the Ambassador sat back to gauge the reaction of the American pilot.

Now Ford leaned forward and picked up his glass and sipped, looking at the Ambassador. "Any boob knows I have to go where there are deep harbors and hopefully aviation gasoline to reach home. It was that last bit about flying across and landing on parts of the British Empire that is the real threat. Keep him talking and soon he'll cast the bait. So just listen. He wants something very badly," the American mused and placing his now almost empty glass back on the table, he nodded for the Englishman to continue.

"Ah, your a cool man, Captain Ford. Your performance this afternoon led me to believe you have a low flash point. But I'm not getting that reading now. You're waiting for me to lay my cards on the table. Good for you. I enjoy a match, especially when I hold all the trump," Sir Reginald thought, eying the American. "Time to shift gears. You don't have the fuel to leave Surabaja and reach Ceylon. So you're stuck here, Captain Ford, unless I step in."

"Captain Ford, your country has been dragged into the war we have been fighting for a few years. Your plane, the Pacific Clipper can mean a great deal in helping us win the war. I am well aware that your Boeing plane sitting out there in the harbor is the most advanced four engine plane in the world and that the technology she possesses is presently being introduced into your Flying Fortress bombers. The Japanese stabbed you in the back at Pearl Harbor. Your government will allocate the great majority of those bombers to the war out here. Of one thing I am certain, no nation, no matter how powerful economically can fight a war simultaneously against enemies as powerful as German and Japan. We know that we can't. Germany is our principle enemy and concern. Whitehall has already planned that in a war with Japan, His Majesty's forces in Asia will have to make do with what they have now. Nothing is coming from England to help out here. England comes first. Knowing how I'd feel if I were an American, I'd want to blast the Japanese to hell. And the Flying Fortress is the plane to do it. Do you agree, Captain Ford?" the Ambassador asked, knowing that Ford was following his reasoning perfectly and had probably already guessed where all this was leading. Leaning back into the plush seat, he picked up his glass and sipped, looking at Bob Ford and awaited the American's reaction.

"Thank you Sir Reginald. I appreciate your taking me into your confidence about the British options," Ford commented. And now he played his first card in this little game the Ambassador had dealt. It would a low one and probably anticipated but he already had guessed what the Ambassador had in mind. Talking about Japan and the Flying Fortress was a good ruse. But Ford wanted to see where this was all leading. He thought he knew but he decided to let the Ambassador play a few more cards.

"But what can I do to help? Right now, unless we get aviation fuel for the Clipper, we don't have enough left in her to get us out of Java. We can take off from Surabaja but where would we go? So what do you suggest, Mr. Ambassador?" Ford asked, with real sincerity written all over his face.

"Mr. Ford, if you ever do get back to America, open a gambling casino or go into politics. You're a fine card player," Sir Reginald thought as he balanced the crystal goblet between the thumb and forefinger of his right hands, looking at the American. "But I hold the winning hand so let us not waste time with all this fencing. You need petrol for your flying boat. I can get petrol. You need safe clearances to land at all these places across the globe. I can provide that safety with fighter escorts by the RAF. However, there is one small detour you'll have to make."

"Captain Ford. Today's possible tragic consequences of the Dutch almost shooting you down because they did not know you were coming could be repeated across this part of the world as you try for safe harbors. There are none. However, there is one exception. You could land at countries that are part of the Commonwealth or allied with us in this struggle against the Axis. But because of the present emergencies, even our people wouldn't be able to help. You can understand that with the war, a commercial flying boat would not rate a high priority considering the demands our people face," Leach stated. "But that could all change if I made sure your plane received every courtesy, especially in getting the aviation fuel."

Sir Reginald reached over and took out the champagne bottle and poured the remaining wine into both glasses. Then he sat back to hear Ford's answer. He knew he had spelled it out for the American and unless he completely misread the man, this pilot knew he was being told that he either did what Sir Reginald wanted or he might not get out of Surabaja.

"Again the threat. Why?" Ford thought before answering. "Unless Mrs. Ford's son is a baboon, what the man is saying is that he wants the

Clipper for England. He'll get us the gas to leave Surabaja and he'll clear us all the way from India, Africa, then across the Med to Gibraltar or Malta, then to London. Otherwise, we'll never leave Surabaja, unless I fill the tanks with automobile gasoline. Which I won't. And if I'm right, he is also telling me that he'd make sure any neutrals beholden to England would make it rough on us. OK... so I'll agree to whatever he wants but with enough caveats that I can get out of here and we'll see what happens when we hit Trincomalee. But slowly now. He may look like someone from central casting but nobody lasts this long in the British Foreign office, no matter what his old school ties or how complete an ass. And this man is not that," Ford surmised and framed his answer on that supposition.

"Sir Reginald. Have you ever seen a movie made... a motion picture, especially a Western?" Ford asked as he began his next move. Ford didn't give a damn how he got the fuel so he was going to get it through the good offices of Sir Reginald Leach, but under Bob Ford's terms.

"No Captain. Why do you ask?" the Ambassador asked, puzzled by this sudden shift to cowboy movies.

"Sir, when the director and the writer reach a point where the story has bogged down and they are stuck for their next scene, the director will holler "cut to the cows" and they will start a stampede so there is action... something happening. In terms of our discussion, I think I know exactly where you are coming from and headed. So I'll 'cut to the cows' and lay it out as I see it so we can get moving. You will get me aviation fuel for the Pacific Clipper so I can leave Surabaja and to fly to Ceylon. For that plus your continued goodwill in making sure we get a warm reception and fuel along the way, you want something from me. What?" Ford stated, his bluntness taking the Ambassador back, somewhat.

"That 'cut to the cows' was a marvelous ploy, Captain Ford. I must remember what it means and how you did it. You will go far, my good pilot. That quiet demeanor, the 'gee whiz' looks, the almost sophomoric questions and then boom! Well done. I either answer honestly or forget it. Honesty will beget honesty. And this is a path that is difficult for me, not having trod it in sometime," the Ambassador thought as he looked at Ford, no longer so sophomoric. And he also knew there was now no need to couch his demands in niceties. Both men knew that.

"Yes, Captain Ford. I do want something. Simply put, here is my proposal. I will get you the aviation fuel you need to fly to Ceylon. At

Trincomalee, the British Naval forces there will service your plane as best they can. I will fly from Batavia with my staff and meet you in Trincomalee. Together, we will fly to England with my office having cleared us from landing to landing, based on your decisions of the route we should fly. Aviation fuel will be available for the Boeing wherever we land and fighters of the Royal Air Force will provide cover for us from India to London. That is my offer," Sir Reginald looked at Ford and was surprised at how simple it was to state what he wanted. Maybe there was something to that 'cut to the cows" idea after all. Now it was Ford's time to reply and when it came, the Ambassador was stunned.

"I agree. You supply the aviation fuel here in Surabaja and wherever we touch down all the way to England. All sites will be advised by a special code we will give your people. British fighter planes will fly cover for us. We have a deal, Sir Reginald!" Ford summed up and rising put out his hand to secure the deal. The Ambassador rose and gripped Ford's hand, almost non-plused at how easy this had been.

The two turned and headed for the door when Ford stopped and looked at the Ambassador. Nodding towards the remaining bottle of champagne, the Ambassador smiled and like two kids sneaking a lick of icing from the cake, they returned to their chairs and His Majesty's spokes person popped open the second bottle. Pouring the glasses full this time, they toasted themselves. "To us, Captain Ford. A successful trip to England aboard the finest plane in the world!" Touching glasses. The two sat back in their chairs and looked at the fire.

"Speaking of the Clipper, Sir Reginald, while we do have extra space aboard her, I do hope that you are the only one from your Embassy that will accompany us. Other than family, that is," Ford stated.

"My family is in England, Captain. However, I would appreciate it greatly if Mr. Finch could accompany us. He does have his limitations but is an excellent man Friday. And along the way I'm sure we will need someone to run errands for us, don't you agree?" the Ambassador stated, putting in his request for his gofer to be allowed on board the Pacific Clipper.

Ford had planned this. He knew that Sir Reginald would be lost without someone to order around and it was proper for an Ambassador to have at least one person to do his bidding. In granting Finch's passage, now Ford had a favor to ask in return, one he knew the Ambassador couldn't refuse.

"Well, we do have the room and I know it is important for you to have someone that understands all you have been doing out here but please do not think we can accommodate every member of the British Foreign office that wants to hitch a ride back to England. Only you and your aide will come with us, Sir Reginald. Agreed?" Ford stated.

"Agreed Captain Ford. I will tell all that you are operating under direct orders from your Chairman, Mr. Trippe and I am just your guest and have no influence. How does that strike you, Captain," the Ambassador asked, stepping neatly into Ford's trap.

"Perfect, Mr. Ambassador. I understand that you have sat on the Board of Directors of British Imperial Airways so you can appreciate how important it is for me to have written confirmation from Mr. Trippe that I have the Board's approval, along with that of your government to divert the Pacific Clipper from my specific orders to bring her to New York. I'm sure that when you advise Whitehall of our plans, they will clear everything with New York, That way, both of us will have the written approval we need. After all, as you so eloquently stated, England and America are allies and we should work together. Getting the Clipper to England seems a great way to do that. Don't you agree?" Ford politely asked, quietly trumping the Ambassador's ace.

"You bastard. You smart son-of-a-bitch. You let me make the offer, you accept and then hoist me on my own petard," Sir Reginald thought as he sipped on his champagne, holding the glass to his lips to hide any expression that might have escaped when Ford made his demand for written authorization. "He has me. I walked right into his trap. That 'cut-to-the-cows' did it..I bit like some fat dumb trout... I should have seen this coming when he agreed so fast. But I bought that wide-eye innocent look... how could I be so naive... 'cut-to-the-cows'... what an ass I am. I can't back out of the deal and I can't call Mountbatten. He'd have my head on a pike at the Tower of London. I'll have to fake it... promise him the authorization, get the gas, get to Ceylon. Once he lands there, he'll be on my turf and I'll have him," the Ambassador thought, furious with himself but still determined to get the Pacific Clipper. What Ford had done to him made him even more determined to take this plane to England.

"Indeed Captain. I recognize your problem. I have dealt with Mr. Trippe myself in the past and have the scars to show for it. I will make sure my government explains to Washington the importance of getting the Boeing away from the Japanese as well as the Germans' in Africa. Since I can vouch for my government, by the time you land in Trincomalee, tomorrow or the next day, everything will be approved from New

York. Since you can't break radio silence, our cryptographers in Batavia will send the message to London and they will move it on to Washington. When we leave Trincomalee, we'll flying under the protection of the RAF," the Ambassador assured Ford, deftly avoiding the trap of an honest answer. "And since we can't fly anywhere without your precious aviation petrol, I suggest we rejoin our host and let him work his powers of persuasion on the man who has your gasoline, the head of Royal Dutch Shell Petroleum in Java."

Rising, the two drained their glasses, placed them on the silver service, shook hands and rejoined the other guests.

Leaving the library, the two went their separate ways knowing they would be back in the room as soon as VanGelder and the Royal Dutch Shell man could meet with them. As Ford walked over to where John Mack and Shamus Ginsberg were standing, Ford noticed the Dutch pilot, Rolph VanderKellen headed to join them. He liked the Dutchman, with good reason. It was his stubbornness that kept them from being blown out of the air. Shaking hands with VanderKellen, he looked at Mack and the innkeeper and answered the question before they could ask.

"The Englishman will use his good offices to help us get the fuel we need to get to Trincomalee," Ford stated and waited for their reactions.

The other three looked at each other and smiled. Then they saw the look and Ford's face and the smiles faded.

"Englishmen bearing gifts, right, Captain?" Shamus commented.

"Bob, what did he want?" John Mack asked.

"We'll have gas every place we land, even fighter cover where possible from the RAF. All we have to do is take the Ambassador home to London, turn the Clipper over to them and they'll build their own Flying Fortresses!" Ford stated, his voice low and filled with disgust. He didn't want any of the other guests to hear him but he knew he had to amplify what he had just told them and was about to further illuminate them about his meeting when he looked up and saw Rolph VanderKellen imperceptibly shake his head. Other guests were passing and smiling at the Americans and Rolph. As soon as they were out of ear shot, the Dutch pilot led them over to a corner of the bar where the four could talk. As they walked over, Ford looked around for Kathleen Elmes and saw her still being shown off by their host. She caught Ford's glance and gave him a "get-me-out-of-here" smile. Ford returned the smile with one of his own, then rolled his eyes in sympathy and joined the others at the bar.

"Did you agree, Captain Ford?" Shamus asked.

"Yes, but only to get the gas. Sir Reginald is to get written confirmation from Trippe himself and have it waiting for us when we land at Trincomalee. In the meantime, if he can get us the gas, we'll get the hell out of here and see what happens when we land there," Ford answered.

"No way Juan Trippe will agree. He hates the English and I doubt that even President Roosevelt could move him on this," John Mack stated. Ford nodded and was about to continue when Shamus cut in.

"It doesn't make any difference, John. The King of England himself couldn't get fuel for the Clipper unless the Dutch wanted to give it to you. I'm sure Colonel VanGelder would agree to give it to you if he had any say. But he doesn't," Shamus stated. "Is that a fair assessment of the situation, Captain VanderKellen?"

"Indeed. I'm afraid Shamus is correct. The Ambassador carries no weight in these matters and neither does the Colonel. There is plenty of 100 octane for your plane up at Royal Dutch Shell. Even with the Japanese coming here soon, all requests for extra rations, even from Colonel Van Gelder must be approved by the governing board at Royal Dutch Shell. And Bob, the Japs could be sitting in the harbor by the time that happens," the Dutch pilot tried to explain.

"What are you talking about. The Colonel has no influence? Hell, isn't he in charge of the defenses of Surabaja. Aren't we allies?" Ford asked as his incredulity at such a situation made his voice rise.

Shamus reached over and put his hand on Ford's arm to calm him down.

"I'm sure that VanGelder and the Ambassador will do everything in their power to get you the gas" Shamus started then stopped as Rolph VanderKellen leaned in and nodded at a late arriving couple. The man was quite distinguished looking and on his arm, a lady of obvious breeding. As they approached their host, many in the crowd looked and nodded to the new comers in respect. The woman acknowledged the greetings with a slight nod of her head while the man looked straight ahead. Colonel VanGelder, spotting them, excused himself and walked over to meet them. This gave Kathleen Elmes her chance to escape and she hurried to join them at the bar.

"Whew. I need a drink. Every time a waiter came by with champagne, the Colonel would introduce me to another couple and I've yet to have a sip. Would someone take pity and get me a glass. I'm so tired of curtseying and getting my hand kissed. Why didn't one of you gentlemen come and rescue me?" she laughed as the bartender, seeing Shamus's signal came over.

"Champagne, a Mimosa or something else, my dear?" Shamus asked.

"A very, very dry Martini, and if they have such a thing, an anchovy olive!" the Lt. asked as the four men looked at her.

"An anchovy olive?" Ford exclaimed. The bartender, standing near, smiled. He reached under the bar and brought out a small jar with the olives in it. Nodding to Kathleen, he poured the silver drink into the goblet and dropping the special olive in the glass, presented it to Kathleen.

Nodding her thanks, she sipped it slowly, smiled broadly to the bartender who smiled back, knowing he'd just received his biggest tip of the evening.

"Thank you Shamus and Captain Ford, how are we doing with the British Ambassador? He was most ebullient when we met a few minute ago. Can he help us?" she asked.

"Kathleen, when the Ambassador and I left the library, I'd have said we were on our way to Trincomalee. But now, after talking to Rolph and Shamus, it seems that the Ambassador's influence with the businessmen in Surabaja is just a tad better than mine. And it those people, not the military that carry the day here," Ford answered, somewhat angrily.

"Well, what is the plan? If the Ambassador can't help us, there must be someone who can!" she stated very firmly, as if Ford had been standing around doing nothing about getting them home. Before Ford could respond, Shamus broke in.

"There is. He just walked in with his wife and they are the reason the Colonel released his deathgrip on you, my lass. The man is Henry Oberveldt and his wife's name is Hortense. If you want aviation fuel, that is the man you'll have to get it from. Right Rolph," Shamus stated.

"As usual, Shamus, you are right on target. Bob, Henry is the President of Royal Dutch Shell in Java. His office is in Rembang, about 100 miles up the coast along the bay. The fact that he is here bodes well for you. I heard the Colonel call him this afternoon and asked them to come to the party. It might be that you'll be meeting soon. But Bob, I caution you. Henry Oberveldt is the personification of the "Stubborn Dutchman," the pilot advised.

Just as the four of them were surreptitiously looking at the Oberveldts, Sir Reginald joined them with the Colonel. Brushing Mrs. Oberveldt's hand with his lips, the group made small talk for a minute until the Colonel's lady joined them. Seconds later, the two ladies moved off and the three men moved to Ford and his group.

"Miss Elmes, Captain Ford and Mr. Mack, allow me to introduce my dear friend, Henry Oberveldt. Henry knows Captain VanderKellen and Shamus," the host said. Nodding to the men, the oilman took Kathleen's hand, kissed it, then shook hands with Ford and Mack.

"Miss Elmes, you are far more lovely than even the Colonel's flowery description led me to believe and may I say your ensemble is easily the most striking and attractive this old town has ever seen. Captain Ford. Mr. Mack, delighted to meet you. Captain VanderKellen, my compliments. And Shamus, always a pleasure," the head of one of the world's great conglomerates said in greeting. Because of the way he carried himself, ramrod erect, Henry Oberveldt, appeared taller than he actually was. Slight of build, a slender face and hair with just the right touch of grey, Ford was suddenly struck again by the same thought the first time he saw Sir Reginald. The oilman was right out of central casting, the writer's version of a business executive. The charcoal grey double breasted suit, white on white shirt, French cuffed, links not showing, a soft yellow tie with dark blue dots, pointed black suede shoes were all perfectly coordinated. All that was missing was the grey homburg and the walking stick and he could play Clifton Webb in any movie!

Turning to Ford, the oilman spoke. "Captain Ford, Sir Reginald and Alphonse have appraised me of the needs of your group. Shall we retire to the library and see what we can do to help you. Miss Elmes, Mrs. Oberveldt is anxious to meet you and asked if you would be so kind as to join her and Mrs. VanGelder while we men meet. Shamus, Rolph and Mr. Mack, I look forward to visiting with you when we have finished," And with that, he turned and led the contingent towards the library.

"Well, I think we'll be getting the gas and be on our way tomorrow. Don't you?" Kathleen stated."John, I know you want to stay here and talk to Rolph and Shamus as I do. But I can't just walk across the room unescorted. Would you mind? she asked.

"My honor, Kathleen," Mack responded offering her his arm. But before they left, Mack looked at the pilot and the innkeeper and he noticed they didn't seem to be as sure as he and Kathleen. Holding her arm, he asked. "What do you to think. Is Kathleen right?"

The locals looked at each other and Shamus nodded to Rolph. He hesitated and looked at the two Americans and Kathleen took her hand off Mack's arm as both waited, now with some trepidation.

"Kathleen. John. I don't know how to read this. Fighter pilots seldom rub elbows with men that head giant companies so I have a friendly but somewhat distant relationship with Henry. Honestly, I can see no reason why he won't help. After all, you're the United States Navy and Pan American Airlines. We are at war. America is our ally and without you there is no hope. So I don't understand why the gasoline trucks were not waiting for you at the dock when you landed," the fighter pilot that saved their lives answered. "Shamus know him much better than I do. Maybe he can shed some light on what to expect."

The innkeeper looked at the pilot and then at the Americans. He sighed and smiled. "My sainted Mother taught me that worrying about things you can't control puts wrinkles on your brow. And we don't want any wrinkles on that pretty brow of your's Kathleen. You've already set this place on its ear and soon the band will be playing so why don't you and John join the other guests and enjoy yourselves. There is nothing we can do. Rolph and I will keep watch and as soon as they come out, we'll grab the Captain and join you. Ok?"

The two nodded and walked across the room to join the others. As they moved out of range, Shamus spoke softly. "Wouldn't want to be in the Captain's shoes. You called Henry stubborn. More like ironheaded."

Inside the library, the four men sat in the same highback red leather chairs, the fire burned brighter and there were two buckets of ice on the coffee table, one with champagne and the other filled to the top with ice. Next to that one stood two Waterford decanters, one filed with whiskey, the other with gin. One of the Colonel's waiters stood off to the side, ready to serve. The Colonel waved him off and without preamble, the host opened the conversation.

"Henry, Captain Ford's plane, the Pacific Clipper needs aviation fuel to get to Trincomalee. Our supplies are far too low at the airdrome and he needs it fast. So, how long do you think it will take for you to have two trucks filled with high octane at the dock in Surabaja?" Van Gelder asked.

The oilman looked at his countryman, the Englishman and the American.

"How much fuel do you need Captain Ford?" Henry Oberveldt asked.

"Close to 3,000 pounds, Sir," Ford responded, his heart beating a little faster in anticipation that their problems might be ended.

"Well, when Alphonse called and invited us to this party, he indicated we'd have this meeting and that Sir Reginald would join us.

So I had my plant manager check on our supply of 100 octane and there is more than enough for your needs Captain Ford."

All three looked at him and smiled. The Colonel dropped some ice in a highball glass, opened the whiskey decanter and poured a glass about three quarters full. As Sir Reginald was doing the honors with the champagne, Henry Oberveldt fixed himself a small gin with ice. Leach looked at Ford to pass his drink to him but what he saw made him stop. Ford had on that poker face, the one he'd learned to respect. Putting the Tattingers back into the ice bucket, he sat back and waited.

"I have given this solicitation a great deal of thought and introspection and as much as I personally want to help you, Captain Ford, it is in the best interests of the Royal Dutch Shell Petroleum Company that I'm afraid I must refuse," Henry Oberveldt stated, quietly but with finality.

All three looked at him. The Colonel's mouth was agape and the British Ambassador couldn't believe his ears. Only Ford showed no reaction and it was he at whom the oilman looked. Ford's eyes told him nothing but he could feel the anger underneath the man's phlegmatic expression. He held himself in from further talking because he knew that in a moment there would be a storm of protest coming for his host and the Ambassador.

He was right. First Van Gelder started in on him... "America, Holland's friend and greatest hope... Pan Am, an important Shell customer, the world's greatest airline... the war... the Japs can't get the Pacific Clipper. It would be disastrous... the honor of all Dutchmen... the basic decency to give them the gas and let them at least try for home... the odds of them making it... what will the Dutch government in exile say... what will the Americans say."

Oberveldt sat there and only the slight reddening atop his cheekbones showed his irritation and embarrassment at being harangued in such a virulent fashion. Finally, Van Gelder stopped. The room was silent but the echo of the Colonel's shouting reverberated throughout the room and probably out into the hall. The host took a deep breath, shook his head and spoke softly to his guest.

"Henry, you have your reasons for withholding the gas these people so desperately need. There is no earthly justification in not helping them and anything that you might say could border on cowardice and treason. So I will leave you in your shame as you try to explain to our allies why Royal Dutch Shell won't come to their aid. Mr. Ambassador. Captain Ford. I will see you after you have finished," And the defender of Surabaja rose and walked from his library.

Now it was Sir Reginald's turn. He had listened to the Colonel's arguments and knew that all he could do was parrot them. He reached over and brought out the Tattingers and filled his glass. As he thought about what he would say, to this man, about the honor of the Dutch and what America meant to all of them, he heard Ford speak and his heart jumped into his throat. "The American has blown it. By St. George. He's sunk us all!"

"How much?" Ford repeated the question that blew the Ambassador's mind. He looked daggers at the American and was about to step in to soothe the Dutchman, who must take umbridge at such an insult when he heard the oilman respond. And the response was reasoned and sober.

"Before I get into that, Captain Ford, let me congratulate you on reading this as strictly a business situation. In a few days, one way or another, with or without my fuel, you and your plane will be gone from Surabaja. And in a week or two the Japanese will come and after a spirited but brief battle, conquer Java. And when they have control, they will come knocking at my door to take over the operations of Royal Shell. They will know from their spies that I have given aviation gasoline to their enemy, you"

Pausing, the oilman leaned over, picked up the decanter with the gin in it, put some ice in his glass and refilled it. Settling back, he looked at Ford and smiled ruefully. "Captain Ford, even if you were alone and flying a beat up crop duster, the Japanese will punish anyone dealing with Americans. Not for dealing with the English, Mr. Ambassador. Nor the Australians, or the French or the Dutch. No. No matter how trivial, just for dealing with Americans. When Alphonse called, I knew the reason. We have known for years of the Japanese plans to conquer Asia. The only thing stopping them was the presence of the Americans. With Pearl Harbor, they took care of that. And while Java has many assets they covet, oil is the most important. Without our oil, their war machine grinds to a halt. Of course, we have discussed just what Royal Dutch should do when the Japs finally arrive. And the consensus was to cooperate. The responsibility to save the company in Java is mine. And giving 3000 pounds of aviation gasoline that let's a plane of such value as the Pacific Clipper escape from Java is not my, or the Board of Director's idea of protecting us from Japanese reprisals. The Japanese will kill a few of the non technical people at the plant, just to impress everyone but they are not stupid.

They'll keep alive the men that produce the oil. I do not expect that the Japanese will find my services necessary. And I have no intention of remaining to find out if I was mistaken," he explained.

Oberveldt leaned forward to add some gin to his glass, his explanation of why he'd not give the Americans their gas left him dry. Sitting back, he looked at the other two, seeing the loathing in the Ambassador's eyes and not giving a damn. It was the American's response he waited for, thinking he knew what it would be.

"How much?" Ford asked again.

"One Hundred Thousand Dollars," Henry Oberveldt responded.

The Ambassador exploded. "By George, you have a nerve, sir. That is a king's ransom! This is pure blackmail. Have you no pride? You should be horsewhipped. Threatening these men with certain death just for your own profit. I will not let this happen. My office will contact your government in London to tell them of this travesty. By Jove, they will order you to give them the petrol."

Ford tuned out the Ambassador. He might as well have tried to drop a charging rhino with a Red Rider air gun. The Dutchman wanted $100 grand and it was up to him to answer. Now he reached over for the bottle of Tattinger and poured himself a glass. "I'm beginning to like this stuff" he thought trying to give his brain a break. "The man wants 100 big ones. Why? I don't give a damn. Maybe he wants us to fly him to the States and that's the price we have to pay for his ticket. Not funny Ford. A hundred grand and I don't have a sou. From where I sit, the son-of-a-bitch has all the cards. And I better come up with something before England's Clarence Darrow pisses him off so much he blows the joint. He is hard headed enough to say "fuck off" and leave me twisting in the wind."

Finally, the Ambassador took a deep breath and before he could continue, Ford stepped in.

"Agreed. You know I don't have that kind of money on the Clipper. Will you take a note?" Ford asked, almost laughing as he said it.

Oberveldt smiled and shook his head. "As you Americans say, cash on the barrel head."

"You're not considering paying this ransom, are you Captain Ford. This man is a blackmailer, a thief, a disgrace, a blight on every Hollander that is fighting the Germans and those that will be fighting the Japanese!" Sir Reginald exploded and looked at Ford. The message in Ford's eyes was not lost on the King's emissary and he backed off. He realized that Ford was telling him he was wasting his breath. This

Dutchman wasn't going to respond to threats. Sir Reginald knew the pilot was right.

"Mr. Oberveldt, as we sit here, there is no way I can come up with $100,000.00 cash. What other form of payment would you consider?" Ford asked. Before the Dutchman could answer, the door opened and their host came in. It took but one look to tell from the faces of the three that nothing had changed except the Ambassador's face was redder.

"Gentlemen, my guests appreciate you keeping them entertained. Even the band was drowned out! I'm back to referee and ask that we all try to keep it down to a dull roar," the host stated and walking over to the table, picked up the whiskey decanter, filled his glass sans ice and took over.

"Sir Reginald, please sum up for me," the Colonel asked.

"Your friend here wants $100,000.00, cash to release the gas to the Americans. He refused to take the promissory note that Captain Ford offered. Since the Captain can't very well wire New York for the money, I now, on behalf of His Majesty, King George VI, offer the equivalent of $100,000.00 dollars in British pounds to purchase the petrol the Captain needs."

The generous offer caught VanGelder by surprise but not Ford. He recognized that if the Dutchman accepted, he'd be obligated to take the Ambassador to England. Ford smiled his thanks to Sir Reginald.

"Henry, in no way am I associated with you in what you are doing but since this is taking place under my roof, I'm involved. Sir Reginald has made an extremely generous offer. If you accept, what are the arrangements for the delivery of the fuel and the payment of the money?" Van Gelder stated, with as little hostility as possible, considering his state of angst.

Ford could read that the rescue attempt by the Ambassador had failed. He was right.

"Ambassador Leach, if circumstances were as black and white as you paint them. Captain Ford would be on the dock at Surabaja supervising the filling of his tanks with aviation gas from Royal Dutch. Let me explain," The oilman paused, reached for the gin decanter and again filled his glass. Looking at the Ambassador, he responded to his offer. "That was quite generous of you Sir Reginald to offer British pounds for American dollars. But that is unacceptable to me. And Alphonse, Dutch guilders are also verboten. It is American dollars I want or there is no deal."

Had Henry Oberveldt questioned the parentage of King George, the sex of Queen Willamena or tossed a pair of black mambas onto the laps of the Colonel and the Ambassador, he could not have gotten a more explosive reaction. The Colonel didn't care if they heard him in Batavia and the Ambassador was just as vehement. And as before, the object of their attack just sat there, frustrating both and making them more angry by his calm demeanor. Ford suddenly sensed that the oilman had had enough so putting two fingers to his lips, he blew a shrill whistle, stopping all the hollering and blustering.

"Please gentleman. The man has stated his demands. It is obvious that he had thought this thing through. The arrival of the Pacific Clipper has brought him a golden opportunity to cash in on our needs and accelerate a plan he has been developing for some time. Correct, Sir?" Ford asked. The other two resumed their chairs and hearing Ford's point, looked at Oberveldt in a new light. If Ford was right, the man sipping quietly on his gin was someone the Colonel didn't know.

Oberveldt, stung by Ford's comments and fed up with the ridicule being heaped on him by the other two, decided to show them they were dealing with someone much more subtle and smart than a petty blackmailer. Taking a sip of the gin then placing his glass on the table, he sat back and looked at them.

"The Captain is quite right. This is not a spur of the moment thing. But after listening to the two of you, it would be a waist of time trying to make you understand. Believe me, there is nothing you can do to me, even telling my wife or trying force the issue with the Dutch government in exile." the oilman began. Ford looked at him with new respect. He wasn't a petty blackmailer and his attitude told him that he couldn't care less if the two ran screaming to his wife that her husband was a thief. So he sat back to watch what promised to be an entertaining few minutes.

"Gentlemen, stop living in the past. Today, there is only one currency that anyone trusts... the American dollar. As of one month ago, Royal Dutch Shell is only accepting American dollars for the purchase of any of our products. If you were an Asian businessman, would you take Dutch guilders when Java will fall in a few weeks? Or British pounds? In Europe, the pound and the guilder are good for lighting fireplaces. Even the Deutch mark is useless except in Germany itself. The same with me. You get me One Hundred Thousand American dollars by tomorrow morning and the Pacific Clipper will have her tanks filled by late afternoon."

Rising, Henry Oberveldt picked up his glass and for a moment, Ford though he was going to offer a toast but he smiled at the three of them and finished off his drink. "Gentlemen, I see no further need for discussion. Captain Ford, believe me when I wish you and your crew God's speed and His protection as you try for home. Your task is indeed daunting. Alphonse, rather than cause any further problems, I will join Hortense and stay a reasonable time before we leave. Gentlemen."

Bowing to the three, the American's hope for aviation fuel turned and left the room. As the door closed behind him, the three looked at each other. There was nothing to say. Finally Ford spoke.

"Colonel, I don't know Mr. Oberveldt. But $100,000.00, while a great deal of money, isn't the reason he is not giving us the fuel. Shamus tells me his wife is quite rich. So it has to be something else. And unless I'm mistaken, he told us. It is the Japanese. The man is terrified of them and he thinks that dealing with us means lights out when they get here. Even if I had the 100 grand, what would he do with it after they got here. No, the money is a ruse. He knows I can't come up with it and the same holds true for both of you. So unless I'm misreading him, he will take his chances with the Japs. Any comments?" Ford asked as he summarized his thoughts on the oilman.

The Ambassador was deep in thought. He sighed and looked at the others. "The Captain is right. It isn't the money so it must be the man's fear of the coming invaders. God in Heaven, Colonel, what possesses the man?" the Ambassador asked, pleading with the Dutchman to explain the unexplainable actions of a fellow countryman in time of war.

Before the Colonel could answer, Ford spoke.

"Gentlemen, I want to thank you for your efforts on our behalf. It hasn't worked out but there is always tomorrow. Colonel, I may have to fill the Clipper with automobile gasoline. Can I call on you tomorrow to make arrangements for the gas and a method of payment?" the pilot asked.

The Colonel looked at Ford and felt ashamed. The whole world was looking to the United States for salvation and he didn't have the power in his own town to help this American get home. With a huge sigh of resignation, he answered.

"Of course. Call at my office in the morning and I'll have the arrangements for the tankers taken care of. There will be no need for payment, Captain Ford. That is the least I can do," the Colonel answered resignedly. "Captain, I wouldn't blame you if you said no but as anxious as you are to get back to your plane and to say good by to us, could you please stay a little longer? All the guests want to meet you. They all know what you are trying to do and want to wish you well. For those of us that will be staying to fight, it would give us a little hope that someday the Americans will return, maybe one hundred thousand of them!"

"Colonel, I'd be honored," Ford replied and the three of them headed for the door, just as they got there, the Ambassador stopped them.

"There is still time. Hortense Oberveldt is an old friend and she might just succumb to the wiles of an old reprobate like me to get us the gasoline. It's worth a go, what!" the Englishman posed and the other two laughed and nodded.

"Good luck, Sir Reginald. That is a mighty chore you're undertaking." Ford responded as they walked through the door into the hall. It was almost empty except for a few at the bars, Captain VanderKellen and Shamus Ginsberg among them. A few minutes earlier, the two had seen the head of Royal Dutch Shell Petroleum leave by the same door, walked right past them, not even acknowledging them. Both looked at each other and without comment, they knew Ford and the others had failed.

The buffet had been special and now as the Van Gelder's servants and kitchen help cleaned up the room, coffee and brandies were being served in the bar. Soon the dancing would begin. Ford, Mack and Rolph VanderKellen were having their cigarettes and coffee, standing off to the side of the bar closest to the library. Shamus was off somewhere and Kathleen was still a captive of the host's wife. Finally, being somewhat alone, Ford brought them up to date on what had transpired with Dutch oilman.

"Why?" John Mack asked, and the other three knew exactly what the First Officer meant.

"I don't know. He doesn't need $100,000.00 from what I'm told by the Colonel. He says he's frightened that the Japanese will kill him for giving us the gas and on the surface, that would make sense. But I'm not buying that. Neither did the Colonel or Sir Reginald. The two of them really gave him a going over. But he is one tough Dutchman. So speaking of the oilman, has anyone seen him since dinner?"

"One of the waiters whispered something to him when they were at their table and he excused himself. Where he went or is now, I don't know," John Mack answered.

Except for the flickering glow thrown off by the fireplace, it was almost pitch dark in the VanGelder library as Henry Oberveldt entered. Just an hour ago he had delivered his ultimatum to the American Captain, the British Ambassador and Alphonse VanGelder. Now he returned and although he could not see the man who had requested his presence, he knew he was sitting in one of the red leather chairs. Oberveldt waited by the door, his hand still on the handle, wishing that all he had to do was reopen it and leave and his problems would vanish. He knew better. Releasing the knob he strode across the Persian rug and slid into one of the red chairs, then reached over to fill a fresh glass with ice, again opening the decanter of gin and filled his glass. Sitting back, he waited as he allowed the ice to cool the silver liquid. Then, without looking, he addressed the man sitting in the other chair.

"Hello Shamus. I received your message. Are you involving yourself in this?" the oilman asked, his voice low, almost conspiratorial but very confrontational.

"Yes, Henry. I am" the innkeeper answered, his voice soft and relaxed.

Oberveldt did not respond. He hated Shamus Ginsberg. To the social and business communities in Asia, he was the urbane, sophisticated leader of one of the great companies in the world. Yet the first time he met Shamus Ginsberg, he knew the Jew saw right through the facade he had erected around himself. Only his wife knew what he was. But she loved him and forgave him for his weaknesses. Hortense Oberveldt was one of the world's richest women. Her ancestors had been original members of the Dutch East India Trading Company and over the centuries, the organization had grown to one of the great conglomerates in the world. His wife's family, the Peeraghur's were in the same league as the Rockefellers and the Rothchilds. And over the last few years Henry had watched as his wife and her family converted their assets into holdings in American companies, protecting themselves against the coming onslaught of the Germans in Europe and the Japanese in Asia. She enjoyed tweaking him about her American Generals...General Mills, General Electric, General Motors and endlessly telling him how successful she was in a man's world. And he hated her with every fiber of his being.

Neither man spoke. The innkeeper leaned forward, filled his glass with Cutty Sark, and sat back. Shamus had prepared for this meeting from the first time he met Henry Oberveldt at his gaming tables in the upper rooms of the Black Swan. He knew who he was and what he was. When word of the VanGelder party reached him, knowing that the Dutch were denying the Americans the fuel under Oberveldt's instructions, he knew that tonight he'd have this meeting with a man he totally abhorred. But Shamus Ginsberg was far too good a poker player to lay his cards on the table and although he hated Henry Oberveldt with a passion, he respected him as a formidable opponent. He had to win this match. So he opened the bidding with a simple statement.

"Henry, I want you to give the Americans the gas they need," Shamus Ginsberg stated and it was not a request.

The gas for the Americans was just a tool as far as Oberveldt was concerned. And the money had nothing to do with it. He'd stolen enough from the company and had it stashed in untraceable accounts in Switzerland so he knew he'd never have to worry. The $100,000.00 was just a move to force the Americans to leave with automobile gas in their engines, making their trip more dangerous, but not impossible. His reasons were simple. When the Japanese arrived, they would know that the American plane was here and hear the story of how the president of Royal Dutch Shell, despite the pressure from his countrymen, refused the fuel. This would ingratiate him even further with the Sons of Nippon. He would make a big show of staying to protect Royal Dutch Shell against the invading Japanese while making sure Hortense and the children escaped. But, of course, to save the companies assets, he had to run it for the Japanese. No one knew he was already a trusted advisor, clandestinely for the Japanese. If they won the war, and he was sure they would, when peace came, he would be their liaison throughout Asia and Europe for all the countries that wanted to do business with the rulers of all Asia. If the Americans won, he would be a hero for staying in Java to protect her natural assets. He could leave Java with Hortense but the coming invasion was his way to be rid of her. And he still had the bank account in Switzerland. He had protected himself and there was nothing this bastard could do to him. So why was he sitting here? In his gut he knew.

"The answer is no, Shamus. As I explained to them, I plan to stay here to protect the assets of Royal Shell. I won't give the Japanese an excuse to burn down our plants because we gave gas to their enemy," Oberveldt, the protector spoke.

"Bullshit. Release the gas, Henry. I know who you are, what you have done and what you are planning. You can con your wife, the Dutch and the rest that think you're some kind of business whiz but we both know that without Hortense, Royal Dutch wouldn't let you pump gas. That is why you have been skimming all these years and stashing the money in Switzerland. Some day soon, Hortense will finally do the right thing and throw you out on the balls of your ass. If there wasn't a war and the Japs coming, she'd probably do it now," the innkeeper quietly spoke, his words cutting into the soul of the oilman. "Release the gas, Henry"

Knowing full well that Shamus had nailed it, and for the life of him he couldn't figure out how he did it, he still felt it was Shamus' word against his. But he knew Hortense would believe the Jew! He was going to leave her anyway. No, his plan to stay and protect the assets of Dutch Shell was still the best. Fuck Shamus and his threats.

"Shamus, I haven't the slightest idea of what your talking about. If this is all to your threat to make me give the gas to the Americans, you've got nothing," Henry Oberveldt stated emphatically. "You're over your head in this Shamus. Stay out of my affairs."

Having called the innkeepers bluff, the oilman should have risen and left. But he didn't. He had to know how much Ginsberg really knew. As much as he despised the Jew, he had to know. It had nothing to do with his gambling debts, he was sure of that.

"Henry, give them the gas," Shamus stated, in the form of an order.

"Shamus, you bore me. No gas," Oberveldt stated, feeling good that Ginsberg had nothing. He reached over to take a sip of the gin. But the glass never reached his lips.

"Amsterdam," Ginsberg whispered. "Tokyo."

Silence.

"How?" the oilman asked.

"I know," the innkeeper answered.

Silence

"Give them the gas, Henry. No one will ever know from me. But if Royal Dutch Shell trucks are not at the dock tomorrow afternoon, filled with 100 octane, Hortense and the Colonel will know," Ginsberg explained.

It was over and both men knew it. "So he wasn't bluffing... he knows about the Germans, and the Japanese... If Hortense ever found out, she'd be the one with the loaded rifle in the firing squad and happily kill me," the oilman thought. He turned to the man he hated and looked at him. As he was about to ask how Ginsberg found out, he knew it was useless. He'd never tell him. He knew the Germans hadn't leaked his relationship with them and the Japanese the same. But Shamus Ginsberg knew. And he'd known for sometime and... he's known since we came to Surabaja! But how?"

"Shamus, how did you know?" Henry asked.

"Captain Ford said he needed 3000 pounds of 100 octane. Make sure he has it tomorrow afternoon. Good by, Henry," Ginsberg said, dismissing the Dutch Quisling.

Mrs. Van Gelder walked to the center of the room and signaled for quiet. The band toddle softly in the background.

"On behalf of the Colonel and myself, welcome to our home. And a special welcome to our American guests," the lady said and led the applause for the visitors. "In a few minutes the band will begin playing and in your honor, Captain Ford, most of the music will be from American composers. Actually, if it wasn't for American music, I don't think there would be anything to dance to. Enjoy!" Mrs. VanGelder smiled and taking the Colonel's arm walked back into the dining room, now the ballroom. As the band struck up, Rolph VanderKellen beat everyone and took Kathleen's arm and led her to the dance floor. Within minutes, all the ladies had a partner and those that didn't waited to dance with Kathleen Elmes. Finally, John Mack got his chance and as the two moved onto the floor, the band leader knew his time had come! He broke off the Rogers and Hart music, and switched to the Dutch rendition of Benny Goodman's "Stompin at the Savoy," Kathleen and John danced as if they had been partners for years and Surabajan society received a delightful look at Americans 'cutting a rug.'

Slowing the pace after that, they played Gershwin, Berlin and all the great American classics. Kathleen danced them all with each and every man there except Bob Ford. When the band took a break, Mrs. VanGelder took pity on her and brought her some champagne and ushered Kathleen away from the men. As she relaxed, she looked around and wondered what had happened to Henry Oberveldt and if Shamus had returned to the Black Swan. They were nowhere to be seen. And she really didn't care. This night could go on forever as far as she was concerned. "Talk about being the Belle of the Ball," she thought. And remembering how many times she'd been asked by the ladies where she purchased such a stunning outfit, she thought she should make a sketch of it and give it Saks. She had told the truth that it was from Saks. She just didn't elaborate. Now the band struck up and before any other men nailed her, she walked over to where Ford stood. She hadn't asked a man for a dance since she was in sixth grade and had a crush on Dick Crawford and he was so shy she had to drag him to the dance floor. Now she'd do the same to Bob Ford.

Ford could tell from the smile in the Dutch pilot's eyes that something was happening behind him and he turned. There, curtsied in front of him was Kathleen Elmes. Rising, she smiled and said

"Captain Ford, would you be so kind and dance with me?" The blush on his face came from the neck up and as he stammered, she took his hand and led him to the floor. Fortunately, others were already there or he might have run away! The music was a Richard Rogers tune, something called the "Most Beautiful Girl in the World" and right away, Kathleen Elmes knew Bob Ford was a splendid dancer. She felt so in step with him and completely at ease that she hardly knew her face just beamed for the whole room to see.

For Bob Ford, the experience was something else. When he put his arm around her waist and took her hand, he felt a slight shock, like touching something metal after walking across a rug. But there were no rugs now and suddenly the problems of gas, the Clipper and the war were not important. He didn't let her go until she whispered something in his ear, about the fact that the music had stopped. Now the band began again and as he moved to take Kathleen's waist, someone tapped him on the shoulder. He was about to ignore whomever it was but turning, he saw it was Henry Oberveldt!

"Captain, may I please. Like every man here, I too would like to dance with Miss Elmes. Miss Elmes, Kathleen. May I?" the oilman asked and not waiting for her reply, took her arm and together they waltzed away. Turning to return to Mack and VanderKellen, he saw Shamus Ginsberg standing with them.

When Ford had told them that Oberveldt had shot down their request for the gas, Shamus was the only one that wasn't surprised. As the three men headed for the buffet, Shamus told the Dutch pilot he'd be in later. The innkeeper waited a few moments then motioned for the bartender. He asked the man to deliver a message to the Van Gelder's major domo. Then Shamus walked over and entered the study. It was his favorite room among all the other homes in Surabaja where he was often a guest As he approached the coffee table, he could see one of the Waterford decanters was filled with Cutty Sark, his favorite whiskey. He filled his glass to three quarters and sat back, smiling. He remembered the shanty at the far end of the wharf on the river Shannon and the first time he went in with the other dock hands, pretending to be older than the fourteen he was. He ordered a whiskey and water. The bartender, knowing Shamus was far to young to drink hard liquor, filled the glass with bar whiskey and gave it to the young worker. When Shamus reached for the pitcher of water to pour over the whiskey, the bartender grabbed his hand and said something Shamus never forgot. "Son, real drinkers never add water to their whiskey!" the older man whispered. Seeing the doubt in Shamus' eyes, he added,

"You know what the fish do in the water don't you?" As the other in the bar broke up in laughter, Shamus put down the water pitcher, grabbed his whiskey and drank the whole glass! Suddenly, his throat was on fire and his eyes filled with tears and he couldn't breathe! He thought he was going to die on the spot, on that dirty floor and with the roaring laughter of the others ringing in his ears, he ran to the door, his eyes filled with tears and staggered down the dock to the little ketch that was his home.

Smiling at the memory of the young boy running away from the poverty that was Ireland, he dropped a couple of ice cubes in his drink. "Ice cubes don't count. Fish can't do anything when the temperature is below freezing!" Then Henry Oberveldt entered.

Shamus watched with the others as Henry Oberveldt led Kathleen to the dance floor and the two swung out to some music that Shamus didn't recognize but they seemed to be doing well together.

When the oilman put his hand on her arm to lead her to the dance floor, Kathleen almost flinched and as the music began and he put his arm around her, she forced herself to relax. "Maybe I can get him to loosen up and tell me why we can't have the gas," she thought. In a second or two, they were moving easily together and Kathleen had to admit that he wasn't a bad dancer. As the music ended, Henry Oberveldt took Kathleen's hand, and bending over it kissed it. He held it for a second and whispering low so she had to bend her head slightly to hear, the Dutchman said, "Tell Captain Ford my trucks will be at the dock about noon tomorrow. The gas is his," Straightening, he looked at the lovely American woman, and smiled. Her mouth was agape. Bowing again, he moved to where his wife was seated, leaving the Navy officer staring at him, awestruck. Had not the Australian attache chosen that moment to trip and crash into a table while coming for his dance with Kathleen, her unladylike "Yippee" might have caused a stir. Quickly placing her hand over her mouth to stifle any further exhibitions of excitement and not laugh at the poor man laying at her feet, Kathleen Elmes deftly stepped around the form and walked over to her escorts. But try as she might, she couldn't hold in what Henry Oberveldt had said and when she was about two feet away, she grinned from ear to ear and announced, "we have the gas!"

0510 hours-19-12-41 Major Thu's Camp above Surabaja

The sun had not yet risen when he entered Major Thu's tent and softly tapped the commander on his shoulder. The Major was immediately awake. With the flaps of his tent down, he reached over and flipped on a flashlight to illuminate the small room. The soldier came to attention but Thu just nodded, rolled his legs over the edge of his cot and looked.

"Sir, the man is here," the commando reported and saluting, turned and opened the flap to admit Jalara, the tailor, who entered and stood as Thu, taking his blouse from the back of the chair, fumbled for a cigarette. Pulling one from the pack, Thu looked at the man and motioned for him to sit. Lighting the cigarette, he signaled to begin.

"Major Thu. The American pilot met with the British Ambassador at the Van Gelder home. My man served them in the library and listened. His report is confusing. He said the American has agreed to fly the Ambassador back to England! But the American still don't have the fuel," Jalara reported.

"What in the name of the Emperor is going on? Tanaka wants me to capture the American plane and now the British Ambassador and who knows how many others are going to be on board. And there is no fuel. But maybe the Americans are taking the Ambassador to Batavia and will refuel there. Makes no difference. I'm here, not Batavia so I've got to do it here," Jalara looked at him and he realized that Jalara had more to tell him. He nodded for the tailor to continue.

"The Americans are not leaving today. They have no gas and their Captain is meeting this morning with Mr. Ginsberg to try for the fuel. It seems that the man who runs Royal Dutch Shell, Mr. Oberveldt, will not give the Americans the fuel they need to leave Surabaja. My man told me there was a terrible argument in the library but the oilman never gave in. He is afraid of reprisals from you and wants to keep the Americans here. The owner of the Black Swan met with the oilman later but my man could not get close enough to hear. He said they spoke in whispers. That is all I can report," the tailor finished his account. He waited for the Major's reaction. After a few seconds, Major Thu reached over and shook Jalara's hand and nodded. The tailor rose and bowed and left the tent following one of the commando in the dark to the path that led down to his bike.

Thu did not even notice the man's departure. His mind was spinning. He had to sort things through. That the Americans would not leave this morning was obvious. He had to alert Commodore Tanaka to that. But before he sent any messages, he had to understand what was happening. Thu lit another cigarette to ponder his problem. He needed coffee and as he opened the flaps of his tent, looking to the East he could feel the beginning of the day. In a tiny, tree covered area, some of the men had a small fire going. As the Major approached, they began to rise but he waved them to stay seated. Thu took a cup offered by the Sergeant and poured himself some coffee. The heat coming through the thin tim cup warmed his hands and he walked away from the fire towards the edge of the hill, to look down on the harbor and the Straits of Macassar. His eyes picked up the Clipper and wondered if the men aboard here had any idea of the trouble they were causing!

"I think I'll send a coded message to Commodore Tanaka. Give him something to think about this morning," Thu thought to himself and a slight grin creased his mouth. 'My dear Commodore Tanaka. The Americans are not leaving Surabaja today, as you planned. The Dutch won't give them any fuel! They want to keep the plane here and give it to us as a present when we take Surabaja. Isn't that nice of them. However, the British Ambassador says he'll get them all the gas they want if they will fly him to London. But the Dutch won't sell him the gas either. Any suggestions?' If I sent that, they'd hear his bellow all the way to Tokyo, even if the Arista was twenty fantoms under the sea!" the Major thought to himself, enjoying a brief bit of levity as he tried to come up with a plan. "The American is stuck another day in Surabaja. But he has enough fuel to get to Batavia. If he leaves before I can get aboard, we're screwed. And the great Tanaka will go home in shame. And somehow that bastard will make sure I go down in flames with him," Thu thought, with disgust. He had to know when the Americans were leaving. And from what the Commodore had said about the American pilot, he'd put automobile gas in those tanks and go, no matter what. When, only Ford will decide. "If we board the Clipper, what happens if the Americans don't leave? So not only do I have to board the plane and not get caught, I have to get them in the air before taking over the plane! Auho says it will take almost a 24 hours, whole day to reach Ceylon. Ford will not want to land on uncharted waters at night. So that means Ford will leave during the morning if he wants to arrive at Trincomalee the next morning."

0750 hours-20-12-41-aboard the Arista, Java Sea

While a Major in the Japanese Army was concerned about a Captain of an American airplane, the Captain of His Emperor's submarine, the Arista, had his own problems. In the few days that Commodore Tanaka had been aboard, Captain Nagoma had begun to wish for the sinking, destruction and even escape of the Pacific Clipper. As the morning of 20 December, 1941 dawned above his ship, he sat below the depths of the Java Sea and realized that the grand scheme of the Commodore had been thwarted. For what ever reason, circumstances had ruined a plan that depended on stealth, surprise and unbelievable luck. The reports Thu had sent, from the Dutch trying to shoot down the Americans to their safe landing to the news that they would not leave for another day because they had no gas had sent the Commodore bouncing off the walls. And he, Captain Nagoma bore the brunt of Tanaka's rage. But Nagoma was an old warrior and accepted the fact that prima donnas like the Commodore had to be suffered in silence. As he dressed and put on freshly pressed khakis, he felt more "commandlike" and smiling, he readied himself for another day with the great man. He wondered if the American Captain, Ford, had such burdens. Probably not. Checking his reflection in the mirror, Nagoma was pleased but sighed heavily as he opened the door and walked down the passageway towards his control center and the Commodore. As he strode towards his men on the bridge, his thoughts returned to the reason he was in the Java Sea, the American plane. "I wonder what is happening in Surabaja."

0845 20 December, 1941-aboard the Pacific Clipper

When Ford and the others returned last night from the VanGelder party, he briefed the crew on the general details of what had transpired, especially about the gas. Now, standing in the stairwell near the galley and sipping on his first cup of coffee of the morning, Ford went over the things in more detail. The whole crew got a big laugh as he went into the details about the conversation with Ambassador Leach. When he told about offering to fly the Ambassador back to London, just to get the gas, Norm Brown, ever the hand wringer, immediately stepped in.

"Pardon me Captain, don't we need authorization from New York to fly to England?" the Second Officer asked. As others looked at Brown, wondering how he could have forgotten where they were and how they got there, Ford tried to explain.

"Mr. Brown, you are quite right. However, things are not quite regulation out here. I have no plans to fly to London. I was just leading the Ambassador on to see if he could deliver the gas we need. And if he could, then we would take it, promise him anything and fly to Trincomalee and hope that Whitehall and Washington would see the folly of the Ambassador's plan. OK?"

"Well, gentlemen do not mislead other gentlemen," Mr. Brown chastised.

Ford just looked at his Second Officer. Now he was having second thoughts on revealing what had really transpired at the Van Gelder's home. He didn't want to raise their hopes too high. And he didn't want to give Norm Brown another shot at him, asking for too many details, details that he himself didn't know the answers to. And the big one was that if the gas was delivered, how was he going to pay for it? All Kathleen said was "we have the gas."

Of all the problems facing them, this was the most vexing to Ford. Pan Am was the world's most prestigious and successful airline and here they sat in Surabaja without money to pay for anything, hustling others like some barnstorming daredevils at a county fair passing the hat for cash! The fact that Oberveldt told Kathleen that his trucks would be on the docks at noon meant that someone had come up with the money for the Dutchman or Oberveldt wasn't a Dutchman! Ford didn't care why the oilman suddenly agreed to give them the gas. If he had to sell his soul to get the gas, Ford was ready and willing to play Faust.

Last night coming back to the plane, he and John Mack assumed that it was Shamus Ginsberg that changed the mind of Henry Oberveldt, much more than a dance with Kathleen Elmes.

Ford thought about what they were assuming to be a fact; that Shamus Ginsberg had somehow convinced Henry Oberveldt to give them the gas. How he did it, Ford wasn't too sure he wanted to know. And the deal had to include the money that the Dutchman was demanding. Or did it? And if Ginsberg wanted to be paid back by the Americans, he'd have to take Pan Am's marker. But what would they do for money when they left Surabaja? If they couldn't get money here from friends of the United States, the Australians, the Dutch and the British, what in the world would they do in India, Arabia, or trying to get across Africa? If this problem was going to be with them all across the underbelly of the world, they'd never get back to the States. They might even end up in one of those 'black hole' jails he'd seen in a Rudolph Valentino movie, held for ransom! What would those buck-toothed Arabs do when they saw Kathleen Elmes! The thought brought a laugh from him as he pictured her horrified look when she appeared in front of some pot bellied wazier and was sold into slavery to pay Pan Am's bills!

John Mack looked at Ford when he laughed and he wondered what tickled the Captain so much. Before he could ask, Ginsberg's car arrived and the two of them walked into the morning sun, not knowing but hoping that their feelings about the innkeeper were accurate.

While the Americans rode in his car to meet him, Shamus Ginsberg sat in his living room sipping on some coffee reviewing the events of the last twelve hours. When Kathleen Elmes raced up to them to mouth the news that they had the gas for their flight to Trincomalee, as everyone crowded around her to get the details, he walked away but not before asking Captain Ford to meet him here this morning. He smiled remembering the excitement of the three as Kathleen repeated what Henry Oberveldt had told her. And Shamus had to congratulate Henry for a very shrewd move, telling the girl. It was a nice touch. It put the British Ambassador on the defensive. His play with Ford would now be to threaten the American with problems wherever the Clipper went. British problems. And Leach could do it, Shamus was sure of that. With what was happening out here, nobody would question the whims of an Ambassador if he ordered a plane delayed or held. There was still a lot of anti-American sentiment in the British Foreign office and he was sure Leach could tap into that if he wanted to. And until the big plane hit the East Coast of the States, for the most part, she would be flying over British territories or lands that were English dominated. That is, except for parts of Africa which were pro German, like the French Territories and Brazil and Argentina in South America. "Poor Bob Ford. America's allies wouldn't give him the gas to leave Surabaja and when he does get away, his British Allies will provide the problems. Then its the German's turn!"

Rising, he walked into the kitchen and poured another cup of coffee. As he stood there, he knew was going to miss Surabaja, miss it greatly. The Black Swan was everything he dreamed of owning all those years of flitting about the Mideast and Asia. He had become rich owning some of the best pubs and gaming places in the Orient. But none had what the Swan had, a perfect location on the mouth of the harbor in a city of liberal citizens, ruled by autocrats that quietly enjoyed the amenities of the Black Swan. What he had bought from Surabaja Sue's successors he had improved on and made himself a viable member of the community, often contributing his time and his people to the charities that helped out the less fortunate. The understanding between he, as the uncrowned leader of the merchants of Surabaja and the ruling class was mutually beneficial to all. Shamus' worldliness and his marvelous gift of tongues made him a welcome guest at the parties given by the good burgemeesters that controlled the country. And when there was a special present that one of the men needed for his wife or girl friend, they would come to Shamus. He never took payment and as time passed, these special favors he performed built for a him a bankroll of goodwill that was far more valuable than the cash he could have amassed.

And he had indeed accumulated a great deal of money, far beyond any dreams he may have had as a young man shipping on tramp steamers, working in taverns and whorehouses, dealing cards and running guns across the Levant, through India, Mongolia and China. The first tavern he actually owned was a small, waterfront hovel on one of the many deltas of the Ganges. He served a good honest drink, made sure the girls were clean and didn't sell drugs. That helped keep the police off his back, along with paying them a monthly share of his profits. His skill as a dealer also helped keep the house in the black. As sailors would come into his place, he kept an ear for news of other towns and cities where an enterprising young man could expand. In a few years he had progressed to a stylish gaming establishment in Bangkok, then onto Saigon, to Shanghai, Singapore and finally to Surabaja. As his wealth steadily increased, since almost all his transactions were cash, Shamus made it a practice to keep a good amount spread among the local banks near where he had his establishments, knowing the local depository would be far more appreciative of his business and protective of him than their bigger brothers. The young boy born in Hells Kitchen, New York City and raised near Shannon, Ireland had become a man of the world and a bank account that would let him live like the Lord Mayor where ever he hung his hat.

The thought of leaving the Swan, his people and Surabaja made him weary and angry at the same time. But Shamus was far too much a man of the world to waste time railing against something he had no control over. The Japanese wanted Java and her resources and there was nothing to stop them from taking this beautiful land. And there was little likelihood that he, the crew of the Clipper and Kathleen Elmes would make one damn bit of difference in the outcome of the war.

But the Pacific Clipper just might. That plane was something unique and although Shamus didn't know an aileron from an airfoil, he knew the Clipper was special. Just the fact that that pompous ass Leach was salivating over the prospect of getting the Clipper to England showed Shamus how valuable she was. And if Sir Reggie saw that, what would the soon-to-be landlords of the Black Swan give to have it! They had nothing to match the Clipper, neither did anyone else, But the Japs could copy almost anything and if they got their bloody hands on her, they'd have the long range aircraft they desperately needed to conquer all of Asia. And in Berlin, put the Pacific Clipper in the hands of the Krupps and in no time the Germans could solidify their grip on Europe, isolate and destroy Russia and sit back and wait for the West to sue for peace, on German's terms.

"Well, goddamn it Ginsberg, get off your ass and make sure the Pacific Clipper gets home!" the innkeeper shouted out loud in his empty kitchen as he turned and marched into the living room and grabbing the wrought iron rail, headed up the winding stairs to his loft and a shower.

0915 20 December, 1996 at the British consulate

"Edward, the Colonel will not be joining us this morning. Last night Captain Ford informed us that he thought he might have the gasoline situation resolved. He said he would call us here to advise on the status of getting the gas from that horrid Oberveldt. Tell Lt. Johns to ready the plane and we'll plan to leave for Batavia around noon," the Ambassador instructed his aide, who did an exact about-face and departed.

Sir Reginald didn't bother to enlighten Finch of the sudden change in the fortunes of the American pilot. He himself was not that sure of what happened. All he knew was that while standing in the main room, watching the dancers, especially the American Naval officer and listening out of one ear as some Dutchman and his wife bored him to tears, he saw the oilman bow to Miss Elmes, whisper something to her and turn away. And the American reacted as if he had pinched her! Then, skirting the fallen body of the Australian, she hurried over to the Ford and suddenly they were grinning and seeming to celebrate. Van Gelder walked over and Ford told him what it was that elated them happy and he smiled. Then the host started towards him and the diplomat made a hasty excuse to get away from the Dutch couple and joined the Colonel. The news from him that Oberveldt told Miss Elmes they could have the gas floored him. Both of them tried to figure out why the oilman changed his mind. So all he knew as he stood looking across the harbor at the tail of the Pacific Clipper was that Robert Ford had his petrol. And the Ambassador ruefully admitted to himself, the American Captain also held all the trump.

"But does he? I wonder. No matter how great his plane's range is, it can't fly to America without stopping for fuel. So when he gets to Trincomalee, where will he go, assuming he can get more gas to continue? I told him he'd be landing on British territory until he reached South America. And what doesn't Captain Ford have...money! He has no money! So how is he going to pay for the petrol for his plane; he'll try to get credit and give a Pan Am marker. But what if suddenly, the Pan Am IOU isn't any good! Now, wouldn't that be too bad. Ha!" the Englishman thought.

Walking over to his desk, he looked at an atlas that Finch had brought to him yesterday before they left for the VanGelders. He had it open to a double spread of the subcontinent, from Malasia to the

Persian Gulf. Wherever Ford took his plane he was landing on British territory. Now the Ambassador knew that fate hadn't smiled only on Ford with the news that Oberveldt was giving the Americans their fuel. Walking quickly back to the window, the gloom of a few minutes ago was replaced in his step and demeanor. Sir Reginald Leach had been dealt a new hand.

"So, my young American friend. You have an angle that got the fuel for you from that bastard Oberveldt. But what will you do when you land in Trincomalee and say, "Fill 'er up, or whatever a pilot says when he needs petrol. And what will you pay them with when they give you the bill? A Pan Am IOU? I think not, especially when they have been instructed to take cash, British pounds only! Yes, Captain Ford, unless you have me along to clear the way for our people to take the Pan Am marker for the petrol you need, you'll rot in Ceylon! And as for that 'cut to the cows' tripe, you never had any intention of flying me to London. But I must think this through," the diplomat mulled.

Looking out the window at his prize across the water, Sir Reginald Leach had made his decision. "Captain Ford, like it or not, if you ever want to see the United States again, you will fly me to London! That is your only way home! I am the British Ambassador and in the name of my country, in the best interests of both our nations, to help us defeat Germany, you and your crew will fly the Pacific Clipper to England!"

Smiling, the Ambassador turned and walked towards the door. "Ah, Reginald, it does feel good to make a decision, especially where no one in real authority is around to know what you're doing," the Englishman thought to himself as he opened the door and strode into the outside office, ready to take on the Americans.

"Mr. Finch," he roared. "I'm changing our plans again."

0945 20 December, 1941 at the Black Swan

Ginsberg's car arrived at the side door of the Black Swan with its passengers a few minutes before their 1000 hours date with Shamus. The two Americans got out and in front of them they could see that most of the chaos of yesterday in the harbor had ended. But across the way, the two old rust buckets they had noticed tied up to the dock yesterday now had smoke whisping out of their smoke stacks. They had fired their boilers and were taking on passengers!

"Bob, if those two ever get out of the harbor, a small swell will sink them" John Mack said. "They are death traps," Ford was about to comment when, from behind them, their host spoke.

"Ah, Mr. Mack. You are optimistic. When they leave the dock, they will come apart at the seams. The captains of these ships would take their sainted mothers out on them for the money they've been paid," their host commented. They stood and looked for a few seconds but there was nothing the three could say or do so they turned and entered Shamus' home. The two Americans again, like the night before at the Van Gelders were not prepared for what they saw. Directly across the living room was a mahogany wall that ran from floor to a beamed ceiling and hanging on that wall was as eclectic collection of great paintings that the two of them had ever seen. Even Ford recognized a Van Gogh. He assumed the others were equally as famous. John Mack, who knew his art, saw a Cezanne, a Degas and a Monet. He was stunned. There were other paintings, smaller with religious themes and over to the right, a painting by an artist he couldn't identify but he loved it. It was of a yellow cow, laughing and frolicking in a field. His host caught his stare at the painting and smiled.

"Like it, John?" Shamus asked.

"Very much but who painted it," he asked.

"Franz Marc. It is called "The Yellow Cow" and the painter is relatively unknown but I like his work. But there will be no more. Marc was killed in World War I. An artillery barrage. Too bad a talent like him was killed in the Great War and a little corporal survived," the Irish Jew commented.

While John Mack and Shamus were discussing the world of art, Ford glanced at the coffee table situated between the two large naugahyde couches. Walking over and looking down, he could see National Geographic maps laying there and he saw at once that Shamus had been plotting the Clipper's course from Surabaja. "Is everyone on this island a navigator? So I guess I can tell Barney there will be one more for dinner. Unless I'm totally wrong, he's the one that twisted Oberveldt's arm. I wonder what he has on the oilman," Ford thought. And he suddenly felt a little queazy about the innkeeper. He didn't know why. Shamus had been the perfect host and their probable savior. It was something subtle but Ford had long ago learned to trust his instincts. Pilots live by the faith they had in their feelings. Ford had it in spades and it was this feeling that suddenly came over him in the innkeeper's living room, an inexplicable sense that told him to watch out. For some reason, Ford felt some doubts about Shamus Ginsberg.

"Ah, Captain Ford. You see when you and I discussed your route back to the States, I'd already done some homework. So that almost "magical" analysis on the deck yesterday afternoon was based on simple logic and some National Geographic maps. Word of your landing had reached me the moment you touched down and I was curious as to where you would go from here. My curiosity has led me to why I asked you to come here this morning." Just as Ford was about to respond, the door from the kitchen and Shamus' house boy came in with a silver tray and coffee urn, cups and accessories and placed it on the table where there were no maps. There was also helpings of French toast with powered sugar, syrup and fresh mangos and kiwis. The man left and the three sat, Shamus pouring the coffee and waving at the French toast and fruit and his guests nodded their acceptance. Quickly the three ate and then settled back to enjoy more coffee. Now the two waited for their host to explain the reason for the meeting.

"Gentlemen, last night I was able to arrange for Mr. Oberveldt to reconsider your request for aviation fuel. About noon today, the trucks of Royal Dutch Shell will arrive at the dock and fill the tanks of the Pacific Clipper. You will then be free to leave Surabaja," Shamus began. He paused as he framed his next statement. He had thought long about this and as he was about to begin, Bob Ford preempted him.

"Shamus, we knew it was you that got the Dutchman to relent. We won't ask how. So, how do we pay for the gas and what do you wish in return?" Ford stated.

Shamus looked at Ford and then at John Mack. He had an elaborate plan to offer to the Americans for his passage and the directness of Ford's statement shook him. He had always prided himself as an astute poker player and looked at the two Americans but could read nothing in either man's eyes or expression. A simple question but how demanding! So he answered simply.

"I want to be aboard when the hull of the Pacific Clipper escapes the waters of Surabaja. As for payment, let us agree that my ticket from Surabaja to Trincomalee is the fuel. The designation of the class of travel and the location of my seat I will leave to you."

Both laughed and relaxed. They lifted their coffee cups in toast to their newest passenger. As Ford sat back, with one problem behind him, he thought of those ahead. Getting out of Surabaja and to Trincomalee was now assured. But what would they do for money after that? They still were broke and if nobody would take his marker here in Surabaja, he'd have to assume the same thing as they flew across the underbelly of the world. As he thought about the places he'd have to land and refuel, India, Arabia, the Sudan, an image jumped into his mind, a tall distinguished man with a trim grey mustache. Sir Reginald

Leach, the British Empire's Ambassador to Indonesia! Ford may not have wanted Sir Reginald as a passenger flying him to London but he sure as hell didn't want him as an enemy, trying to thwart them as they tried for the States. He had to figure a way to mollify John Bull's man in Southeast Asia.

Ford's sudden departure from the conversation brought Mack and Shamus to silence as they watched him deep in thought. Suddenly, the silence intruded and Ford realized they were waiting on him.

"Sorry. Other things suddenly grabbed my attention and I'm afraid I let my mind wander. Please, let's continue," Ford apologized.

"Anything I can help with, Captain" John Mack asked.

"I wish you could, John. It is what we talked about. Cash or the lack of it and what do we do with Sir Reginald. Now that we have the gas, thanks to Shamus, we don't need him to leave Surabaja. But until we reach the Congo, we'll be flying over and landing on British territories. He could play hell with us if he wanted to. He is a powerful man and he wants the Clipper for the British. No, Sir Reginald has to be put to rest before we leave here. And for the life of me, I don't know how you placate an Ambassador!" Ford explained, detailing his concerns.

"Captain, I wasn't present at your meeting with the Ambassador. But from what you've told me and what I gleaned from the others, the Ambassador was going to get you the gas in exchange for your flying him back to England. Is that about it?" Shamus asked and with Ford's nod, continued.

"Not a bad idea but he failed. He knows you have the gas to get you as far as Trincomalee. So his main thrust at you would be that you need his good graces to be able to pay for supplies and not be bothered when you land on British waters or those of their friends. Right?" Shamus asked and again Ford nodded.

"First to finances. Here you are in Surabaja without a sou and no one will take your marker, the IOU of the world's most famous airline. And you have another 20,000 miles to fly to get home. So, let my getting you the gas for the first leg of this odyssey be my ticket aboard the Pacific Clipper. Now, without bragging, the marker of Shamus Ginsberg is good all across the subcontinent. So here is my proposal. Whenever you or the members of the crew have to purchase something, from fuel and whatever supplies the plane needs to fly to underwear and booze and food, I will pay the expenses. You will give me the Pan Am marker for everything and when we get to New York, Juan Trippe will cover them. If we don't make it, wherever we'll be, we won't need money!" the innkeeper offered. "Now what do you say to that, Robert Ford."

Ford grinned from ear to ear and put out his hand. "Agreed, Shamus. But why?"

"Easy. You're my ticket out of here, and hopefully, to America. I have enough liquid assets that I can easily underwrite the trip. You see, like Henry Oberveldt, I knew the only money that would be worth anything in the world was the American dollar. When I would go to Hong Kong or Macco to make my deposits, I always brought home some American dollars. I wanted enough money to be able to get away from the Japanese. They'll take what's in the banks in Hong Kong, Macco and here plus the Swan herself and there is nothing I can do about it. What is in the banks is a small fraction of what I've squirled away at the Morgan Guarantee Trust in mid-Manhattan. And, here at the Swan, I've more than enough cash to get us to the States, in style," the innkeeper explained as Ford and John Mack both felt the elation of knowing that money was no longer one problem. They knew there were many others, including a hard headed Englishman. As for his prior concerns about Shamus Ginsberg, Ford pushed them to the back of his mind. This was one gift horse he wasn't going to look in the mouth!

"Again, welcome aboard, Shamus Ginsberg!" Ford said with a big grin on his face. Ginsberg smiled and rose from the sofa. Looking at them, he began. "Gentlemen, as a rule, I take no libation during the day and only a sip of champagne during the evening business hours. However, this morning let us enjoy this moment and celebrate it with my favorite drink, besides Cutty Sark, Irish Coffee. I have a 12 year old bottle of Bushmills that I've been holding for such a moment," Walking over to the door to his kitchen, he pushed it open and nodded. Out came his servant carrying the silver coffee tray with three tall silver goblets. Shamus took one of the goblets from the tray, and began. "First, I've developed a taste for cinnamon in my Irish. That may set off some purists back in Dublin that will shudder but that's too bad. So I drop a cube of sugar into the bottom of the glass, add a pinch of ground cinnamon, pour in the Bushmills, filling the glass at least half way to the brim, then add the coffee. Now here is the trick. Most waiters and even first rate maitre'ds will take a tablespoon of whipped cream and drop it on top of the coffee. Wrong. The way to do it is like this. Take a clean spoon, turn it over so the back is up and the front resting on the lip of the glass. Then with the other spoon, take a healthy heaping of the whipped cream and put that on top of the inverted spoon. The whipped cream will slowly slide into the glass, then will sit quietly on top, not mixing with the coffee. Otherwise, if you just drop a spoonful of cream into the glass, what you'll have is creamed coffee, not Irish Coffee!"

The aroma emanating from the goblets as the cinnamon and whiskey merged in the coffee filled the room with a pleasant, relaxing ambience. The three sat in silence until Ford spoke. "Shamus, aren't you suppose to mumble some mysterious Irish incantation asking the Little People to bless our flight," Ford asked.

Laughing, their host picked up his goblet. "Captain, all the good luck amulets of the Jews and the four leafed clovers of the Irish together are overtaxed on this mission. So I'll excerpt from an old Irish prayer for this moments. "May the wind be always at our back and may God hold us in the hollow of his hand," Ford and Mack added "Amen" and the three lifted their cups in silent prayer. Sipping on the 'Irish' the two found them to be as delightful as Shamus had promised.

"Shamus, neither Bob or myself have had a minute to really try and digest all that has happened since Pearl Harbor. Not to us but I mean, well, what happened? You know these people, the Japanese. Why? Why did they attack and what is going to happen," John Mack asked.

Shamus looked at the two and wondered how much background they needed to understand what the Japanese did. He doubted that even he did. But he knew he knew more than they so he decided to give them a quick lesson in foreign affairs, Black Swan style.

"What President Roosevelt called "the day of infamy" was rightly named, if you're an American. We were stabbed in the back. In Japan, it is their greatest triumph. America is the enemy and they just took advantage of the famous American trust. Here in Asia, everyone understands. That is the way things are. Now you can see what you're up against. Think like Occidentals and the Japanese will blow your balls off, just like they did at Pearl and every other place in the Pacific. The Japanese need the resources of the other nations in the Pacific to conquer Asia. Only America stood in her way and now nothing does. In a few days, Java will be part of the Japanese Empire. They wanted this war. Now they have it and unless America can do something about it, they'll hold Asia for decades, maybe even centuries."

"But Shamus, there must be some in Japan that see the folly of a war with us!" Ford exclaimed.

"If there are, they are all dead or in prison. Gentlemen, you and the rest of the world better wake up. This is no paper tiger that will be blown away by the first American protest. Even if somehow the Army and Navy could come back, look at what they have to reconquer just to get near the home islands themselves. It will take years. The Japanese people are willing to die for their homeland. Are Americans willing to die for the Hawaiian Islands, the Philippines, Guam or Wake Island? They might if the Japs had bombed San Francisco or LA. And remember, the Germans have just declared war on us. So that means we have to arm ourselves as well as the Allies and fight the two greatest military forces on earth. Crap. I was told by an American seaman not too long ago his younger brother had joined a National Guard outfit back in the States and they drilled with broomsticks instead of rifles because there weren't any rifles. And we're going to fight Germany and Japan at the same time?"

Shamus' vehemence took Ford and Mack back but there were still questions in their minds and Shamus tried to end the discussion because it was going no where and getting them upset. "Gentlemen, there will be plenty of time on the Clipper to discuss the war. All I can say for sure, from what I know of the Japanese mentality, they will never admit defeat until they are totally destroyed. And I'm not talking about the soldiers and sailors and pilots. No, it is the civiliansthat will never quit. No nation can defeat the Japanese on their home soil. Even if every soldier is dead, the old men and women and children will fight to the last person. A bullet from one of them kills just as dead as from a soldier. And if the Americans invade Japan, millions could end up wounded or dead before the Japs surrendered. No, my friends, the most vicious, toughest fighting force in the world has attacked us. God help us if we don't know it. Maybe Pearl Harbor will wake us up. Christ, I hope so. Maybe the Pacific Clipper in her own way can help get the weapons we'll need to defeat them. All I know, if America thinks it can defeat Japan by invading her homeland, we'll be in for another Hundred Years War!" the innkeeper ended.

"Christ Shamus. You paint one hell of a picture. I'm sorry John asked," Bob Ford stated. Shamus just looked at them and then shrugged. The two Americans rose, shook hands with the innkeeper and departed to returned to the Clipper and await the visit of the British Ambassador to Indochina. Ford wasn't looking forward to it.

He had used the phone in Shamus' room to call the British Ambassador and tried to put him off but Sir Reginald wasn't having any of that. Ford had no choice but to meet with him. They understood that you don't tell the British Ambassador to 'shove it', especially when you're going to be landing on his turf most of the way home. Ginsberg's driver brought them back to the Clipper and Ford, getting out an looking at her, decided that the lousy camouflage job had to go. He asked Tacki for help and Shamus' man said he'd get it done. Getting on board, he called the crew together to tell them that Shamus Ginsberg would joining them on their trek to America and also advised that Sir Reginald Leach, the British Ambassador would be coming by for a chat. Dismissing them, he went up to his room, lay down for a half hour and rested. Before he dozed off, he could hear Brown yelling instructions to Tacki and his crew. He was happy Norm had someone to oversee.

Ford was standing on the dock when the Ambassador's Rolls Royce pulled up promptly at 1600 hours. Ford strode over to greet him and as the Ambassador emerged, Ford again was struck by movie star quality about the man. Sir Reginald looked at the Clipper, now almost free of the camouflage paint and quietly admitted that she did make the Sutherland seem inferior. "The Aussie had it right, I must admit," Sir Reginald thought as he walked towards Ford. The two shook hands and Ford escorted him into the plane. The King's representative was very impressed with the richness and luxury of the Clippers interior; tan leather seats, widebacked, obviously quite comfortable and with plenty of leg room.

"Mr. Ambassador, would you like to see the bridge, flight deck?" Ford asked. He followed the Ambassador up and standing in the center, Ford pointed out the different instruments and stations on the deck. Sir Reginald nodded and smiled as Ford carried on like a proud father. Ford quickly realize that all the Ambassador wanted to talk about was going home to London so he cut the cook's tour short and the two of them went down to the lounge. Ford had made it clear that he wanted to be alone with the Ambassador so the passenger level was empty except for Barney. Sliding into the plush tan chair under the starboard wing, the Ambassador looked around and was impressed. Barney Swacki appeared from the galley and Ford introduced his First Steward to the Ambassador and when Sir Reginald inquired where Barney was from, he replied, "Chicago," The Ambassador raised his eyebrows and all three laughed. Barney was use to foreigners thinking all Chicagoans were part of Al Capone's gang. Offering coffer or tea, Barney waited. The pause by the Ambassador indicated something more tasty so Barney excused himself and returned immediately, with a silver ice bucket, two crystal goblets and a bottle of champagne. As Barney, towel over his forearm showed the bottle to the Ambassador for his approval, the subtle touch was not lost on Sir Reginald. He smiled at Barney and as the steward expertly opened a bottle of Dom Perignon and filled their glasses, the Ambassador nodded to Ford.

The two men looked at each other. The Ambassador let his eyes sweep again through the plane and nodded his approval. Ford just sat there, not having the faintest idea of how he was going to turn down the British Ambassador's request to fly to London.

"Captain Ford, when are you planning to leave Surabaja and is Trincomalee still your first stop?" Sir Reginald began. Unlike Ford, he knew exactly where he wanted this conversation to lead and end. This time he would not fall for that wide-eyed country bumpkin look. He knew Ford had to fly over British territories all the way to South America. So unless Ford agreed to make his final destination London with him aboard, Sir Reginald would promised the American that their troubles were only beginning when they touched down in Trincomalee. But Sir Reginald was far too much the diplomat to hit the American right between the eyes with that. He wanted to lead him along, be 'a pal' and then drop the hammer. He felt good watching Ford ready his answer. After last night and that "cut-to-the-cows" business, he enjoyed watching the Captain squirm.

As Ford listened to the opening gambit in a match he'd hoped had been ended last night, he knew he would not beat the Ambassador with that "aw shucks' play. "Yes, Sir Reginald. We do plan to fly to Trincomalee, tomorrow," Ford responded.

"Yes!" What kind of response is that my young American. Of course it is yes!" the Ambassador though to himself, wondering how simple that answer was. And now it dawned on him. The answer wasn't simple. Now I have to respond with another idiotic question or take it right to him. Yes! God, where does he come up with such simple but difficult responses."

Ford smiled at the Ambassador and sat back and thought. "I'm beginning to enjoy this, champagne in the evening, Irish Coffee in the morning, more champagne in the late afternoon. I have to thank you Ambassador. You've shown me the good life. Now let me really cut to the cows. Here comes a high hard one Sir, right between those baby blues of yours."

Leaning forward, Ford spoke softly. "Sir Reginald. As I told you, where we go after we leave Trincomalee is in the lap of the gods. Obviously, wherever we land, we hope to avail ourselves of the hospitality of the people there and purchase supplies from them. Your kind offer last night that you will make sure when we land on the King's possessions we will receive every courtesy is greatly appreciated.

And I plan to take you up on that generous proposal. The cooperation of your people as we go across the subcontinent is vital to our successful flight home. But Mr. Ambassador, unless I receive written orders from Mr. Trippe directing me to fly you and the Pacific Clipper to London, I intend to take my ship back to the United States," Check and mate!

Ford's words "written orders" struck the Ambassador. His heart sank. The pilot had touched the Achilles' heel of his grand design. He could threaten Ford with no cooperation no matter where they went, that he would order the British Embassies along the way to seize the plane and he was angry enough to do that right now. But as he looked at the American he knew it wouldn't work. As his mind raced through the options he had, he quickly realized that unless he was prepared to cause a major disfunction between his government and the United States, all he could do was be spiteful and have a couple toads along the way cause Ford problems. And he knew Ford would best them! So here he sat in the lounge of the plane that he hoped would bring him back to London and the glory that would come from that. He looked at the American and suddenly Ford became all that he envied, the representative of a young, vigorous society, fully confident in their destiny, their abilities as individuals and as a nation to solve any problem, overcome any crisis. There would be no glory for him. The game was over and sitting in this beautiful plane in the backwaters of an ancient nation, he was looking at the future in Ford while the grandness that was the British Empire was fading. He knew that without the Americans, there might not be a Britain. He felt old. He'd go back to Batavia then on to Bombay and wait while they decided what to do with him. And right now, he didn't give a damn. The early evening sun bounced off the waters in the harbor and streamed into the cabin, adding flickering shades of yellow and green to the teal blue. Sighing, he reached for his glass, now almost empty. Ford took the bottle of Dom Perignon from the silver bucket and filled both glasses. Sir Reginald raised his to the American and said. "Mate."

1750 hours-20 December 1941, Aboard the Arista-Java Sea.

The Commodore was climbing the walls. After his "discussion" with Nagoma, he had avoided any contact with the crew and the Captain. Self imprisonment inside the tiny cabin was his penance for that stupid display of anger. Objectively, he knew that Nagoma had been right. But objectivity was not one of Tanaka's strong points. Compounding the feeling of rage at Nagoma and disgust with himself was the total lack of communications with Thu. His whole body ached to climb to the top of the sub and shout to Thu to tell him what was happening! His wish was answered by a soft tap on his cabin door. In one stride his hand closed on the doorknob and as he was about to fling the door open, he stopped, gathered himself and remembered that he was a Tanaka. No further displays of emotions from him. Walking back to the tiny chair, he sat and softly bid the person enter.

It was the same poor wretch of a radioman, the one he had terrified yesterday! He recognized Nagoma's insult by sending the same sailor but ignored it and took the paper from the messenger. The radioman bowed and backed out of the room, forgetting to close the door as he fled down the passageway. Tanaka didn't care. He ripped open the message and read in code, "FORD DEPARTS 0830-21/12/41. READY. THU."

Tanaka grinned and looked at one of the schematics of the Pacific Clipper that his Intelligence group had cut out for him. They got it from an American magazine that featured a story about the new Boeing 314A. "Ah, the Americans. Ask them a question about anything and they'll tell you all they know or where to go to get the answers! Publishing the exact details about the finest plane in the world in a trade magazine, unbelievable"

Looking at his watch, he saw that it already 1725 hours. In another hour or so, it would be dark and Thu and his men would begin to board the Clipper after midnight. With no cargo or passengers with luggage, the two figured the cargo hold would be empty and therefore no reason for Ford or any of the crew to inspect them. But to be on the safe side, they agreed the boarding would take place when the crew was asleep. He doubted Ford would put a watch on in Surabaja. They had nothing to fear.

Now that the moment was near, Tanaka faced the biggest weakness in his whole plan. Even if Thu and his commandos got aboard, even if they overpowered the Americans and captured the plane, it did them no good unless the Pacific Clipper was airborne. Only then with Thu's pistol pushing against Ford's head would the American to fly to Kota Bharu to say hello to him! He had thought this through and what had happened to Ford coming to Surabaja gave him the final touch, the piece d'resistance to make sure Ford was airborne when Thu struck. He would stage another air raid!

"The Dutch are so jumpy now, and so is Ford, that they'll believe anything. I'll send Thu a coded message as to the details of the plan. I'll have a fake message sent from the Arista to the Dutch in open transmission. When that air raid siren sounds, Ford won't know if it is real or not. And he can't take the chance that it is a false alarm. He'll bust his ass getting the Clipper out of the harbor and into the air. Once Ford is airborne, I have him!" the big man thought. "If I can shake him up, think that out fighters are coming, he and his people will be looking for planes in the sky, totally unaware that we'll be attacking from inside the Clipper! Brilliant, if I do say so myself," the Commodore thought to himself. Feeling almost ebullient, Tanaka left the cabin, his imprisonment over. He was ready to execute his plan. His long strides quickly took him to the bridge and Nagoma.

1940 hours-somewhere in the mountains of Surabaja-Major Thu's camp

Thu was ectatic. The coded message from his commander pumped him up and the plan for the fake air raid to get the Americans in the air was brilliant. He and his men were ready and as he thought about Tanaka' plan he saw a way to embellish it, to make the Dutch really believe the invasion was beginning. There had been a number of false alarms, like the one welcoming the Pacific Clipper to Surabaja so another might not achieve the desired results, getting Ford and his ship into the air.

"But maybe I can get them to think this is the real thing. What if word was spread by responsible local citizens that they had seen Japanese troops moving through the forests and along the beaches above the city, headed for the oil fields. That would shake them and when the open transmission came from the "tramp steamer" saying that they had seen Japanese warplanes headed for Surabaja, that would surely stamp this air raid as real. To the Dutch, this would surely mean the beginning of the invasion. And Ford couldn't risk staying in Surabaja! He'll haul his ass into the sky and away from here," the commando thought.

Now Thu got busy with his part of the ruse. He had Sergeant Yuban alert the tailor, Jalara, to come to his camp. An hour later, Jalara appeared. Without elaborating on the plan, he told the agent to have some of the men in his group tell the natives of seeing Japanese troops in the hills above Surabaja. Then Jalara was to have others report they had seen small patrols of Japanese troops headed for Rembang. Knowing human nature and because the rumors would begin at night, by daylight, the number of soldiers spotted by the natives would rival the real invasion force! The Dutch and Javanese forces had to spend the morning tracking down the rumors and when the fake message was received from the bogus steamer, everyone would believe the invasion was started. The Japanese often sent in troops to hide behind enemy lines just prior to an invasion. When the Americans were told that

Japanese soldiers were seen advancing towards Surabaja and Rembang, they wouldn't sit around to check the veracity of the reports. They'd pour the gas to those engines and get the giant plane away from Surabaja as fast as they could. With Thu and his men in the holds!

1950 hours-20 December 1941-aboard the Pacific Clipper

Ford looked at his watch and decided to get something to eat. He'd been pouring over the maps on Steers' navigator's table and his back was beginning to tighten up. He was alone on the Clipper except for John Poindexter. The rest of the crew, along with Kathleen Elmes had gone into town to spend the night at the Orange Hotel. Shamus had made all the arrangements and they would join him for dinner at the Black Swan. When the crew had gone, Ford kept the doors on the passenger level open so he and the radioman could enjoy another beautiful evening in Surabaja. The soft evening breezes brought in the aroma of the scented flowers, trees and shrubs that surrounded the city and it made for a relaxing evening.

Nodding to Poindexter that he was going to eat, the two walked down to the galley and broke out the club sandwiches that Barney had prepared. Taking a couple of Australian beers, something called Fosters from the ice box, they sat in the lounge and enjoyed the quiet of the empty plane. To Ford, having done more talking in 24 hours than he had in 24 years not having to make idle conversation was heaven. And Poindexter, naturally tired from listening to empty air punctuated by foreign languages from the ships at sea also enjoyed the quiet. So, of course the two talked up a storm. Finishing their snacks and policing the area, they returned to the flight deck. As is the habit of all radio men in the air or at sea, when working at their console, they automatically put on their ears and flip the ON switch to listen. In a few minutes, a radio transmission began. Poindexter idly noted the time, 1940 hours and continued on his assignment of figuring out a "radar" like conversion of the radio to help if there were to be any night landings of the Clipper. He'd paid little heed to the transmissions over the radio since they landed. Suddenly, he heard something and sat upright in his chair. Ford saw Poindexter's movement out of the corner of his eye and turned away from his maps to see what was going on. Seeing Poindexter scribbling rapidly, Ford moved into his seat, put on his ears and listened. It was a code he didn't know but suddenly, he knew it had something to do with his ship! And he felt very cold. The breeze that a few seconds ago was soft and filled with fragrance, now felt icy. Ford looked down at his bare legs and could see goose bumps on them.

Poindexter stopped writing and when Ford looked over at the radioman, he stopped breathing. Poindexter was ashen! He was actually frightened. Ford didn't say a word, knowing his man would tell him everything.

"Bob, yesterday I told you about the transmission I picked up when we were landing in Surabaja. It came just minutes after we knew the Dutch would let us land. Neither Kathleen or I could understand the code but I told you the sender had a special touch and I'd recognize it if I heard it again. I just did. It originated from here, from somewhere in or near Surabaja. Since there was no acknowledgement, like last time, I can't triangulate but I know it is the same sender!

Ford knew the message was about them but he couldn't let Poindexter or any of the crew know he was worried. But he was. He felt something was going on and it involved them. But smiling at the radioman to get him to relax, Ford shrugged it off with an explanation that there was a war going on and Java was soon to be invaded. "Come on John. The message might be from the same source as yesterday's but why do you think it involves us. Java is going to be invaded soon and its possible there are some Japs already put on the island. The odds are a million to one that anyone cares about us. Christ, Pan Am hasn't even tried to find us!" Ford stated, trying to get his man to see why this transmission was probably for Japanese commandos on the island. Ford didn't know how right he was!

As Poindexter was about to reply, there was a banging on the side of the plane and both men almost jumped out of their skins! Then a voice came through from the entryway, shouting "Hello in there. Anybody home?" The two looked at each other and laughed at the momentary fright the pounding had caused and rising Ford led the way down. There standing in the entryway was Rolph VanderKellen and his three cohorts from the Royal Dutch Air Corps!

"Permission to come aboard Sir," Captain VanderKellen requested, finishing it off with the traditional salute of a visiting officer to another's vessel.

"Permission granted!" Ford laughed as he returned the salute, somewhat less military than the Dutchman's, then shaking hands with the pilot. Ford did the honors introducing Poindexter and Rolph reciprocated introducing the three Lieutenants. The six sat around one of the lounge tables and VanderKellen pushed the gifts towards Ford.

"A few small tokens from us and out best wishes for a safe journey back to American," the Dutch Captain began. "We ran into some of your chaps in the bar at the hotel and had a grand visit. When informed that you were staying onboard, we decided to use that as an excuse to bring you some libation and hope that we could impose on you for a quick tour of the Clipper. After all, the four of us feel a very parochial interest in her!"

The surprise visit by Rolph VanderKellen and his compatriots was a welcome relief to the two Americans, especially after they were so busy scaring themselves with mysterious radio transmissions. To Ford, it was especially salutary. Every man luxuriates in explaining to another his particular specialty in life. And the opportunity to show off the Pacific Clipper to a fellow pilot was especially gratifying to Ford since it was to someone as valiant as the Dutch Captain. Shamus had told him of VanderKellen's heroics over the Straits of Dover. In the 36 hours since the Dutchman had saved their ass, Ford had come to regard the Captain very highly and that a combat veteran, a fighter pilot felt the same towards him was very complimentary.

Ford didn't bother with the passenger level, knowing pilots wanted to see what made the Clipper tick. Standing on the bridge, the fighter pilots were quite comfortable and the younger pilots kidded Ford and Poindexter about all the space and luxury they had. Quite different than the cockpit of a Brewster. Lt. Heyden, asking permission, opened the door to the starboard wing and whistled, staring in disbelief at the size of the Wrights and that the engineers could work on the engines while in flight! The two Pan Am men answered each and every question as the four sat in the different chairs and marveled at the instruments the flight crew had at their disposal. Almost an hour passed before Captain VanderKellen called a halt.

"Gentlemen, give the Captain and Mr. Poindexter a break. No more questions. Let us retire to that beautiful lounge and pop a cork or two to toast our friends and their safe journey home," When the Dutch pilot finished pouring the champagne, he raised his and was about to offer a toast but he stopped. He just looked at Ford and nodded. Ford understood and nodded back. He reached into his blouse pocket and brought out a pack of Chesterfields, shaking one loose and lighting it. Looking up, he noticed the eyes of the four Dutchmen on the pack and laughed.

"Anyone want to try an American cigarette?" he asked.

His question was greeted by laughter and affirmative nods. As the fighter pilots helped themselves to the Chesterfields, Poindexter got up and walked to the galley. In a second he returned with a dozen or so cartons of a mixed bag of American brands; Old Golds, Camels,

Chesterfields, Lucky Strikes and placed them on the lounge table. Ford then piled them up into four sets and pushed them over to their guests.

"Bob, we can't take these. Where you're going, they may be more valuable than money!" Rolph Vander Kellen explained as he pushed his back towards Ford.

"Nonsense, take them Rolph. We have plenty on board and there is little else we can give you to thank you for yesterday and all the help you've been getting us the gas," the Clipper's commander countered.

The Dutchman nodded his thanks and all of them sat back and enjoyed the champagne and the cigarettes. One of the pilots, Lt. Anders, asked Ford about the range of the Clipper and Ford told him that if necessary, the Boeing could fly 5000 miles before refueling. That got a raise out of the fighter pilots whose maximum range in the Brewsters was 500 miles! Then Lt. Heyden asked about their planned course back to America. Captain VanderKellen looked angrily at the young officer but Ford just laughed.

"Lt., our first stop, hopefully, will be Trincomalee, in Ceylon. There is a British naval base there and we hope to be able get more 100 octane. After that, my plan is to head for Karachi, India, then across Arabia to Khartoum, onto the Congo, then across the South Atlantic to Brazil, up the Caribbean to Trinidad, then non stop into New York. That's our plan. But you know the old saying about the 'best laid plans,' Ford answer. The fighter pilots just looked at him, almost in disbelief and finally VanderKellen spoke.

"That's never been done, Bob, by anyone. From what you've just said, you'll be circumnavigating the world, in a commercial plane, at that and one that can only land on water! I know some military planes have done it but they were always able to go to and from places where there were services for their planes. After here, you'll not find any help for a ship like the Clipper."

"Rolph, ever since Pearl Harbor, wherever we have gone, we've been told that we can't make it. Well, we're here in Surabaja and we can stay and wait for the Japs or try to make it. What would you do?" the Clipper's pilot asked. The question was rhetorical and all knew it. "Speaking of the Japs, what are your plans for them when they come?" Ford asked.

"When they come, we'll be here," VanderKellen replied phlegmatically.

"Any idea of where they are?" Poindexter asked, looking at the four. One of the others replied. He was Uve Balh, a good looking red-haired young man, the Dutch pilot that remembered seeing the newsreel of Madeline Carroll and the Yankee Clipper. His excited warning had delayed their destruction long enough to get the Dutch command to reconsider and allow the Clipper to land.

"Starting tomorrow, we'll be sending up searching sorties to see if we can spot them. They'll be coming," the young man commented. His fellow pilots nodded and looked at Captain VanderKellen. Their leader just looked at them and then at his champagne glass, still filled. He drew down on his cigarette and looked at Ford and Poindexter. He nodded that the redhead was correct. Then sipping on his drink, he looked at his host and explained what, in his opinion, would happen.

"Where they will land is problematical but my best guess is that they'll hit about 100 miles from here, at Rembang, where the Royal Dutch Shell refinery is located. Their ships have to come up the Macassar Straits and we have the range to inflict what ever damage we can when they come that way, we'll take some of them with us," the angular Dutchman commented on their own no-win situation.

The six just sat there, each with their own thought of the problems he faced. After a few seconds, the irrepressible Uve Blab broke up the wake.

"Captain Ford, please forgive me for asking, but I have to know. Lieutenant Elmes, I mean, Captain VanderKellen told me how good looking she was but tonight when I saw her at the hotel, I mean,, wow!, sorry, but, how in the devil did you get her to fly around the world with you!" the flyer asked. Ford broke up laughing as did Poindexter and the immediate embarrassment of the Dutch pilots quickly gave way to laughter as they saw that the Americans took no offense to the question.

"Lt. it would take the rest of the evening and much of the night to explain her presence on the Pacific Clipper. Rest assured that it is with the complete approval of the United States Navy and the Department of State. She is an accomplished linguist, a respected member of Naval Intelligence and will be a great help to us going home. And it is much nicer to have a beautiful woman aboard than a homely one, don't you agree, Lt.?" Ford answered.

The redheaded fighter pilot blushed and nodded as his friends laughed at and with him. And as Rolph VanderKellen poured the last of the champagne into the glasses of each man, he again looked at Ford and nodded towards the open door that lead to the dock. Ford looked at his watch and nodded. Both raised their glasses as the others, sipped and finished their drinks. Then all six rose and shook hands, all around. Ford put his arm around the shoulder of the Dutch captain as his men led the way to the exit. They stepped onto the dock as Ford and the fighter pilot paused in the exit way.

"Well, Bob, Good luck. I wish you had more time here to allow me to show you how beautiful our island is but there seems to be something coming that makes that impossible. We've only know each other for a day plus but if there is a pilot in the world that can pull off this odyssey of yours,, it is you. And the Pacific Clipper is the only plane flying in the world that can do it. I'll be down tomorrow to see you off. Good Luck," the Dutch pilot said as his right hand gripped hard on Ford's,

The American was struck with the futility of it all. Here in the middle of a part of the world he never expected to see was a man he could call friend and he was leaving him here in Surabaja. A sudden, sharp pang of near tearfulness gripped the taciturn American and he pulled the Dutchman to him and hugged him hard, as much to show his affection as to hide the tears that welled up in his eyes. A second passed and Ford was back in complete control but the moment wasn't lost on the Captain of the fighter squadron. He too felt the same and quickly turned and strode from the Clipper across the dock to their car. VanderKellen got into the passenger's side in the front seat. The other three Dutchmen were in the back and waved at Ford and Poindexter. As they pulled up the small rise to the street. Rolph VanderKellen did not look back.

As the Dutch car started down the street towards Surabaja, Ford remembered an old wives' tale he'd heard a few years ago from the mother of a girl friend of his. She had grown up in a logging camp in Northern Wisconsin and when she was six or seven, her father, an engineer on some now forgotten feeder line, went to work and as he climbed into the cabin of the engine, he waved good by to her. The little girl watched the train and her Daddy go out of sight beyond a small hill and he never came back. To this day, the woman believed she was responsible for her father's death because it was bad luck to watch a loved one or a friend go out of sight. Ford, totally devoid of any belief in the occult, turned quickly so he wouldn't see VanderKellen's car disappear.

He walked back to the Clipper and Poindexter joined him. Checking his watch in the moonlight, he saw that it was almost 2300 hours. Time to hit the sack. Poindexter began cleaning up the lounge as Ford closed the doors to the port and starboard entrances. Locking them, he began a routine security check of the Clipper. First to the anchor hatch, entering the small room and pulling on the lines for the anchor and those tied to the dock to make sure they were secure. Satisfied, he bent down to enter through the small door into the rooms of the holds. Flipping on a switch the whole area was suddenly bathed in light. It was eerie down in the almost empty holds and cold. He shrugged his shoulders and left. All was secure.

"All secure, Captain?" John Poindexter asked.

"All secure, John. How about some sleep? I'm going to use the forward compartment upstairs. Do you want to use the aft?"

"Might as well go up. Want me to set an alarm?" he asked.

"No John, I doubt I'll sleep late not with what we'll be doing tomorrow. Anyway, I expect the rest will be back around 0700. Shamus is to be here at that time and the Dutch will be down to see us off any time after that. Preflight check at 0745. The harbor patrol boat should be here a half hour later to take us out into the harbor. We'll leave these waters at 0830," Ford stated, ticking off the takeoff schedule. "But you know, there is always the unexpected. Who ever gets up first, start the coffee. Good night John," Ford said.

"Good night, Bob. Tomorrow really begins it, doesn't it?" Poindexter asked.

Ford leaned down from the bend in the steps and looked at his radioman. He smiled and nodded. "Maybe it won't be too long before you'll be sending a message to your wife, John. This time with an ETA for New York. Night, John," Within minutes, both men were asleep and the only noise was the soft slapping on the hull of an occasional small swell.

Chapter 8

The Japanese Strike

0200 hours-21 December 1941-Water's edge-Surabaja Harbor.

The mid-December moon was full and its beams lent the murky waters of the harbor a gossamer sheen that made the undisturbed Bay shine like an giant ebony mirror. Surabaja harbor lay still and quiet. An occasional kingfisher disturbed the shore waters with his talons as he searched for some adventurous fish too near the surface. There were no lights burning in the city as the curfew and blackout were in effect. The Black Swan had closed at 2100 hours and the crew of the Pacific Clipper were sleeping soundly at the Orange Hotel. Tomorrow more natives would try to escape Surabaja while others prepared for coming invasion. But now, all was silent.

On the shore about a quarter mile above the dock area, where trees came down to the edge and their roots stood exposed to the waters, six men appeared. The bright moonlight cast their shadows back onto the maze of limbs and bushes but they were so clad that it was impossible to tell them from the black roots and trunks. Their faces were stained black They wore a skin tight, one piece dark olive rubber suit that went from their throat into the black gym shoes on their feet. None wore a belt and even the metal eyelets of the gym shoes had been removed. Except for their eyes, the men were almost completely devoid of any color. Major Thu leaned out slightly from the cover of one of the trees and looked down the shore towards the dock. What he saw pleased him. His prey was bathed in the moonlight, glowing like a giant silver swan, sitting there awaiting he and his men. His eyes, perfectly accustomed to the night, searched for any movement that would signal him of the presence of others. But nothing moved. He and his men had been at this point for an hour and had seen nothing to tell them that anyone or anything was moving about. Except for the kingfisher. The noise of the insects and tree frogs was constant and reassuring.

Now he turned to his men and nodded. Swiftly and silently, a small, rubber raft appeared and slid into the water near him. The man in front kept the raft close to the shore and Major Thu stepped into it. The others followed and each slid down into raft, Thu as well. Then the man in front loosened the rope that had been tied to a trunk of a tree and pushed the raft away from the shore. A few feet out and he took a small rubber paddle from beneath the front of the raft and began to slowly, silently propel the craft towards the huge plane. The man kept the raft almost on the shore, under the overhanging branches of the trees.

In a few minutes, the raft stopped. They had come up to the fenced-in area of the dock that jutted out into the bay. Atop the wooden barrier was a barbed wire mesh that stretched back to the corner of the dock. And on the other side, about 300 yards away, sat their target. The wooden barrier ran about 50 yards out into the water. Using his hands, the man let the raft softly bump into the wooden barrier to stop it. Major Thu easily scaled the wooden wall so he could see over the barrier. His observations that the dock area was empty didn't ease his caution. He climbed back into the raft and nodded towards the end of the dock and the bay.

Within minutes, the raft and the commandos were around the wooden barrier and approaching the Clipper. They were in the shadows of the dock, darting in and out of the open areas under the wooden platform. Thu would pause every thirty yards and listen but nothing was heard. Gradually the plane grew bigger and suddenly, they were within ten yards of her. Now Thu was most concerned. He had memorized, as had his men, the insides of the Clipper but the next few feet would be the most difficult. They had to board her and there were four place they could try. He had earlier in meeting with the other commandos ruled out trying to enter from the spontons, since that was where the doors led into the passenger cabin and he knew they would be sealed. That left the hatch in back where the plane took on its heavy cargo. This was where he had planned to go first but looking at the tail, he saw that it was quite secure. He had brought along long thin steel bars that he would have pushed through the rubber seals and lifted the Clipper's bars off the braces. The problem with that was leverage. In a raft, unless they could hold onto the plane while the bar was inserted and then the lifting done, they would probable slide around in the water and possible awaken anyone on board. And his intelligence had informed him that Ford and another were on board. So it would be the anchor room on the bow of the plane.

The forward docking rope tied the nose of the Clipper to the dock but she also had her anchor out and in the water. So the hatch was probably ajar and they wouldn't have to pry it open! Thu tapped the paddler on the shoulder and waved him ahead along the port side of the Clipper.

Not touching the plane, the paddler brought Thu and the men to the front of the Clipper and Thu's heart almost jumped out of his body as he saw a small crack in the skin of the ship. A crack where the line for the anchor came out from the plane and into the water. That hatch had been left ajar! Thu had his opening into the Pacific Clipper. Now the trick was to get in without rocking the plane and waking anyone inside. They had rehearsed how they would climb into the plane without causing the plane to bob up and down. Thu utilized the old circus pyramid routine. The hull of the plane rested in about six feet of water. Sgt. Yuban as the tallest as well as the strongest of his men, would form the base. He slid off the edge of the rubber raft into the still waters and when his feet touched the bottom, his mouth was just at the water line. Then Thu, grasping Yuban's hands, swung his feet onto the sergeant's shoulders. The Sergeant's head bobbed under the water but he had taken a deep breath and with two steps, was at the side of the plane next to the anchor rope and the line to the dock. Thu was high enough above the line to lean against the plane and grasping the rope, pull it taunt. The plane didn't bob and he easily shimmied up the rope to the anchor room hatch. Slowly opening it, he slid in and grasping the two ropes, held them so as each of his men grabbed them, their weight wouldn't move the plane towards the dock. Within half a minute, all but the Sergeant were on board. The rubber raft had to be disposed of and the small arms for the men passed up and into the hatch. Reaching under one of the sides of the raft, Yuban brought out a package, about the size of a shaving kit and passed it up to the last man. Then the Sergeant, keeping one hand over the valve, opened it and slowly released the air from the rubber raft. When all the air was out, he took his knife and swiftly slashed the rubber into shreds. Then the shaving kit that had held the small arms was passed back to the Sergeant who stuffed it with the shredded raft. Yuban passed the kit back to the man inside and then grabbing tightly held rope, pulled himself up and into the anchor room. Then he joined the others in the main hold. Major Thu had already assigned each man to a specific spot in the hold and there was no need for any artificial light. As dark as it was, the soldiers, acclimated to the darkness, went to their assigned areas. And like soldiers everywhere, now they waited. Thu was very pleased. They had accomplished their first goal, getting aboard the Clipper. Now they would wait. If Commodore Tanaka's timing was good, a few minutes after the crew arrived, the sirens would crack out their warning of the coming air raid and Ford and the crew would be far to busy hauling their ass out of Surabaja to look for stowaways.

0430 hours-21 December, 1941-aboard the Arista in the Sea of Java.

The Commodore had left instructions that he be awakened at 0430 hours. Five seconds before it was time, one of the crew rapped softly on the door to the Commodore's room. As the sailor raised his hand to knock again, the door flew open and Commodore Tanaka, dressed in pressed khakis, nodded to the crewman and walked past him to the conning tower. Captain Nagoma was there to greet him. Bowing slightly, as the Commodore came towards him, the Captain waited for his orders. Tanaka stopped and rose to his full height thinking he would further intimidate Nagoma. The sub Captain caught the Commodore's act too often on this voyage to have any fear of the great man.

"Captain Nagoma. Good morning. A beautiful day, isn't it," the commodore intoned. The Arista was ten fathoms below the surface of the Java Sea but this was Tanaka's special day and he felt grand. In a few hours Major Thu and commandos would capture the Pacific Clipper and bring the great plane to him at Kota Bharu.

"Captain Nagoma. My best estimate is that we are about 200 miles from Kota Bharu. We can send the false alarm signal from anywhere and there is nothing we can do here to assist Thu. Assuming the Major effects the capture sometime after 0830, it will take them about four hours to reach Bharu. Should we not consider changing course and head for our rendezvous there to be waiting when they land?" the Commodore asked.

Nagoma considered the request, knowing that it was an order but it made sense to him. Walking over to the navigator's table, he did a quick guess estimate and agreed. If they left the Sea of Java and headed for Kota Bharu, they could be there when Thu arrived with the American plane. The fake alert signal could be sent from anywhere. And he very much wanted to be there to see the plane that had taken his ship out of the war and gave him Commodore Tanaka an enemy for life!

"I agree, Sir. If we surface, we could do 18 to 20 knots and be there when Thu lands. You had planned to radio the false alert at 0745 hours. That would put us about here," Nagoma offered, pointing to a spot on the map that meant nothing to Tanaka. It was just closer to their destination. Nagoma looked at the Commodore and waited for his comment or observation. After a stage pause, Tanaka, knowing the whole bridge was waiting for his decision, nodded imperiously to Nagoma and the Captain order a change in course that moved the Arista towards Koto Bharu. The submarine came to life. They were going somewhere. No more sitting and bobbing around. The whole crew felt a great relief and excitement at the same time. Word swept through the Arista, "Kota Bharu, going to Kota Bharu," Every man had known from the minute Commodore Tanaka came on board what their mission was. Now that they were headed for Koto Bharu, then the Pacific Clipper had been captured!

0545 hours-21 December 1941-aboard the Pacific Clipper

Ford woke. He reached over and flipped on the small table light and looked at his watch. O545 hours. Ford didn't know what woke him but he knew it was too early to rise. So he turned off the light and rolled over and fell back to sleep. His last thoughts were of being with Colonel VanGelder at the Dutch airbase and hearing the British at Trincomalee confirm in code that they expected the Clipper. Below him in the hold, the Japanese commander and his troops slept soundly. Major Thu had already checked the ways he and his commandos would attack the Americans, through the anchor hatch in front and the trap door in the Master Suite. While Ford and the flight crew were busy getting the Clipper into the air, the rest would be strapped into their seats. When he and his men burst upon them, only the people on the deck would be free to fight them and he knew that he and Auho could neutralize them. Sergeant Yuban and the other three would take care of the others. Thu fell off to sleep, knowing everything depended on the "fake attack" from Tanaka.

Ford checked his watch again as the sun streamed into the bridge. He'd already shaved and put on a clean set of whites and at 0645, he waited for the rest of the crew to return. Poindexter was down in the galley getting the coffee ready. Looking out the window from his pilot's seat, he saw the cars arrive with the rest of the crew. Getting out of his seat, he quickly slid down the stairs to the passenger level. Poindexter had the door open and Ford went out to greet his people. Swede Rothe got out first and behind him, the tech rep from Boeing, G. Brown. Ford had taken to calling him G. Brown to distinguish him from Norm Brown. Out of the other car stepped Kathleen Elmes and looking at her, Ford wondered if he'd made the right decision staying on the Clipper last night!

Kathleen smiled at him as she approached. "Too bad you didn't join us Captain. We had a great evening. I don't think we talked about today and the rest of the trip more than every minute last night!" the Navy Lt. kidded. "She's right, Captain," John Mack added, coming up behind her. "We have it all planned. All you have to do is fly it."

Ford laughed and felt good about the crew being in such a healthy humor. No matter how big the Clipper was and how few there were of them aboard, it was still confining and twelve people rubbing elbows each day and night could get on anyone's nerves. So a night on the town was a relief for all, especially Ford. Swede Rothe put his overnight case on the sponson and came back to him. Although they didn't need to, the two of them made another quick check of the exterior of the Clipper. Ford was very please to see the camouflage gone and the Clipper all shinny and clean. Tacki and his men had done a great job. As Ford thought about paying them, he shook his head again at the ridiculous position he was in, commenting to himself, Broke!

Looking at his plane, Ford saw that the American flag was painted back on the nose, just below his window. All things considered, the Pacific Clipper looked almost as good as she did when they left the States. Everything was ready. As they turned to board the Clipper, the gates opened and another car came down the ramp. Ford, Mack and Kathleen turned and watched at Shamus Ginsberg got out. His driver opened the boot at the rear and took out one suitcase and a small carry on. He put them on the pier and grabbed Shamus' hand and kissed it. The innkeeper hugged the driver and pushed him back into the driver seat. As the car rolled up the ramp and away towards Surabaja, Shamus watched for a few seconds, turned and picked up his luggage and walked towards the Clipper.

"Gentlemen, today seems like a marvelous opportunity to fly somewhere. What say we see how the Irish Coffee's are in Ceylon? It is only a short hop from here, just some 4000 miles across the Bay of Bengal," the innkeeper said as he walked towards Ford and the others.

He had gotten almost to them when another car swung down the ramp, screeching to a halt. Tacki jumped out and raced over to Ginsberg.

"Boss. Boss!" the driver yelled. "One of the men from my village says he saw Japanese soldiers in the hills, early this morning. He says there are thousands of them. All over the hills"

"Easy Tacki, easy," Ginsberg said soothingly to his man. "We've been hearing of these sightings for weeks now and nothing has happened except they have scared hell out of us. Now, tell me slowly what you've been told."

"Boss, I wouldn't have come back if I thought it was another false alarm but Sammi, the driver for Mr. Jalara said that some of his people, had seen the soldiers. Others told Mr. Jalara that they had seen the Japanese moving along the shore towards the oil fields. I wouldn't have come to see you but two sighting from different places made me think. Plus Sammi told me that Mr. Jalara called the police," Tacki reported.

Ginsberg turned and tried to explain what Tacki was reporting. "Jalara the tailor is highly respected by the Dutch and all the locals. He is a most reliable person. If he put credence in these reports, there might be something happening. We know the Japs are coming and it would make sense they had sent in commandos ahead of the invasion. But who knows."

Turning to his friend, the innkeeper put his arm around him and tried to calm him down. Walking him back to the car, Ginsberg whispered in his ear. Like the other driver, Tacki kissed Ginsberg's hand and got in the car. He drove away and didn't look back. Shamus watched him go up the ramp as he turned towards Surabaja, the innkeeper spun around so he wouldn't see Tacki go out of sight. Looking back towards the Clipper, he saw Kathleen Elmes standing in the doorway and he quickly moved towards her, smiling. "Ah, Lt. Elmes, at last. Now we will be aboard this great ship and you'll have no place to hide from me!" All of them on the dock laughed as the new bursar of the Pacific Clipper boarded.

0725 hours-aboard the Arista

"Admiral Yamamoto's message to attack Pearl Harbor 'Climb Mount Niitaka' took only three word," Captain Nagoma thought. "Tanaka has been in my cabin writing the 'false alarm' for an hour. It better be good," the submariner thought and as he turned to check the status of operations on the bridge, Commodore Tanaka emerged.

"Ah, Nagoma. Here is the message. I wish your opinion. The code we'll use is one they should be able to decipher but not too easily. The trick is to make the Dutch think the invasion is beginning. With Thu's people circulatingthe rumor that some of our troops have landed, this should get the sirens wailing and Ford leaving in a rush. What do you think," the tall man asked as he passed the note over to Nagoma.

Nagoma looked at it and nodded his approval.

To: Commander, Admiral Tossco, Second Imperial Fleet, aboard His Imperial Majesty's carrier Hoyso

Fr: Commodore Tanaka, Imperial Naval Intelligence, aboard His Imperial Majesty's submarine Arista:

"The hawks will fly today. Empty the nest. Repeat. The hawks will fly today. Empty the nest. Tora! Tora! Tora!"

The radio officer turned and followed by Tanaka and Nagoma, walked over to the radioman and handed him the coded message, the code that the man used was one they knew was familiar to all Japanese ships and one that Tanaka was sure the Dutch, British, Americans and even the natives of Bali could break. As the sender tapped out the message across the waters to the Hoyso, docked at Koto Bharu and alerted by the Arista of the false message, Tanaka grinned at the Arista's Captain. Nagoma smiled back but with far less relish than he felt. He had his reservation but now it was up to the Americans to take the bait.

In the three hours since they began their race to Kota Bharu, Nagoma was confident the sub would be at the island when Major Thu arrived with the Pacific Clipper. He was sure about the Arista. Thu's arrival was still a long shot, no matter how clever the ruse. If the Boeing was everything the Commodore said it was, then the man that commanded her had to be Pan Am's best. And if he was good enough to be in charge of the finest plane in the world, then he would eventually determine if the mission was a success or not. Like all plans drawn up, on paper they looked fool proof. When executed, things didn't always pan out. This American captain might just be the one element the Commodore might have underestimated.

The radioman had finished his transmittal and they awaited the planned reply from the Hoyso. Within a few seconds the acknowledgement came back. The radioman easily translated the coded message and handed the response to the radio officer who handed it to Captain Nagoma, who passed it over to the Commodore. Both had understood the message but Tanaka was delighted to have it in his hand to read.

To: Commodore Tanaka, Imperial Naval Intelligence aboard His Imperial Majesty's submarine Arista.

Fr: Admiral Tossco, Commander, Imperial Second Fleet, aboard His Majesty's carrier Hoyso.

"The hawks have left the nest. Repeat. The hawks have left the nest. Banzi, Banzi, Banzi."

He glanced up at the clock showing it was already 0750 hours. Nodding his thanks to the radio officer and his man, he and Nagoma walked back to the navigation table and looked at their position now, relative to Java and Surabaja.

"It is not quite 0800 hours. Assuming that the Dutch intercept and translate the message, it will probably take them 10-15 minutes to decide if a raid is coming. Thu's idea of starting the rumor of our troops on the ground already should make it plain an attack is coming and they'll react with an air raid alert. The question is what will Ford do? I must confess Nagoma, that in these past hours I have envisioned every conceivable reaction by the American, all of which would destroy our plan. But I always come back to the knowledge that Ford is going to do everything he can to get home and if the Dutch tell him there is an air raid coming, he'll take off. And when he does, Thu and the men will take the Pacific Clipper!" the Commodore summed up.

Nagoma bowed as the tall man left the bridge. "You better be right, Commodore. Or you might just be shoveling coal into the boilers of the garbage scow I'm commanding in Sappuro."

0755 hours-21 December 1941-Dutch Airdrome

The young Dutch soldier had just gotten up fix to himself a cup of coffee. The office was empty and as he looked out the radio room window across the field, he could see the six Brewsters all lined up, ready to roll. Looking at them, the man thought of yesterday evening when he drove Captain VanderKellen and the other pilots to the dock and saw the Pacific Clipper for the first time. The gateman had walked down and the two of them visited. The sheer size of the plane brought an almost stunned reverence to him. As much as he tried to be casual about the plane, the man understood.

"Some piece of work, isn't she, lad. One of the crew told me each of those engines has 1600 horsepower! God, that could light Surabaja for a month," the older man said and the soldier appreciated his taking him into his confidence. Now, standing with the hot coffee mug in his hand, he wondered what it would be like to fly a plane so big. Looking at the Brewsters, planes that he loved, he shook his head thinking about all that power those huge engines gave the Americans. And the range! Almost 5000 miles without having to land.

He heard his radio behind him at the desk begin chattering and he walked over to listen. He was about to put on his headset but since the office was empty, he let the transmission play as he listened to it. If it was important, he'd write it down but it sounded like some gibberish. He couldn't tell where it was coming from and all he knew was that it was some kind of coded message. Eric Stroom, the code expert wasn't here this early in the morning so the soldier just ignored it. The radio went silent and he looked at it, expecting something more. When noting came, he went over to refill his cup. As he was pouring more coffee, a new transmission came through. He dropped the coffee cup and raced to his radio as the first words hit him.

"Attention, Surabaja. This is the tanker Albatridge. We are fifty miles South East of Java. Our radio operator has just intercepted a coded message from a Japanese carrier, the Hoyso. As best we can decipher, they are launching an air attack on Java. Repeat, our radioman says he knows this Jap code and the carrier Hoyso has launched an air attack against Java. The radioman says the transmission came from somewhere in the Macassar Straights. Good luck."

The young Dutch soldier, looking at what he has written down, reached over and pressed down the air raid alarm button.

Bob Ford was on the dock with Swede Rothe finishing their preflight check when the air raid sirens' call blared forth from the loud speakers down near the end of the dock. The gateman rushed to the phone near his station and began calling the airdrome. Ford and Rothe look at each other and it didn't take two seconds before they were racing to the hawsers that held the Clipper to the dock. Ford grabbed the bow rope and flipped it free of the cleat it was tied to while Rothe is doing the same with the stern lines. As the wailing of the sirens continued, Ford jumped aboard the Clipper.

"What is it, Captain?" John Mack ask.

"Air raid. Barney, haul up that anchor," he hollers to the First Steward standing in the galley. "Everyone, you know the drill. Let's get our ass out of here."

As Ford starts up the stairway to the flight deck, Kathleen Elmes yells at him.

"Captain, the dock guard is running over here, yelling at us!" she informs him.

"John, crank her up. Norm, make sure everything is locked tight. Officers to the flight deck, the rest of you strap yourselves in," Ford orders as he rushes out the entryway to greet the guard.

"Captain Ford, Colonel Van Gelder is on the phone. He says that they have been warned that the Japs have launched an air attack on Surabaja. He said to tell you it isn't confirmed but don't take any chances. And he adds, God speed. So do I," the guard reaches over to shake Ford's hand who without being aware of it, shakes his. He sees Swede Rothe standing at the front of the Clipper as John Mack starts the engines. Turning, Ford in two steps vaults through the entrance and bolts up the stairs to the flight deck. All lines have been released and behind him, on the dock, Swede Rothe, with the help of the dock guard is pushing the Pacific Clipper's nose away from the dock as her engines leap to life.

Ford hits the bridge running and in one stride slides into his pilot's chair, taking the controls from Mack. Looking out the windows across the harbor, a scene of utter chaos greets him. Boats of all shapes and sizes are racing everywhere, fleeing towards the harbor's mouth and the open sea. His pilot's chair is twenty feet above the water and that gives him a panoramic view of the madness in front of him as he slowly pushes the throttles forward on the starboard engines. The Clipper glides away from the dock and into the deeper waters of the harbor. With the sirens still blaring, Ford maneuvers the huge plane towards the center of the harbor very carefully. "Christ, we'll be rammed and sunk by some goddamn junk before the Japs have their shot!" Ford thinks as he views in almost total disbelief the bedlam in front of him. John Mack searched the harbor for the police boat that was to escort them to their watery runway. He couldn't spot it. Mack looked at Ford and shook his head. Neither had even faced a situation, trying to take off with boats racing across their bow.

"John, we can't wait for the police boat to clear away those damn boats. Lean on that fog horn and blow us a path to the middle of the harbor," Ford orders.

The First Officer leans over to his right and pushes the red button on the side of his console. Immediately, the ear splitting roar of the horn adds to the cacophony of the harbor but it had its immediate effect. Boats near the Clipper move away and as Ford sees the lane open, he adds power to the other engines and the Clipper races into the void. The churning harbor waters from all the traffic make the Clippers' ride out to deeper water very bumpy. The wakes of some of the biggest boats bounced her around and the rest of the crew below, strapped into their seat feel the pitching and bobbing of the plane. On the bridge, because of its height above the hull, Ford and the other three, Mack, Steers and Poindexter sway with the rising and falling waves. Some of the troughs are so high the plane rises some eight to ten feet in the air then slams down as the waves passed beneath them. To Ford, it was just an irritant. He's taken off flying boats in swells that almost made some passengers sea sick. Finally, the Clipper turns into the wind and her prow points towards the mouth of the harbor and the open sea beyond. John Steers, holding on to the back of John Mack's seat, flare pistol loaded and cocked, waits at the open window by Mack's station.

He hopes the damn plane stops pitching long enough for him to reach out and fire the flares without hitting an engine or the wing! Ford wants the flare fired when he began the Clipper's run.

Now Ford begins to bring the thrust of the four 1600 horsepower Wrights up to full throttle, while holding the flaps up, forcing the body of the Clipper to sink deeper in the water, acting as her breaks. Suddenly, silence. The damn sirens stopped and Ford releases the flaps. In one shuddering moment, the Pacific Clipper bucks like a wild bronco trying to rid itself of a spur-raking rider. Slowly the powerful engines start to pull the huge plane through the watery clamps of the harbor and the Clipper gathers momentum as she lumbers down the path Bob Ford had chosen as their lane to reach take off speed. Faster and faster, 20 knots, then 40 as Mack reads the air speed indicator out loud, a little edge and more timber to his voice since he's trying to be heard over the rushing wind through his window. Suddenly John Steers' fired off one flare and the noise scares hell out of Mack and the others. Then the second and with the engines roaring and the flares exploding, Steers let out a shout, "Ride 'em Cowboy! Come on Clipper, you can do it!"

Now Mack picks it up. "At 50 knots, Captain, 60, 70, Holy shit! Look! There, ahead, cutting across our bow, a goddamn sampan, he doesn't see us! Get the hell out of the way, you asshole," Mack shouts at the ship steaming across the path of the Clipper, five hundred yards away. Now two hundred yards and no time to cut the engines. The Pacific Clipper is going to broadside her. Forget America, they're going to sink in Surabaja harbor! Steers hadn't even sat down as he watched with horror the panic on the faces of the people on the sampan as the Clipper shoots across the water like a winged torpedo at the midships of the boat.

Then it disappears! The boat is gone! And they are airborne. Somehow Bob Ford had done it. A football field, just 100 yards from the sampan, he put all flaps down, pushed the throttles forward for every ounce of power the four Cyclones had and the Pacific Clipper lifted off the waters of the harbor at Surabaja. The suddenness and acute angle of the lift off had thrown Steers off his feet and all the way back to his navigators' table where he bounced when hitting the steel legs. But he was all right. He quickly gets up and straps himself into his chair, the exhilaration of what they had just done made him feel like he was on Cloud Nine. He could have had a skull fracture and wouldn't have felt a thing. He looks at Ford and can't believe it! The Clipper can't do what she had just done! No plane can. But they are airborne and climbing to altitude. Steers' leans his head back and begins to grin.

John Mack looks at Bob Ford and grins. Ford looks at his co-pilot and winks. "You know what you just did can't be done," the co-pilot said as he leans his head to the left to holler at Bob Ford. Mack's window is still open and the roar of the engines and incoming air forces him to yell. Ford looks at his friend and just snorts. Glancing at the instrument panel and quickly checking the engine pressure, everything looks perfect. Slowly Ford began banking the great plane to the left and begins their climbing slowly to 8,000 feet and the start of a peaceful flight to Trincomalee. He reaches over to flip the seat belt sign off and thinks better of it. The air is still choppy and the coffee and rolls can wait until things have smoothed out. And until his heart left his throat and went back into its usual place!

Below, in the hold, Major Thu realized he'd made a big mistake the minute the Pacific Clipper began moving away from the dock. As the plane started bouncing on the choppy waters, he and his men were thrown around the hold of the plane. Quickly, Thu stood and motioned his men to do the same and hang onto the ribs of the fuselage. Even with that, the men still had a hard time keeping their balance. When Ford slowed the Clipper to begin revving up his engine prior to take off, Thu signaled his men to get to their appointed positions. He, the pilot and one commando moved close to the door leading into the anchor room. Here he could hold on to the door handle and the other two braced themselves with their backs against the door frame and feet pushing on a metal strut. When Ford released the Clipper and began her run down the waterway, Thu had no idea what was coming. The sudden lifting off the water of the Clipper threw him against the anchor room door and it opened! The Japanese Major fell in and panic gripped him. He looked around and to his great relief, the other door leading into the passenger part of the plane was closed. Thu motioned for Auho to join him and nodded to his commandos to wait. Crouching next to the entryway, Thu looked away from the pilot to hide his embarrassment but as he thought about what just happened, it was a small stroke of luck. Had a Pan Am crewman been in the anchor room, their takeover of the Clipper would have begun much earlier than he had planned. As Thu regains his composure, the Pacific Clipper begins to climb to its cruising altitude and Thu relaxes a little. He looks at the commando waiting with he and Auho, his eyes asking about the three in the rear of the plane. The commando looks down the darken hold and sees the others are ready and nods to the Major. Now Thu leans over to his pilot and whispers.

"How long will it take them to get to cruising altitude?" he asked.

"My best guess is twenty minutes," Lt. Auho responded.

Looking at his watch, Thu noted that it was just a few minutes past 0800 hours. The timing had been almost perfect.

"If they will be at cruising altitude in 20 minutes, we better get going. We can't have all their crew walking around. They are in their seats now, probably waiting for Ford to level off. Better go now while they are strapped in for the takeoff," the Major thought. He looked at the commando, crouching, half his body in the anchor room and the other half in the hold. Thu nodded to him and put his right hand, palm down to his throat, then in a slashing move, brought it across his throat. This was the signal to begin the taking of the Pacific Clipper.

Kathleen Elmes and the rest of the Clipper's crew were strapped into their seats. Each had selected a window to spot the incoming Japanese planes or if they went out far enough, maybe a Jap carrier or battleship. Shamus Ginsberg wasn't looking for Zeros or Mitsubishi bombers. He was trying to spot the Black Swan and as Ford continued the wide banking turn to the north, Surabaja lay directly below.

"There. There she is!" Ginsberg shouted.

"Where? I don't see any planes, Mr Ginsberg," Norm asked.

"Not planes, Mr. Brown. The Black Swan. There she is. Look out to the left, towards the back, what do you flyers call it, something o'clock," the Innkeeper stated.

Sitting behind Shamus, Third Officer, Jim Henriksen spoke.

"You mean about 8 o'clock, Mr. Ginsberg. We use the face of a clock to give general directions. The Black Swan is now about 7 o'clock," the Pan Am officer informed their guest.

"Thank you, sir," Shamus began, turning in his seat to look back at Henriksen to express his gratitude. "I knew it was something, "
As the voice of the Irish Jew tailed off, Kathleen looked over from her seat to see why Shamus had stopped. Before she could ask him what was wrong, her eyes followed his towards the rear of the Clipper.

"Ahaa, Ahaa, " the Navy Lieutenant's voice croaked. Her gasps brought the heads of the rest of the crew around. And standing in the aisle were three men, clad in black, each holding a pistol pointed at them. Then the door to the anchor room burst open and three more in black raced from the room, with two running up the steps to the flight deck. The third stopped and trained his pistol on them.

As the other two raced up the stairs, Jim Henriksen shouted a warning. "Look out, Captain Fo, ," his voice dying off as the pistol in the hand of the biggest of the invaders crashes across his skull. The blood exploding from his head splashes against the cabin wall and the window by his seat and Henriksen collapses. The others try to come to his aid but they were all captured by their seat belt and the pistols covering them.

On the flight deck, the disturbance below was drowned out by the roar of the engines as the crew concentrated on getting the Clipper away from Surabaja and the on-coming Japanese invasion forces. Mack hadn't closed the window on his side and now that they were airborne and hadn't crashed into the side of that sampan, he reaches up and closes it. As the sudden quiet engulfed the cabin, the end of the warning from Henriksen is heard.

"What the hell was that?" John Steers asks. "Did you hear something? I thought I heard, Holy Christ, who the hell are you?" Steers yells as Thu and Auho bound onto the flight deck. Ford, Mack and Poindexter turn and look into the pistols aimed at them by the two, Thu covering them as Auho does the same to Steers and Poindexter.

"Captain Ford. In the name of His Imperial Highness, I commandeer this plane for the Emperor of Japan. I am his humble servant, Major Seishu Thu, of the Imperial Japanese Army. You will fly this plane to Koto Bharu. Lt. Auho of the Imperial Japanese Air Force will monitor your movements and if you deviate from my instruction, I will kill you. Lt. Auho is fully qualified to fly this plane. As of now, the Pacific Clipper is a war prize of the Imperial Armed Forces of the Empire of Japan," Thu announced.

"I beg your pardon, Major. What the fuck do you mean, we are a war prize. We are American citizens, civilians, flying back to the United States. This is a direct violation of the Geneva Convention," Ford announced, stalling as his brain searches desperately for something he can do to recapture his plane.

"Too bad, Captain Ford. We are at war with your country, or haven't you heard about Pearl Harbor and the glorious defeat of your Navy. So don't waste my time pretending you don't know what has happened to your pitiful Army and Navy. Enough, the people below are under the guard of my troops and any incident by you or any of them will mean a bullet in the head of the offender. Do you understand, Captain Robert Ford? Your plane is now ours. You can fly her to Koto Bharu or I'll put a bullet in your brain and Lt. Auho can fly the Clipper," the Japanese Major informs the American pilot and taking two steps, walks over to Ford and puts the cold barrel of his pistol against Ford's temple.

Ford had held the Clipper in a long, gradual turn to port as he was climbing to cruising altitude. He was still in that mode when the Japanese commando leaned over to lay the barrel of his gun against his temple. Ford in one motion, pushes down on the rudder pedal with his left foot while he pulls the stick hard to port. The huge plane spins on its axis and begins to roll over and down. Ford holds the stick as far to the left as he can and the Pacific Clipper spins out of control and flashes down towards the water. Everyone not seated and held in their place by a seat belt, goes airborne and crashes into the sides and ceiling of the Clipper. The two officers on the flight deck suffer the same sudden weightlessness, with Thu's momentum carrying his body into the flight panel as his head crashes into the steel compass. The pistol in his hand falls to the floor as his unconscious body lands over the throttles, pushing them down. The motors of the Clipper race to full power as Ford tries to bring the plane out of its spin. The racing engines drive the Clipper faster and faster down towards the water. Mack reaches over to pull the dead body of the Jap off the throttles. Flipping off his seat belt, he fights against the dead weight of Thu. Pushing his left knee into Thu to raise him, Mack gets one leg loose enough to bring his body upright in seat and climb over the Jap's back. Grabbing the knocked out Major by his neck and his crotch, Mack pulls the man off the throttles. Ford immediately pulls them back to slow the spinning Clipper but it's too late. He can't slow the dive or the spin. So Ford pushed forward on the stick and the huge plane began to slowly drop its nose and begins to inch to the starboard. Slowly, the Clipper starts to come out of her spin but the water rushes up to meet her. Now Ford reaches over and pushes the throttles forward. As the engines race and pick up speed, the Clipper begins to respond and with the nose pointed down, Ford brings the stick as hard to starboard as he can. The Clipper shakes violently from its port roll towards the starboard. Now Ford pushes the stick forward and the pull of the roll to the right and the forward movement of the controls brings her back towards horizontal. Ford tries to level the Clipper off but her momentum is too great and they giant plane flashes towards the sea. Ford cuts the power on the inside engines and pulls back on the stick. The big ship responds beautifully and begins to level off. Ford, checking the altimeter, blinks and blinks again. It reads 50. He has leveled the Pacific Clipper at 50 feet off the deck!

Chapter 9

Escape From Surabaja

1350 hours-21/12/1941 Aboard the Arista, Kota Bharu, Malasia

No word. Nothing. The Arista's radio had not picked up any transmission from Major Thu aboard the Pacific Clipper. Now as Captain Nagoma brought his ship towards its docking area, he could see through the afternoon haze that some of the buildings were still just rubble and further in the hills, many of the trees were splintered and felled, tribute to the devastation of the Japanese bombings. Nagoma knew that General Yamashita's 25th Army was marching down the Eastern shore of the South China Sea from here towards Singapore. And it was the land based planes from this port that had helped sink the Repulse and Prince of Wales. Now as he shepherded the Arista towards the pier, his thoughts went down to the man below, the man who at 1015 hours left the bridge of the Arista and retired to his cabin. Commodore Tanaka knew his plan had failed. Other than the usual complement of seamen to help dock the Arista, there was no one to greet them. If the American plane was here or even on its way, the dock would have been crowded with officers and men, waiting to welcome the heros. But there were only the dock hands. Relaying his orders to the helmsman, the Arista came easily within a few feet of the dock and stopped. The mooring lines shot out from his men and were smoothly caught by the men on the pier and within seconds, the Arista was safely docked. The men of the Arista raced from the hatch on the deck to line the sub from bow to stern. Seconds after they came to attention, Commodore Tanaka appeared, turned to Nagoma atop the sail, saluted and walked down the short gangplank to the dock. Behind him, came one of the Arista's sailors carrying the Commodore's seabag. As the tall man's feet hit the wooden dock, a staff car came around the corner and rolled to a stop where the Commodore stood. A soldier jumped out, opened the rear door and the tall man got in, without looking back.

As his First Officer stood on the deck looking up at him, Nagoma signaled with a nod and the officer dismissed the men. As they climbed back into the sub, Nagoma walked to the rear of the conning tower and looked back to the open sea. Alone, he smiled for the first time since Tanaka had boarded his ship. "Capturing the American plane was a million to one shot and Thu couldn't pull it off," he thought. "Goodby Commodore. Only the gods know what fate awaits you but somehow I feel you'll survive. Hara Kiri, the honorable way isn't for you. You'll find someone back in Tokyo dumb enough to buy your siren's song. I don't know what it will be but you'll keep after the American until one of you dies. I'm rooting for the Captain of the Pacific Clipper." Captain Nagoma took a deep breath and when he let it out, he felt great. "Now I can get back into the real war," he thought as he walked to the ladder leading down to his command center and his men.

0835 hours-21 December 1941-Aboard the Pacific Clipper.

Ford could feel the blood returning to his head and his heart begin to slow its furious beating. His hands gripped the wheel so tightly that it took a few seconds before the signals from his brain to relax his grip got through to his muscles. He opened his clenched hands one finger at a time. The Clipper was still on the deck, skimming over the water. Ford was vaguely award of noises behind him but his whole being concentrated on slowly bringing the great plane off the water and up. Gradually, he pulled back on the yoke and pushed the throttles forward and the plane responded smoothly and began her climb. Ford looked ahead and his eye caught the mangled form of the compass. Then he remembered the Japanese soldier holding a gun against his temple and after that, the rest was a blur. He had blocked out everything from his mind as he put the Clipper into a death dive and then fought to bring her out of it. And somehow, while he was fighting to save the Clipper from a watery grave, his men had overpowered the Japs.

When Ford pitched the Clipper into her steep roll and dive, the Jap major was thrown into the windshield, smashing his head into the compass and collapsing on top of the controls. The Jap pilot also lost his balance and fell back into John Steers. The navigator was strapped in his chair but he grabbed the little man and choked him with a hammer lock, taking away his gun. The Jap fought and bringing his head back, hit Steers in the face, bloodying his nose and mouth. Steers squeezed even harder, closing off the pilot's windpipe and he passed out. While he was choking the pilot and stripping him of his gun, Steers could see John Mack wrestling with the body of the Major. He didn't know Thu was knocked out and for some reason began to laughed when he saw his friend throw the body of the Jap across the deck where it crashed into the legs of Steers' navigator's table, bending them and sending the atlases flying. As the powerful Mack came after the Jap officer, the spinning of the Clipper sent him sprawling across the room and crashing through the door of the Observatory.

When Jim Henricksen's warning shout was cut short by the blow across his skull, the other two Japs turned their guns on the rest of the Clipper's crew. Then three others tore out of the anchor room, with two going up to the bridge and the third training his pistol on them. Only seconds passed when the Pacific Clipper suddenly pitched to her port side and began to roll and dive. The four commandos were suddenly airborne, their guns flying from their hands as they crashed into the seats. The big Jap righted himself and began to look for his pistol. Barney Swacki, strapped in a seat nearby, in a flash freed himself and yelled. As the Jap turned, Barney hunched his shoulders and launched himself, head first at the Jap's face and the man dropped like he was poleaxed. Blood spewed from Barney's head and as he fell to the deck, he hooked an arm onto a leg of one of the seats as the spinning plane sent the big Jap bouncing and rolling down the aisle right into the anchor room, bleeding and unconscious.

As the plane began her spin, the commando on the stairs lost his balance and his body smashed into the passenger door. Dazed, he turned just as the Boeing Tech rep hit him with his shoulder, knocking the wind out of the commando. G. Brown lost his balance as the Clipper continued her dive. He was thrown into the open door of the anchor room, where the inert body of the Sergeant cushioned his fall. The commando slid across the aisle and banged his head into the stairs, knocking him out.

The third Jap fell into the grip of Swede Rothe, who locked his arm around the man's neck and twisted the man's head so that his screams could be heard over the roar of the Clippers engines. The dive ended as suddenly as it had begun and as Ford leveled the ship out, John Parish was out of his seat looking for the fourth Jap. He found him, crouched down between seats 12A and 13A, a long knife in his hand. As Parish loomed over him, the Jap lunged. Parish didn't hesitate. He kicked him in the face as the man rose, breaking his nose and dropping him unconscious to the floor of the plane. Parish took the knife, left the Jap on the floor and went to find some rope to tie all of them up. Barney, looking around saw that everyone seemed to be ok, except Jim Henricksen. Kathleen Elmes and Shamus were already attending him. With the passenger level secure, Barney went forward to the galley to get some water and cloth for bandages as Norm Brown headed for the flight deck.

As Ford fought to bring the Pacific Clipper out of her dive, the inert bodies of the two Japanese officers began to slide towards the nose of the plane. John Mack crawled back out of the observation room and seeing the body of the Jap major headed for Ford's feet, dove like a football player going after a fumble. He grabbed the commando just before the man hit Ford's seat. Steers had grabbed the nape of the neck of the little pilot to keep his dead form from sliding down at Ford. The gun was still rattling around on the floor and Steers was trying at the same time to get himself free of his seat belt, hold on to the pilot and get the gun when out of the corner of his eye, he saw Poindexter leave his seat, drop to the floor and slide towards Ford and the gun. The radioman grabbed the spinning weapon off the deck just as he hit the wall on the other side of the cabin and as his body spun towards the nose, Ford somehow brought the Clipper out of her spin and began to level off. The three Americans just looked at each other and then at the bodies of their two erstwhile captors. John Mack shook his head and for the first time noticed that he was bleeding from small lacerations on his legs and arms. Looking at Steers, he saw the navigator was bleeding from his mouth and nose. Poindexter's shirt was torn but otherwise, the three were in good shape.

Ford slowly turned in his seat and looked over his shoulder. His eyes picked up a scene he couldn't believe. Poindexter was holding a gun on one Japanese, the pilot, if he remembered correctly, slumped on the floor next to Steers. John Mack stood guard over the man that had just seconds ago held a pistol against his head. Major Thu was his name, Ford recalled and he was stone cold out. As he looked at his men, he could see blood on John Mack's pants, Steers' nose and mouth bleeding, and the radioman's shirt was torn. As he was about to say something, Norm Brown came bounding up the stairs, holding a long dagger in his hand.

"Jesus Christ, Captain, you guys OK?" the Second Officer yelled. "We had a hell of a fight. Parish and the others are tying up the four Japs. Mr. Henricksen's pretty beat up... pistol whipped by one of those bastards but Miss Elmes and Shamus are tending to him. The rest of us are alright with a few bumps and cuts. When the Clipper began to spin we thought they had shot you! How in hell did you keep us from going in?"

Ford looked at his crew, shook his head and laughed. "Give us a few minutes Norm to get the Clipper up to altitude and back on course. Then I'll be down. John, can you straighten out that damn compass so I know where in the world I'm heading."

John Mack, stepping over the unconscious body of Major Thu returned to his seat and reaching up with his left hand, twisted the compass back to its regular position, the frame somewhat bent but the compass operational. Now Ford and his co-pilot settled down to bring the plane back on course and up to cruising altitude. Steers and Poindexter took their prisoners below.

Oscar Hendrickson, the Second Radio Officer, the two engineers and the Boeing Tech were binding the hands and feet of the soldiers with electricianstape and when that was done, the four were shepherded to individual seats where they were strapped in with the seat belts and their legs taped to the bottom braces of the seats. Major Thu and his pilot were also given the same treatment. With the six Japanese commandos tied up, the crew members with cuts and bruises began to move to the galley where Kathleen Elmes was playing Florence Nightingale. Other than Henricksen, his head wrapped in gauze with an ice pack placed over the bleeding wound and stretched out on one of the Pullman-like berths, the rest of the crew had just scratches and slight cuts. Although the Clipper was climbing and the flight was becoming bumpy, none of them could sit. And while it was still morning, Shamus Ginsberg and Barney Swacki broke open a couple of bottles of Scotch... for medicinal purposes!

John Mack returned to his pilot's chair after visiting with Kathleen Elmes downstairs to have his cuts tended. A little iodine and a few soothing words and the First Officer was back at work. As he strapped himself in, he checked the altimeter and the air speed indicator. The first told him Ford had the Clipper climbing through the 4000 foot mark and they were moving at 110 knots. The compass indicated a course of east by northeast. The clock said the time was 0927 hours. Mack did a quick double take when he looked at the time. He couldn't believe it. To him it seemed like just minutes ago when the Japs tried to shanghai the Clipper but almost an hour and a half had passed since Ford jumped the plane over the sampan and went airborne. His mind swiftly sorted through the events in a split second; the air raid alarm, the race across the waters of the harbor, somehow missing the huge sampan, the Japs appearing out of nowhere, Ford spinning the plane and him throwing the Jap major across the room. Now as he sat in his seat, he looked over to his left at Bob Ford and smiled.

"How in the hell did you do it? How did you put this bird in a spin like that and bring her out of it? We know what the engineers said about Gs and the few she can pull before the wings fall off. You did two or three times that! How? It can't be done! What did you know?" John Henry Mack asked.

Ford looked over at his co-pilot and smiled. He checked his climbing ratio to speed and leveled off at 5,000 feet and slowly pushed ahead on the throttles, bringing his cruising speed up to 150 knots. A quick scan of the rest of the instruments showed that the Pacific Clipper was preforming perfectly. No warning lights blinking red, the tachometer readings showing normal, oil pressure and engine temperatures right on the button. Reaching over the wheel, he flipped on the automatic pilot and leaning back, he looked out the window before answering.

"John, about a year ago I spent some time studying the results from Bob Stanley's original test flights of the first 314s. You remember how screwed up everything was, especially trying to turn the bird, how Stanley had to rotate the power from the starboard engines to the port side to get her to turn and moved the flaps up and down to control her vertical movements so he could land the damn thing. Well, last spring when I was down at Edwards testing some Corsair for the Navy, I tried some spins to see how by using just the flaps I could pull out of a free fall. What I found out was that in a spin, if I put the flaps down and pushed forward on the stick, I could much more easily control the spin and pull the plane out of her dive. When I tested the Clipper, I tried the same thing. It is the flaps and how I used them that gave me control of the dive. All I basically did was raise and lower the flaps on one wing to the other after I put her into the roll. That gave me the control of her. Actually, it was the suddenness of the roll that was far more frightening that the actual Gs we were pulling. The damn Japs forced me to put her into the dive much closer to the water than I would have ever tried if we were just seeing what her limits were. Anyway, don't believe everything the engineers tell us. They just design and build them. We fly 'em," the pilot explained.

John Mack looked at his Captain and shook his head. As he was about to comment on Ford's explanation, Norm Brown came bounding up the stairs from the passenger's level.

"Captain Ford! We've tied up the prisoners. What do you want us to do?" the Second Officer asked.

Turning, Ford answered. "Ok, Norm. I'll be right down. If he hasn't already, ask Barney to get a pot of coffee going. John, she's all yours. I'd have you join us but with all that has happened, I want one of us at the controls all the time. Ok?" Ford instructed and Mack nodded. He reached over and turned off the automatic pilot, taking the controls himself. Checking his compass, he reached down to the throttles and began to add power to the four Wrights and pulling back on the stick, raised the nose of the Pacific Clipper and began climbing to her cruising altitude of 8000 feet. Smoothly, quietly and powerfully, the engines lifted the huge body of the Boeing higher and faster. Rolling his broad shoulders and wiggling his rear end deeper into the cushion on his chair, the former Stanford fullback settled in comfortably to fly the Pacific Clipper.

Ford stopped on the last step and looked around. Down the aisle he could see the commandos strapped in the seats and midway, Jim Henricksen laying in one of the Pullman berths. Moving down to his Third Officer, he saw that he was in obvious pain.

"How do you feel, Jim?" Ford asked.

"About as bad as I look, I guess Captain. Got one hell of a headache," Henricksen said, with a laugh that made him twitch in pain. "That spin. How in the world did you pull that off?" he asked.

Ford smiled and answered. "I'll tell you all about it when we're having drinks in Trincomalee. Now you rest and I'll try to help relieve the pain with something from Barney's larder, dark brown, hot and I don't mean coffee," Kathleen Elmes was at his elbow. "I gave him some aspirin and hopefully the ice bag will help staunch the bleeding. But he needs a doctor... stitches. That wound is deep," she commented.

Ford's anger was building and as he looked down the aisle at the Japs, he wanted to grab the Major and beat hell out of him. But he turned and walked back to the group. Barney had a cup of coffee waiting for him and he smiled his thanks and turned to the others. He didn't want the Japs to overhear anything so he sat on the third step and motioned for them to come closer. Before he could say anything Shamus Ginsberg spoke.

"Captain. These men of yours were terrific. Even when we were spinning, they somehow got free and beat hell out of these buggers. And looking at the two that Mr. Steers brought down, I guess the same happened above," the innkeeper advised.

Ford smiled his thanks to one and all then got serious. "Besides Mr. Henricksen, anyone got anything more serious than cuts and scrapes?" They all shook their heads and Kathleen Elmes asked the question for all of them. "Are we going back to Surabaja so Mr. Henricksen can be treated by a doctor? And who are those people back there. I mean, I know they are Japanese soldiers but what were they trying to do?"

"No on returning to Surabaja and they were trying to shanghai the Clipper. Wanted me to fly it to some place called Kota Bharu," the pilot answered. As Kathleen Elmes began to speak, Ford's look silenced her. "We know that soon, today, tomorrow or in a week the Japs will steam into Surabaja and Java will fall. I want to be to hell and gone when that happens. There is a British Naval detachment at Trincomalee so Jim will get proper treatment from their doctor. Now I think it is time for me to talk to our uninvited visitors. Lt. Elmes, please wait here. I don't want them to know we have someone on board that is fluent in Japanese. Shamus, you know these birds better than us. Please join us. Norm, you too. Any questions?"

"Captain, what are you going to do with the prisoners?" John Steers asked.

"Right now, I'm thinking of opening the cargo bay and seeing how good they are at free falling. I'd just as soon feed them to the sharks," Ford answered and began to walk down the aisle, Norm Brown and the tavern owner trailing as his crew nodded their approval of his solution.

The six were tied up in the last three rows of seats and a couple looked like they could use some medical attention. The one whose face got in the way of John Parish's foot was still bleeding. Ford didn't give a damn. His eyes swept the six until they rested on Major Thu. Ford waited for Thu to look at him but the Jap continued to look straight ahead. Ford knew Thu spoke English and he wondered if any of the others did. Knowing it was useless to question them, he began to talk to Shamus and Mr. Brown, trying to get a rise out of one of the prisoners.

"This man put a gun to my head. Said he was bringing the Pacific Clipper back to Japan as a present to his Emperor, Tojo. Calls himself Major Thu," Ford began.

"Captain, the name of the Emperor of Japan is Hirohito," Norm Brown corrected as Ford knew he would.

"And there was another one with him but I didn't get a look at him. The Major said he'd fly the Clipper if I didn't follow orders. Do you see anyone big enough here to handle the Clipper, let alone fly it? Mr. Brown? Shamus?"

"No Sir," Brown responded.

"Neither do I Captain" Shamus answered "But it seems to me that the name of the Japanese Emperor, is Tanaka. But maybe Mr. Brown is right. The Emperor's name is Yamamoto."

"Hirohito," Brown corrected. And one of the soldiers nodded. Thu caught it out of the corner of his eye and Ford caught both the soldier's nod and Thu's look that would have sent the soldier back to his ancestors. Ford now knew that Thu's men understood English.

Ford smiled at Thu. "Major, please tell me what in hell you and your men hoped to do? Capture our plane? Why?"

The Jap just looked straight ahead, a slight smirk across his lips. Ford was tempted to reach over and belt him but he knew that would give the little bastard some perverse sense of satisfaction. He'd already failed in his mission and now one of his men told the Americans they understood English. Hitting him would give him some small triumph, having the American captain lose his temper.

"Shamus. What should we do with these men that tried to steal our ship?" Ford asked.

Shamus, quickly following Ford's lead, answered.

"Captain, far be it from me, a man of peace and brotherhood to tell you what retribution these men should suffer but there is a delightful one the Balinese use when any of their women are violated. Now the Pacific Clipper is a flying ship and ships are "she's" so we can say that "she" has been violated. Ergo, if you wouldn't mind putting the Clipper down near one of these islands, lets us cut down some strong limbs from the trees, strap the asses of these six to them, kill a pig, spread the blood over them and shove them out to sea. We can even make it a sporting proposition. Give each a number, select your favorite and the first shark to strike one of them, that number wins. How does that sound Captain Ford?" the Irish/Jew recommended.

"I like it, Shamus. Adds a bit of sporting fun to it. Yes, we could relax on the sands while watching the sharks play with our friends here. That fat bastard there that pistol whipped Mr. Henricksen would go last. After the sharks had their appetizer with these little farts, the big one would be the main course," Ford commented. "Any other ideas?"

"You said it earlier. They wanted you to fly them somewhere. Just open the cargo door and see how far they can fly. Let's make it the airplane's version of walking the plank" Ginsberg laughed gleefully at the idea of the six flapping their arms, trying to stay airborne as they fell towards the sea.

Norm Brown had heard enough. He couldn't believe the Captain would ever do anything like this but he knew Bob Ford had a terrible temper and there was no denying he was about to explode in anger. So he decided to try stop things now.

"Captain, I must protest. We are Americans and do not torture prisoners. And we also represent Pan American Airways, an American company. As representatives of a country that has signed the Geneva Convention, we must treat these prisoners humanely," the Second Officer stated, knowing he was doing his duty. Out of the corner of his eye he caught a brief flicker of a smile cross the lips of the big Jap that had wounded Henricksen and as he shifted his eyes to the Jap major, Brown knew he was being laughed at!

Ford was pissed and let Norm Brown know it. The frustration and anger were real now. And Brown felt it!

"Mr. Brown, these men invaded our ship with the express purpose of shanghaiing her. That is a violation of the laws of the sea and the air. They'd probably dump us somewhere over the South China Sea without parachutes. So don't go preaching that bullshit that we can't do to them what they surely would have done to us," Ford shot back and Shamus couldn't tell if he was really mad enough to do what he'd suggested earlier or still bluffing.

As Brown was about to speak, Ginsberg interrupted.

"They didn't sign it," he stated quietly.

"What do you mean, Mr. Ginsberg," the Second Officer asked. "I thought all nations signed the Geneva Convention after World War I."

"Mr. Brown, far be it from me to give you a history lesson after what we've been through but the Geneva Convention was signed in 1864. And Japan was not a world power then and not invited to join. No one thought much about it until the Japs began using Chinese women and children for bayonet practice. And when the world protested, they told us to stick it up the "you know what," Ginsberg stated in a very matter-of-fact voice.

"You mean they can do anything they want to prisoners of war, soldiers and civilians? And they don't have to answer to anybody," Brown asked, incredulous at what Ginsberg was saying.

"You got it," Shamus answered a dumbstruck Second Officer.

Ford was getting tired of all this. As his anger abated, the much more pressing problem of flying across the uncharted underbelly of the world moved him to put an end to this little charade. Norm Brown had played his part perfectly, although he didn't know it. The old 'good cop, mean cop' routine may have planted some kernel of worry in the mind of Thu. But, unless something else happened, he'd turn the prisoners over to the British when they landed at Trincomalee. Too bad, it might have been fun to tie their asses to trees and float them out for the sharks, as Shamus had suggested.

"Mr. Brown, you will take the prisoners below and make sure they are secured. Have Barney and John Parish help you. I will determine their fate later," Ford instructed.

"Yes, Sir," Brown responded as Ford moved past him towards the forward part of the cabin, not looking back at the Japanese. Shamus Ginsberg stayed for a few seconds, calmly looking at the Japanese officer. Then he stood, looked at Norm and winked as he also moved forward.

Major Thu knew all of it was for his benefit. He also knew that Ford would do none of the things suggested. But it was the wink from the civilian to Mr. Brown that got his attention and caused him a moment of doubt. For he understood completely that the one called Shamus would feed them to the sharks in a second if he were in command.

"What a strange performance. Had Mr. Brown talked openly like that to his superior in front of the enemy, he'd have been shot on the spot if he were in our Army," the Major thought. "There are still many hours of flying and who knows what opportunities might arise. But it is I that is tied up, not Ford and his men. I will not underestimate him again."

TANAKA AT KOTA BHARU

The Port Commander, Lieutenant Commander Fuyo stood aside as Commodore Tanaka entered the conference room. Two other officer rose as he entered and strode to the head of the table. A celebration had been planed in this room. When the American plane never came, the ranking officers that were there left for Guam before Tanaka got off the Arista. The only other officers to greet the tall man were two Lieutenants from Naval Intelligence in Tokyo. Junior in rank and far below Tanaka in social status, they would not question the Commodore about what happened. So when he sat, so did they, at attention. Fuyo looked at the two bus boys standing by the buffet, ready to serve and with a nod of his head, dismissed them. No one spoke.

"Thu failed. The reports from Surabaja said that Ford took off from Surabaja when the sirens began. If Thu hadn't been able to get aborad, he'd have let me know and I'd have ended the Clipper's journey with a couple of Zeros. So that means he got aboard but didn't effect the capture. The plane could have crashed or Ford and his men bested mine."

Just the thought of Ford brought the Commodore's powerful right palm slamming down on the conference table, the impact ringing like a rifle shot in the silent room. His anger and frustration boiled over in that one act and he sat back in the chair, seething with hatred for Ford. He'd placed his faith in Thu but Ford won. It was done. Now he had to regroup. The Commodore was not one to second guess himself and waste time on "what happened?" It had happened. Thanks to Thu's failure, he'd lost the advantage of having Ford in his back yard. Now he'd have to chase him across the world. And he better come up with a plan that Tojo would buy. He knew Japanese agents around the world would keep Naval Intelligence advised of where the Clipper landed and took off. It was up to him to figure where he could intercept Ford and his plane.

"And I have to justify my continuing to try for the Clipper. The idea of duplicating her design and technology is over. There is no way I can shanghai her. And I don't have any commandos at my disposal," the big man thought. "What earthly rationalization can I come up with to continue tracking Ford and the Clipper across the world? Yet, I shall never give up. The Pacific Clipper has become Ahab's whale to me. And if I have to destroy the plane, so be it,"

Sitting back and looking down the table, he still didn't pay any attention to the other officers. His mind was spinning with all possible options and he thought about Tojo. What could he do to appeal to Tojo that would get him the Prime Minister's support. He suddenly remembered a time almost a decade ago when his uncle had introduced him to a young Lt. Colonel Tojo. The Baron said the young officer was becoming a major factor in the War Party and supported his ideas of world conquest. And he mentioned something that the nephew never forgot. "Isodecki, there is one great flaw in the man's character. He loves to be in the limelight, to hear his own voice. Propaganda is his strength. It could be his Achilles' Heel," the Baron told him and he had been so accurate. Tojo loved to talk. "So Uncle, how can I take Tojo's love of himself and get him to allow me to keep after Ford after this debacle? What can I do that will be so spectacular that Tojo will go for it, where he can get on the radio and tell the people of another Japanese triumph over the hated Americans. Something other than capturing another base, something that the people will understand was very special? What was it I just thought... something about Ahab's whale... destroying it... " and with that, Tanaka again slammed his hand on the table and jumped up out of his chair. Pacing around the room and not paying any attention to the others, he knew he had the germ of an idea that could possibly offset the failure to bring back the Clipper for duplication. Even if they had succeeded, Tojo would take no pride in saying that it was American 'know how' that built the plane the Japanese airmen were flying to dominate Asia. "The Pan Am planes have been a thorn in our side for years, flying across the Emperor's Lake with impunity, showing how their technology was superior. Which it is but that isn't the point. Ford will try for New York. He has to. And if he makes it, the press and that bastard Trippe will splash his exploits all across the country. But if I can destroy her there, in New York, what a propaganda triumph! That will shock American, coming so soon after Pearl Harbor. They'll know that no place is safe from Japan, when we can so easily sink the vaunted symbol of their air supremacy. This will be another tremendous shock to their psyche. I have to think this through but I think that is the answer. Sink the Pacific Clipper in New York harbor!"

The excitement of his novel idea brought a small smile to his lips and he returned to his chair, again slapping the table top with his hand but this time in anticipation of the chase and the destruction of the Pacific Clipper. He would use the time flying back to Tokyo to refine the idea so it was ready for Tojo. That he would see the Prime Minister on his arrival was a given. After all, he was a Tanaka. Leaning back, he finally took notice of the other three officers, two of whom he recognized. Looking at the Port Commander, he spoke.

"Commander, I am thirsty. Some tea, please," the Commodore ordered. As the Port Commander rose and looked for one of the bus boys to serve his honored guest, Tanaka turned his gaze on the two men from Tokyo. Looking at them, his demeanor was as imperious as ever, exactly as they expected. The two officers sat in silence.

As Lt. Commander Fuyo returned to his chair, the bus boys coming in behind him to serve the officers, Tanaka looked at his comrades from Naval Intelligence and spoke.

"What arrangements have you made to fly me back to Tokyo?" he asked, looking at the two. They looked at him, then at each other.

"You, Lt. Hiki. Speak. Do you have any instructions?" the tall man ordered.

"No Sir. We were planning to fly back to Tokyo with you on the American plane," And as the words flew from his lips, Lt. Hiki wished he were dead!

Tanaka's eyes flashed and the color drained from Hiki's face.

"Your statement is noted, Lt. Hiki and will be remembered. Commander Fuyo, what planes are here that can take me to Tokyo?" Tanaka asked.

Before the Port commander could answer, there was a soft tap at the door and Tanaka didn't bother to even look that way. His eyes were on Hiki, whose total embarrassment was almost physical, and Tanaka knew it so he kept staring at the poor officer. A soldier entered and handed a message to Fuyo. Tanaka assumed it was unimportant. The messenger was, the message wasn't. Fuyo read it and paused.

"Sir. This message concerns you. The plane that took the other officers to Guam is being rerouted to get you and bring you to Guam," the Port Commander spoke, walking towards Tanaka with the message for him to read. Fuyo was barely able to hide his delight, knowing that the rerouting of a plane carrying such important officers just to pick up Tanaka meant that the haughty Commodore was in deep shit in Tokyo!

Taking the message and reading it, Tanaka smiled. His importance was being acknowledged and bringing the plane back with those others that were jealous of him showed how high they regarded him in Tokyo.

1115 Hours -21 December, 1941- Aboard the Pacific Clipper

Ford had gone back to the flight deck and within ten minutes, Norm Brown reported that the Japanese prisoners were secured, the six tied to the metal struts inside the holds, spaced about twenty feet apart as directed by Ford, Major Thu had been tied up nearest to the port side vent that supplies air to the holds, the vent that would allow Kathleen Elmes to eavesdrop on whatever conversation might take place between the prisoners. With the prisoners tied up, Ford called the crew together except for John Henry Mack piloting and John Poindexter monitoring the air waves.

"Look, we've got over 3,500 miles to fly before we get to Trincomalee. That's about twenty two hours plus in the air. Lt. Elmes, Mr. Brown tied up the Jap major directly underneath the port vent. It will take a few hours before he'll feel he can talk with his men. In the meantime, you get some rest. Ok? Barney, keep the coffee pot full. We've got a lot of air to cover so when all of you have competed your duties, get to bed. Who knows when we'll get another chance to rest!" Ford ordered.

As the crew broke up and Kathleen Elmes headed for the Master Suite, Ford climbed the stairs up to the flight deck. He suddenly felt as if each step was ten feet high and realized that he better get some rest. "Christ, I'm beat. Mack's been flying for the last half hour and Steers will relieve him in another hour. I'll grab a quick nap. I've got a feeling that I'm going to need it."

1750 hours-21 December, 1941-Aboard the Pacific Clipper

Ford rechecked his compass readings for the tenth time in five minutes. It still was the same... 130 degrees Northwest by 60 degrees South. If all the dead reckoning the John's, Mack, Steers and Poindexter had done with the atlases Bill Mullahey swiped, they were headed for Trincomalee, Ceylon. It was quiet on the bridge and Ford was alone. He had told Mack to keep the controls when he returned after making sure the Japanese prisoners were secured in the hold. As he told John, "I'm just going to lie down for a few minutes. I'll relieve you at 1115 hours," When he did crawl out of his small bed behind the bridge, it was already close to 1700 hours. He'd slept almost six hours! They had let him sleep while Mack, John Steers and Norm Brown took turns flying the Pacific Clipper. There was no danger. They were damn good pilots and had an emergency arisen, he felt confident any of them could have handled it. Fortunately, there wasn't any. Now he had the Clipper all to himself. Norm Brown had reported that the prisoners in the hold were quiet and he was going to take some well earned rest himself. And in the solitude of the flight deck with just the beauty of an early evening sky over the Bay of Bengal and the soft, steady drone of the powerful Wrights to keep him company, Ford again went back to "Why?"

"Why would six Japanese commandos try to shanghai us?" Ford thought to himself. He check his gages, especially the fuel, knowing this was the longest part of their flight, thus far. All showed enough to make Trincomalee, easily.

"But why?" he mulled again. "Let me think it through. The Japs bomb Pearl Harbor and at the same time destroy almost all of our bases. Coincidence? Yes. With the exception of Noumea, all of our bases had military detachments on them; Guam, Wake Island, Midway, Manila, and of course, Hawaii. So when we get to Auckland, we're stuck there with no way to return home. And after a week when we finally decide to try for home, there is no compelling reason for anyone to worry about us. And except for the brawl, nothing happened in Darwin. Then on to Surabaja and although we almost had our asses blown away, it was "friendly planes" that came after us."

Ford looked out the port windows of the Clipper to enjoy the magnificent sunset. The Clipper was flying at her cruising altitude of 8,000 feet and the rays of the sun bounced off the clouds above and below the plane in hues that took his breath away. The whole spectrum of colors and all their variants were there and he tried to recall the names of some of the more exotic. There were different shades of blue, like indigo filtering through some of the darker clouds, along with soft sky blues from the thinner ones. The yellows ranged from ocher to lemon and Ford had to look away when the clouds parted and the sun shone directly in his eyes. The reds and the greens, especially the reds offered him their whole assortment of colors and as almost every time he saw a sunset like this, he thought how lucky he was to be alive to view God's painting of the sky.

Ford took his eyes away from the spectacular handiwork of the Almighty and his eyelids closed. Opening them, Ford went back to reconstructing their journey to see if he could find a reason six Japanese soldiers were tied up in the hold of the Pacific Clipper. Ford knew there was a reason and he had to figure it out. Not that it meant anything anymore. Once they got to Trincomalee, he felt very confident they'd have nothing to worry about from the Japanese. Then he thought about Pearl Harbor, Guam and how swiftly the Japs had so totally taken over Southeast Asia and the Pacific and he wasn't so sure anymore. "These bastards are tough. Christ, look at the territory they have gobbled up in less that a couple of weeks... Guam taken, the Philippines will be gone soon, New Guinea and Malasia any day now. They've kicked us out of the Pacific. Singapore will fall soon, the British have no Navy left, ours sits in the mud at Pearl, the French will surrender, as the French always do. And after seeing what the Dutch have out here to stop the Japs, forget it!" The though was very sobering.

"Wait a second! What was it Jocko said? He told me something on the dock that night... something about how their shore patrols had intercepted a transmission from somewhere in the hills that they thought was from Japanese infiltrators. And Pan Am was mentioned. Could it have just been idle reporting of our arrival? Probably. But what if it wasn't. No, but there were Japanese commandos on Java. From the little I know of military thinking, six commandos don't go off on their own and try to grab a plane just for the hell of it. No, there is a reason. There has to be!" the pilot thought. "Why would six men, including a pilot, try to shanghai the Clipper. A pilot... which meant someone that could fly the Clipper. So, there must have been plans all along to capture the Clipper. But why? She's has no military value. She's the best plane in the world... for flying passengers and cargo... but nothing else," the pilot mused. He leaned back in his seat and again gazed out at the sky. In just a few minutes the colors had changed, now darker but just as stunning. Ford felt so relaxed as he gazed at the kaleidoscope of colors Old Sol and the clouds were providing for him that he didn't want to think anymore. But his mind kept spinning and when the rays of the sun bounced across some of the clouds, they reminded him of the rays streaking out of the sun on the flag of the Japan and he was back trying to solve the enigma of why the Japanese would try to take his plane.

For whatever reason, something Shamus Ginsberg had said when he was frightening he and John Mack with stories of how powerful the Japanese were while having their Irish Coffees with him popped into his head. "They plan to conquer the world!" Shamus had said and to Ford that was ridiculous. That little country, with its bamboo shacks, small fishing villages, and almost no industry to build planes and bombers and ships planned to conquer the world!

Then Ford stopped laughing. "Why do I keep underestimating these guys? Look at what they have done in two weeks! Maybe it is because they are physically small. Or because we were brought up thinking anything that said "Made in Japan" was a cheap imitation, not worth the money," Ford thought. And suddenly Ford understood! It was simple. "Of course. Imitation! That's it. What can the Japanese do better than anyone else? Steal products and copy them. Shamus said they planned to conquer the world. But they can't do it with just their Army. In ten years, they haven't been able to take over China. And while their Navy with those aircraft carriers has been spectacular, those carrier based planes have a limited range. They'd have to sit off the West Coast to bomb LA, Frisco or Seattle and our bombers would blow their fleet out of the water," Now the pilot of the Pacific Clipper sat back in his chair and thought. And when he came up with his answer, it scared the hell out of him!

"That's it! That's why they want the Clipper! They need long range bombers. And with the Clipper in their hands, they could copy her: the technology, the engines, the navigation equipment and build their own fleet of bombers, like our Flying Fortresses! That has to be it! Shamus, get up here. You too, Miss Elmes."

Then Ford realized he was talking to himself. He flipped on the Intercom and was about to summon the two of them when he knew that his request would be heard by Thu below. So he simply reached across the Intercom and pressed a button that would signal the galley that the Captain wished to speak with whomever was on duty.

When the light went on in Bob Ford's head, the man who was responsible for taking the Pacific Clipper back to Japan was sitting in the gathering dark of the Pacific Clipper's hold. The Americans had not gagged them or even tied their feet. Thu was amazed at their stupidity. The feet could be a more lethal weapon than the hands. Now with the inside almost totally dark, he put his finger against the bulkhead and tapped out a message to his men. "They will come to feed us. Eat and do nothing," Thu knew that the Americans would feed them. At least one person would think of them when they were eating and the soft-hearted Americans would bring them food. They would eat and the next time the American came, he would have his men ready to capture one of them. He knew the Americans' strong feelings for the individual and if they could just overpower one of the Clipper's crew, he'd have a bargaining chip against that bastard Ford.

But someone had to get his hands free. How? The ropes binding his hands were thick, heavy duty cargo ropes. But maybe the thickness of the ropes might just allow one of them to work their smaller hands free. It was a chance and Thu quickly began, knowing his men would follow his lead. After an hour, he was bathed in sweat even at 8000 feet and exhausted. Now darkness had totally blackened their prison. Thu closed his eyes to allow them to adjust to the darkness. Then he opened them and in a few seconds, he could discern the shapes of his men. And there it was, the teeth showing a smile from Corporal Izoah! Then, he saw Izoah was waving his free hands at him from across the hold. With a great sigh, Thu mouthed instructions for the corporal to free all the rest of them. Seconds later, a door opened at the bow of the plane and a light came on and bathed the hold in brightness. Thu almost fainted. As he looked across at Izoah, the young man was still tied to the strut. Or was he?

When Barney, following Ford's instruction, had knocked on the Master Suite door to awake Kathleen Elmes and ask her to join Captain Ford on the bridge, he'd had already alerted Shamus Ginsberg who had been stretched out sleeping across three passenger seats. Kathleen thought that she had just put her head down for a few minutes but when Barney's knock finally awakened her, she realized she'd been asleep in her clothes for most of the afternoon. Taking a few seconds to straighten up and splash her face with water, she hastily put on some lipstick, ran a comb through her hair and opened the door to follow Barney down the aisle and up to the bridge. Reaching the top, she saw Shamus standing by the navigator's table and John Mack in his co-pilots chair. The three were chatting as she approached. In a strange way, she suddenly felt as if she were a close and important part of the team. John Mack rose and invited her to sit in his chair. She smiled her acknowledgement of the honor but indicated she'd stand with Shamus.

"I've been racking my brain to try to figure out why the Japs below would try to shanghai our plane. I think I've got it but I wanted to run it by you," Ford began. "They want the Clipper so they can copy her, build bombers based on the Clipper's technology, her engines, the sophisticated electronics we have, the navigational and radio systems. The Clipper has no military value except for what she is, and has. If a nation could capture her, reproduce her but change her configuration to make her a bomber, they would have now what it has taken us years to produce, the Flying Fortress. Your thoughts."

The three pondered for a few moments but the Captain's analysis seemed on target. "Captain, you're right. That can be the only reason, as far as I can see," John Mack reprised.

"That has to be it, Captain. They thought by shanghaiing the Clipper, flying her back to Japan, they could duplicate her! That has to be the reason," Shamus Ginsberg agreed.

The three of them looked at Kathleen Elmes for her input. She knew more about the Japanese and if anyone could punch holes in Ford's analysis, she could. Kathleen didn't respond. She was lost in thought. "It makes sense. Why else would six Japanese commandos try to steal an American commercial airline except to copy her. The Japs know that Boeing planes have been flying labs for our military. But who is behind this. Not that Major." As she was about to comment, something she knew that Naval Intelligence had followed back in 1938 triggered a possible connection.

"Bob. John. The Hawaii Clipper. Does that ring a bell?" Kathleen asked. Both looked at each other and back to her and nodded. John Mack spoke.

"Didn't the Hawaii go down in a storm flying from Manila to Hong Kong a couple of years ago?" Mack stated and asked.

"Yes and no," Ford commented. "No one ever found any wreckage. Not Pan Am or the Navy. And this is the strange part, the weather was perfect yet later they said she went down in a storm. But Kathleen, what has this to do with the six Jap commando's in the hold below?"

"Naval Intelligence has never gone along with that explanation. Neither did Pan Am but the State Department asked that there be no charge of espionage. There had been other instances of the FBI catching Japanese trying to sabotage Clippers ships. But tensions were already high between our two countries," Kathleen explained. "So to sum up, there is a history of the Japs trying to sabotage Pan Am planes and the Hawaii Clipper went down without anyone ever finding any wreckage. And this will blow your minds, our agents in Japan have reported that at the Mitsubishi Naval works, a duplicate of the Martin 42 has been built but its tests show it hasn't the range to be a bomber! But the Wrights on the Pacific Clipper do! I'll bet that's the reason why they tried to shanghai us," she expounded.

"Jesus Christ! You knew all of this and didn't tell us," Ford exploded.

"I never connected the Hawaii Clipper to what happened today," she shouted right back to him.

Ford glared at her and then shrugged his shoulders.

"You're right. I'm sorry. No need to blow up at you. I'm just frustrated knowing some slant-eyed bastards are trying to take my plane," startling Kathleen and Mack with an apology. Shamus just laughed.

"You two are going to have a stormy marriage but you'll have a hell of a lot of fun," the Innkeeper said with a broad smile on his face. John Mack laughed as Ford looked away and Kathleen blushed. Just then, Norm Brown's head come up the passageway and things calmed down.

"Captain," the Second Officer began, "it is supper time and Barney wants to know what you guys want for dinner. Also, how do you plan on feeding the prisoners? One at a time or bring the food down to them?" he asked. And Shamus Ginsberg blew his stack!

"Why would you even consider such a thing!" Shamus Ginsberg shouted at the Second Officer. "Mother of God, Mr. Brown, are you some kind of bloomin' St. Francis of Assisi? Stay the hell away from them. Keep 'em tied up until you turn them over to the Brits at Trincomalee. Or dump them out the end of this beauty and be done with them. Feed the bastards? Mr. Brown, grow up. They ain't humans. They're Japs!" the ex-owner of the Black Swan exclaimed.

"Please Shamus, aren't you a little paranoid about them?" Kathleen Elmes chimed in to support Norm Brown. Shamus turned to her and took a deep breath. He didn't want to make an enemy of her and thought for a few seconds before replying. Brown's request was the height of stupidity but it was humane and that appealed to the Lt. He'd have to use all his wiles, not only to keep her as a friend but also to bring Mr. Brown around.

"Mr. Brown, please accept my apologies for reacting as I did. Let me explain why I'm advising against going down into the hold. Forget about the issue of feeding these men. The reason I can say that is these men, and the rest of the Japanese army can go days, even weeks, without eating. They are trained to live off the land and they can stay alive on insects that would make a maggot sick. But consider if you will who they are," the Irish/ Jew innkeeper began.

"They are commandos; the toughest, best trained, deadliest fighters in the Japanese Army. These men have been in combat for almost ten years and you know that Major was hand-picked for this mission by whomever thought it up. And Captain Ford, I'll bet my bankroll you're right on when you think the reason for the attempt to take the Clipper was that the Japs want to copy her to build long range bombers," Shamus continued.

"Now Kathleen, as a Naval Intelligence officer, answer me this. With our fleet at the bottom of waters at Pearl Harbor, what would be your estimate of America's chances be if the Japs had planes that could fly 5000 miles to deliver bombs?" he asked.

"If they took any of the Aleutian Islands, they could bomb the West Coast with impunity... from Seattle down to San Diego," she replied, softly.

"And if they had such a weapon, do you think they would use it?" Shamus asked rhetorically.

"Of course. Any nation at war uses all the weapons they have to defeat the enemy," Kathleen replied, stating the obvious.

"So all I'm saying is that we got lucky. Let's not let the genie out of the bottle. I don't know how far we are from Trincomalee but even if it is another week, we are safe as long as they are down there. Correct Lt.Elmes?" the Irish/ Jew summarized and asked for Kathleen's support.

Now Bob Ford spoke. He had been listening and had no intention of allowing Mr. Brown to feed the Japs but it was good that Shamus's arguments had carried the day.

"Mr. Brown, recheck their bindings down there. Make sure their legs are tied. Ask Swede, John Parish and Barney to assist you. We have a lot of air to cover and like Shamus said, these are deadly foes," Ford summarized, dismissing the three while John Mack sat back in his chair.

Two members of the Pan Am crew stepped inside the hold from the anchor room door and turned on the overhead lights. Thu recognized one of the men as the officer that had the argument with Ford. Mr. Brown. Thu had hoped that he would be the one that came down to feed them. The bigger one he didn't recognize. And unless the food was hidden behind them, these men were not here to feed them. They weren't. Now two more entered, neither carrying food. One had that black roll of tape and the other a shotgun. The Americans didn't speak as they began their work. The one with the shotgun, Barney they called him, walked up to the Sergeant whom he had knocked out earlier, and placed the barrel of the shotgun on his forehead. Then he cocked the gun. The sergeant didn't move. The other man bent down and quickly wrapped his ankles with the tape, then checked the bindings on the hands. Looking at the door, Thu could see that both men had drawn guns and were standing so they covered the prisoners as well as their crew mates. It was very professional and Thu was impressed and quite surprised. They saved him for last and when finished, the two walked back to the anchor door and joined the others. Without looking back and flipping off the light, they left.

Fifteen minutes after the four went down, they returned. Norm Brown went up to the flight deck, and not saying a word, gave Ford and John Mack the thumbs up sign. The two looked at Norm, smiled and then settled back to do what they did best, fly.

Midnight aboard the Pacific Clipper, somewhere in the Bay Bengal

It was the cold that woke him. Thu stirred and coming out of his sleep tried to figure out where he was. Then he remembered. He was a prisoner, tied up in the bowels of the American plane he was suppose to capture. He tried to figure out the time and remembered when the Americans had come down to tie up their feet, the aroma of food cooking whiffed down into the hold. He used that as a time check. From the time they had been locked up after the debacle it was little things like that fragrance that gave him his orientation to the time. Since the Americans always ate their big meal around 6 or 7 PM, it must be around midnight now, with the hold being so cold. Thu knew he didn't have much time to come up with a way for them to still complete their mission. But he had not given up. He was awake but he had no answers. The key to solving the predicament they were in was getting one man free so he could untie the rest. Once that happened, Thu knew he'd fulfill the Tanaka mission. But he had to know if any of his men had worked themselves free. It had been hours since they had come down to tie up their feet. The American were probably asleep by now. He decided that the time was right to tap out another message to his men. So he began.

For Kathleen Elmes, after talking to Ford and the others about why the Japs tried to capture the Clipper, it was time to go to work. Swede

Rothe and Oscar Hendrickson, the Second Radio Officer had rigged up a Rube Goldberg listening contraception for her. Taking an extra radio head set, they had clipped off the end of the wire that would usually be plugged in the radio counsel. They replaced that plug with another ear piece so that Kathleen could sit with the ear phones on her head while the wire cord with the new ear piece acted like a doctor's stethoscope, letting her listen to any conversation coming from the hold. The piece was placed just inside the small air vent on the port side, and the vent then closed with black masking tape, to keep any light from the cabin filtering down into the hold, alerting the prisoners that they were being monitored. Kathleen brought her note pad that contained her breakdown of the Japanese code as she remembered it from the work done on the Purple machine. She had changed from her Navy uniform into her cream colored slacks, a navy blue sweater and had white flats on her feet. She was comfortable in the big passenger seat and ready for work. It was past 2030 hours and the Japanese had been in the hold for over half the day. She hoped that they were ready to talk and give her some clue as to who was behind the shanghai attempt. She was excited and anxious, feeling that at last she was contributing. This was her time!

Two hours later, she was stretched out across the seat, her flats on the floor, her legs curled under her, her head resting on a pillow Barney had provided, a cigarette in her hand as she flipped through the pages of Vogue. She had not heard a thing but still had her "ears" on. Now as midnight approached, weariness was finally catching up to most of them. The lights in the passenger area had been dimmed. Kathleen shifted on her seat and crushed out the cigarette in the ashtray when she heard something. She froze. Now silence. Still she didn't move. And as if some signal went out from her, the rest of the crew slowly moved towards her seat. She looked at Oscar Hendrickson and raised her eyebrows, answering his question. He nodded and silence reigned. To Kathleen, it seemed like an hour before she heard it again but it was only a few minutes. There it was, some kind of tapping but not metal against metal, more of a dull thud. Slowly, she sat up straight and picked up her pencil, opened her note book and began to record the sounds. "Dash... dash... dash... dot... " Kathleen's pencil flew across the page, entering the code, not bothering to try to read it. Then suddenly, the tapping stopped. Collectively, they held their breath. Time stood still. Then she nodded and continued to write.

"Dot... dash... dash... dot... " As she was writing, she shook her head, then looking at Oscar, mouthed "different man," She continued to make her notes and then stopped, looked at Oscar and whispered, "get the Captain," As Hendrickson moved towards the stairs to the bridge, Kathleen heard more tapping, coming from the first man she had heard. Again she scribbled furiously, trying to keep up with the swift transmissions emanating from the hold. She was convinced the man tapping was Major Thu. Who had responded she didn't waste time guessing. The response, when translated would tell her. Then it stopped. And somehow, Kathleen knew it was ended. Looking up, she saw Bob Ford and John Poindexter headed down the aisle towards her. Kathleen smiled at them and nodded. She took off the head set, and reaching down, lay it quietly on the floor next to her listening vent. The she rose and handed her notes to Ford.

He smiled at her and looked at them. They meant nothing and wouldn't until Kathleen and Poindexter could decode them. Ford nodded to the crew and they began to disperse as he, Kathleen and the radio man went forward to the starboard lounge. Spreading Kathleen's three pages of code on the table, they began to try to decode the tapping Kathleen had recorded.

"This page is when I first heard the tapping, this is the second and this the third. I didn't try to decode it while I was writing but looking at it now, it no way resembles anything I've seen transmitted by the Japanese that we decoded in Washington. So lets get at it," the Navy Lieutenant stated. Poindexter and Kathleen began to decipher and Ford knew that there was little he could do here. As he rose to go back up the stairs to the bridge, Giles Brown, the tech rep came up.

"Captain Ford, it might be smart to keep someone on the headset while Miss Elmes and Mr. Poindexter are deciphering the message. I know that Mr. Hendrickson is sitting upstairs in Poindexter's chair so unless you have someone else in mind, I'd be pleased to assist," the tech rep offered. Ford looked at him and smiled. "Thank you, Mr. Brown. Go ahead and keep us informed if you hear anything," the pilot responded. The tech rep nodded and went back to where the ear phone lay next to the vent. Picking them off the floor, he sat down in Kathleen Elmes's seat, put them over his ears and looked at the crew watching him. Smiling, he nodded to them and then got down to the business of listening.

Forward, the Navy Intelligence officer and the Clipper's radio operator began their deciphering. Kathleen had recorded the codes in simple Morse Code. So she approached the task of trying to convert the obvious into the complex. She thought the transmissions would be in one of the numerous Japanese codes she had studied and deciphered for the last couple of years in the confines of the Navy Department. So she took the first page and tried to figure out what the first dash meant. Then she went to the second and on through her note until she looked at John Poindexter, totally frustrated. And she saw him just sitting there, smoking a cigarette and smiling at her. And suddenly, she blushed.

"Just Morse Code?" she asked him.

"That's it, Kathleen. Sorry. I know you expected it to be something that Yamamoto would send but it is just Thu telling his men to try to get free," the radio man answered, smiling easily, knowing how much she wanted something much more important and exciting to bring to Ford.

"Nothing else?" she asked, hoping.

"The second code came from one of the men just says that no one has been able to get free," Poindexter answered. "Don't be too disappointed. What we now know is that they are still very active and dangerous. Forewarned is forearmed, Kathleen. They haven't quit and we had better stay awake," the radio man spoke, tying to tell her what she had done was very important and knowing she was disappointed it wasn't that dramatic. "Don't worry. The Captain will appreciate this.

Kathleen smiled at him and knew he was trying to assuage her little hurt that she had not heard something that would have made Bob Ford really respect her. Then she realized she was acting like some airhead blond trying to impress the big man on campus.

"Thank you John. Is there anything that Thu is asking his men other than to get free?" she asked.

"No. It is that cut and dried. If one of them can get free, then he'll free the rest and all hell will break loose. So you better take this information up to the Captain and let him figure out what to do," John answered, making it easy for Kathleen to go atop. She smiled and rose, and walked over to the stairs. John Poindexter smiled as he watched her ascend, thinking that Shamus Ginsberg hit it right on the head. The Captain and Kathleen were made for each other.

Thu had no idea that the Americans had heard his message. The response from the Sergeant told him that none of the men had been able to loosen their bonds but would keep trying. So he moved his body around to try and get comfortable and think. He yawned and set his mind to the options available to him. And after reviewing them, he yawned again and closed his eyes. "The Americans will have to give us the opportunity. There is no way we can do it with out their fucking up before we get to Ceylon. We need Buddha's help," the Major thought. as he again tried to get comfortable. The cold didn't bother him but a piece of steel that stuck up from the floor of the hold under him did. Skewered to the bulkhead, no matter what he did, he couldn't escape that damn piece of steel. Just as he was about to concede defeat to the piece tickling his ass, he heard a tapping from above. It happened only once but he his heart skipped a beat. For he heard the universal call for help... or the answer. Dot... dash... dot. SOS! Someone on board the American plane was a friend!

"It was simple Morse Code, Captain. Mr. Poindexter translated it. The Major was telling his men to try and get free and thus far, they haven't been able to," Kathleen Elmes reported to Bob Ford. The pilot noticed the slight disappointment in her voice and smiled at her.

"Don't feel bad, Lt. That's good news. At least they are still tied up. John, see if Shamus is awake and bring him up here. Kathleen, please stay here. I think it is time for a small war council. We still have at least another eight to ten hours before we hit Ceylon and our biggest problem is below. And have Norm Brown join us," Ford ordered. With John Steers already on the flight deck, Ford would have all his key lieutenants, plus Shamus and the Naval Intelligence officer together. Maybe among all of them they could come up with a solution to the problem below. Ford felt like he was sitting atop a time bomb that he had to defuse quickly. As the others arrived, Ford flipped the automatic pilot to "ON", climbed out of his pilot's chair, stretched and leaned against the back of it.

"Kathleen picked up some code that the Japs were tapping below. Major Thu is asking his men to try to get free. That is understandable. They have to try. And we have to stop them. We can keep sending men down to check on their bindings but I want something more solid, something that will let us relax. Well, not relax but you know what I mean. Any ideas?" he asked.

The others just looked at each other and seemed as lost as Ford to come up with an answer. Then John Mack came up with a suggestion.

"How about trying this?" the First Officer began. "The Major is their leader. Let's take him away from them and maybe that will stop them from doing anything. Maybe with Thu in our hands, they'll just sit there."

The rest just look at John Mack. Then Bob Ford responded. "John, that is a hell of an idea. Norm, get your crew together, arm yourselves and be very careful. Bring the Major up here," As Mr. Brown left to complete his instructions, Kathleen Elmes looked at Ford and the others and spoke.

"Has anyone searched the prisoners?" she asked. "I know none of us are trained interrogators but shouldn't we have searched them before we sent them down to the hold?"

"No need to do it to all of them. If I know the Japanese, only the Major would have anything on his person that would give us some information," Shamus commented.

"That is exactly what I heard in Naval Intelligence. The commanding officer on any clandestine operation always has somewhere on his body a copy of his orders," Kathleen supplemented Shamus's comment.

The door from the anchor room opened and the four Americans entered the hole. Thu looked at them and his hopes soared. "Maybe the man who sent the SOS is among them. But if so, how would he help?" he thought as he watched them come in, again with the guns pointed at he and his men. The one called Barney and Mr. Brown walked over towards him. And as he looked up, Barney put the pistol upon his forehead as Brown began to check the bindings on his men. Satisfied they were all still secure, Brown walked over to him. Then to his complete surprise, Mr. Brown began to untied his ropes. Thu searched his face for some hint that he was the sender of the SOS. Hoisted to his feet and with Barney holding the barrel of the gun against his temple, Thu walked to the exit and through the anchor room door, while the other Americans covered his men. Once through, he was pushed up the entrance he had half a day earlier charged up. Now he was the prisoner.

As he walked up the steps, Thu saw Ford and the big shouldered officer that almost killed him standing there, their pilots chairs behind them. Then he saw the older man, the one they called Shamus and the woman. He'd noticed her briefly when they were tying him up in the passenger chair. "Why would a woman would be allowed to be in such an important place?" Thu wondered. That she was permitted in the command center of the plane shook him. He knew Ford was too good a commander to allow a woman up here unless she was very valuable.

As he walked towards Ford, he wondered why they brought him here. He hadn't talked before and would not now. So why? And suddenly Thu understood. "Cut off the head and the body will die," Thu remembered the old adage and now knew what Ford was doing. By separating him from his men, they would be leaderless and he would be still a captive. All the time Thu's face didn't change expression and his eyes never left Ford but his peripheral vision took in the whole flight deck.

Ford watched the Japanese Major climb the steps and look directly at him. "This is a tough son-of-a-bitch," Ford thought. "But alone, away from his men, he might just tip something."

"Ah, Major Thu. Thank you for joining us on the flight deck. We all understand how cold it can get at night down in the hold and befitting your rank, courtesy dictates that you should be comfortable the rest of the journey to Trincomalee. Please be seated," Ford began as he indicated that Thu should sit on John Steers's navigator's seat. As the Jap major walked to the seat, his arms still tied behind him, Ford mulled over the idea that of letting Thu's have his hands free. Then he remembered Shamus' warning and decided against it. Thu could probably beat hell out of all of them by himself! No, the thing to do was try to break down his smug attitude of superiority, shame him into some reaction that would help them understand why he was on his ship. As he thought about it, Ford liked it. "That arrogant bastard thinks because they caught us napping at Pearl, all Americans are assholes. It's about time we get a shot at wiping that smile off his face. And what could be more embarrassing than losing what the Asians call "joss," Now the thing to do was do it. But how?"

"Major, we were going to interrogate you about your mission but there is no need for that now. We know," Ford began and then stopped. "The bastard twitched!" Ford thought to himself. "He was surprised. And look at him. He doesn't look quite so sure of himself. Now what do I do? I've got him shaken but where do I go from here?" the pilot mulled as he looked at the Japanese commando. Looking at the others, they all seemed well aware that the Thu had reacted to his casual throw away line about knowing his mission and they waited for Ford's next move. Looking at Shamus, then at Kathleen, the idea jumped into his mind. "Joss." He would humiliate the Major. He knew how most of the Oriental males treated their women and the Japanese were the worse. How humbling to be searched by a woman in front of men, and Americans at that! Asking Kathleen to search him was just the extra little touch to demean Thu even further.

"Major, we are civilians. So we have little knowledge of military protocol. However, Lt. Elmes is a member of the United States Navy, on special assignment and flying back with us to America. She reminded us that we had not searched you so she asked that we do that now. So if you'll stand, I'll ask Lt. Elmes to conduct the search," Ford told the startled Major, as well as shocking the hell out of the Naval Intelligence officer!

Thu was incredulous! In just a few seconds Ford had destroyed him with the knowledge that they knew why he and his men tried to capture the plane and now a woman, an American woman was going to search him! He looked at Ford to see if the man was serious and the look he got from the American captain showed that he was, deadly serious. He stood there and waited for the woman to come over to him. Just the thought of this woman touching him made his skin crawl and he felt his face flush as he stood, looking straight ahead.

"Captain, these bastards are experts at hiding things on their bodies, in places that someone as sensitive as the Lt. might not look. I suggest you let me and Mr. Steers take the Major into the little room back here and do the honors. I can assure you it will be thorough," Shamus Ginsberg volunteered, as Kathleen Elmes quietly blew him a kiss.

"Fine, Shamus. You and John do just that," Ford commented as the two led the Jap major into the navigation room. John Steers flipped on the light switch and as Shamus and the Major entered, he looked back at Ford and winked.

As the door closed behind them, Kathleen Elmes looked at Ford, totally angry.

"What do you mean telling him I was going to search him?" she hissed.

"Joss, Kathleen, joss," Ford responded, trying to look serious but then breaking into a big grin. John Mack and Norm Brown smiled and as she looked at the three of them, she began to laugh. The four of them grinned at each other. In a minute, the door from the navigation room opened and John Steers led the Jap major back onto the flight deck, followed by Shamus. He looked at Ford and with a slight shake of his head, indicated that they had found nothing. Shamus pushed Thu down onto the chair and stood behind him. Thu looked at Ford, expressionless. Ford didn't seem too upset. Thu was here and would stay out of the hold. And without their leader, maybe the rest of the trip would be uneventful. Just as the was about to order Norm Brown to take Thu down and retie him, Ford noticed the Jap's tennis shoes and the face of Mr. Moto, Peter Lorie, popped into his mind. Ford turned away and looked out his window at the midnight sky. "What is it, Ford" he asked himself. "What does a Japanese movie detective have to do with this... The shoes! Moto solved a murder because one of the suspects had hidden something in his shoe. But Christ, no good spy would do that. But Thu isn't a spy! He is a commando. If captured, he'd claim prisoner of war status. Spies get shot. Even out of uniform, he'd be granted that if he could prove he was on a mission for his government. It's worth a try," the pilot thought to himself. Turning back to the others, he just nodded.

"Mr. Brown, would you and Shamus please escort the Major down to a seat on the passenger level. And, keep him on the aisle so he can't tap messages to his men below," Ford instructed. As Thu stood and moved towards the stairs, Ford stopped him.

"Major Thu, I know it is the custom in Japan that visitors always take off their shoes when entering a house. This is our house. Since you are a visitor, albeit an unwelcome one, would you please show us the same consideration and leave your shoes on the deck?" Ford asked.

Thu looked daggers at Ford, then lowered his eyes. Ford saw it and almost jumped out of his skin knowing he had Thu. Thu also knew. Not looking at his feet, the Jap put his right foot behind the heel of the left shoe and pushed the left shoe off. He repeated the maneuver and as the second rubber shoe came off he stood in his bare feet and bowed. Ford nodded as Shamus led Thu down the stairs and Brown followed. Ford walked over and pick up the tennis shoes. They were still damp and he looked at them as he began turning them over in his hand. He passed the left one over to John Mack and began to study the right. Looking up at Kathleen, he smiled.

"A Mr. Moto movie," he explained and she shook her head in question. "He solved a crime when he found a clue hidden in one of the suspect's shoes. Since John and Shamus didn't find anything on Thu, if there is something that will give us a clue, it has to be in the shoes. OK?"

Kathleen nodded and watched as Mack and Ford began to examine the rubber shoe. John felt inside and pushed on the sole. Nothing. Then he turned over the shoe to see if there was any possible opening on the outside. Nothing. Ford found the same. Pulling up the inside soles, neither found anything. Ford was sure that there had to be something but the shoes provided no clue. There was nothing.

John Steers reached over and took the shoes from Ford and Mack. He reached inside his the back pocket of his white Bermuda shots and pulled out a small pen knife. Expertly, he sliced a thin cut through the bottom of each shoe. Then bending the soles, he looked to see if there was anything there. Nothing. He handed the shoes back to Ford and the four of them just looked at each other. Ford was sure the shoes had something for them. But they didn't. Then Kathleen Elmes reached over and took the shoes from the men. She pulled the shoelaces from each and looked at them. Then she laid them out length wise on the navigation table and with her finger, flattened them. She slowly moved her finger along the top of one, then the second and halfway down, she stopped and looked at John Steers. He passed her the pocket knife. Like a surgeon, she made an incision at the middle of the lace, and moving her finger down, she stopped and made another below the first. Picking up the lace, she bent the top cut open and looking closely, she smiled and showed it to Ford.

He took it. Then looking at the lace, he could see there was something inside. He smiled and as the two John's joined him, he began to work the piece free from the inside of the lace. When enough of the it showed, he pulled it out. It was a piece of microfilm. Looking at Kathleen, his eyes asked how she knew.

"Return of the Thin Man," she answered. "William Powell and Murna Loy as Nick and Nora Charles and Jimmy Stewart is the guilty one. Great movie. Safety deposit key in the hem of the murdered woman's dress. Remember?"

"You're a movie buff?" Ford asked.

"Big," Kathleen answered, watching Ford lay postage stamp piece of film on the navigator's desk. The four bent over to look at it.

"Need a magnifying glass," Kathleen stated.

Steers walked into the Observation room and came back with one, a large one. Three hadn't the foggiest idea of what they were looking at. One did.

"My God!" Kathleen gasped.

"What is it, Kathleen?" Ford asked.

Raising her hand to silence any questions, the expert on Japanese language and tradition and secret codes slowly read the orders that Major Thu had hidden in the laces of his shoe. Finally, she straightened up and looked at her companions.

"Tanaka" she reported. And the three just looked at her.

"Commodore Isodecki Tanaka. He is the one behind all of this. And it fits," she stated. The three men looked at her and the questions on their faces almost made her laugh. "Commodore Tanaka is the nephew of Baron Tanaka, the Prime Minister of Japan in the late Twenties. He formulated Japanese foreign policy, including the invasion of Manchuria. An American newspaper man heard that there was a position paper called the "Tanaka Memorial" that spelled out the Baron's plans for Japan's conquest of Asia. Somehow he got a copy of it and it was published in the States in 1929 by the Minneapolis Tribune, I think, and of course, the Japanese totally denied it. But we know that it was the blueprint for Japan's aggression in the Far East and probably the attack on Pearl. The Baron died in the early Thirties but before he died, Tojo and the war clique came to power and implemented the "Tanaka Memorial. Now we see that his nephew is after the Pacific Clipper. The Baron is said to have warned that for Japan to conquer Asia, she had to have aircraft that could reach an enemy thousands of miles from Japan. Ergo, long range bombers. And since they haven't the engineering or technological skills to build long range aircraft, I suspect the Commodore convinced Tojo and the high command to try and capture a plane that already had it... the Pacific Clipper," she answered.

Looking at Ford, she saw she had his complete attention and continued. "Consider the following. The Clipper is a 314A, far and away the finest plane flying and a vast improvement over the original 314s. The Clipper is making her maiden flight to Auckland. This is big news and your itinerary was well publicized. Even if it was secret, the Japs would have know your route. Obviously, Commodore Tanaka knew when Pearl would be attacked He also knew there was no way the Clipper could get back to America on her regular return route. So where would you go if you decided to try for home?" Kathleen asked, looking at Ford.

Ford just looked at her. It was so obvious. Obvious if you bought her analysis. But could there be another explanation? Ford quickly went through the other possibilities and he knew she was right. "That has to be the explanation," Ford thought to himself. "With the regular way home denied us, only flying across this route gives us a chance. Tanaka could figure the Clipper's route from Auckland, knowing we'd go to Darwin first. After Darwin, Java, then Ceylon. He had us nailed all the way!

Ford sighed and looked at Kathleen. "It doesn't matter now that Tanaka is after the Clipper. We are almost to Trincomalee. There is no way he can bother us anymore and we have his commandos in tow so why worry," Ford questioned the Lt., hoping she had the same opinion. She didn't. She smiled at him then shook her head.

"I hope you're right Captain Ford. All I'm doing is explaining who Baron Tanaka was and who his nephew is. We have know about him for years in D.C. He was the head spy in Washington for the Japanese and we all knew it," she offered. And as the words left her mouth, the Lt. of US Naval Intelligence knew she had made a very dumb gratuitous comment.

Ford exploded. "Wait a minute. Are you telling us again that you knew something about this guy and didn't do anything about him?

Good Christ, what in the hell is having Naval Intelligence, the FBI, and the rest of you cloak and dagger guys if when you know something you can't do a goddamn thing about it or tell anybody. What kind of dumb bastards run our country! It seems the American Intelligence community knows who are the bad guys, what they are planning and didn't or wouldn't do a damn thing about it. Kathleen, I don't mean to holler at you but you're the only one here that seems to know what is going on and all I hear is 'we knew that the Japs were going to attack, but we don't know where or that this asshole Tanaka was spying all across the country and nobody did anything.' Don't you think that is strange or is that SOP in Washington? The rest of us just have to guess what happened when the shit hits the fan. I'm dumbfounded. You knew what Tanaka was doing, about his uncle's grand design that included long range bombers, and yet neither Naval Intelligence or the FBI bothered to tell Pan Am about this!"

Kathleen Elmes started at Ford as if she was about to hit him and she stopped, realizing that he was perfectly right. He should be angry but there were other things involved and as she was about to try an explain the "big picture" to him, she realized how stupid that would be. Here was a man trying as best he could to fly a plane across waters and lands no one had ever flown across before, being chased by an enemy he didn't know and all she could say was "well, we knew but!"

"I'm sorry Captain. You're right. It is inane that we who have information can't share it with the people that might be involved," Kathleen agreed. Picking up the piece of film, she turned and looked at the two Johns, then at Ford and shrugged.

Ford was looking at the Naval Intelligence Officer with a kind of "how in the world did I get myself into this" look. Then he took another deep breath and spoke. "Look, in a few hours we'll be in Trincomalee. We have Thu up here and the others in the hold and with any luck, we'll be rid of the bastards soon. We know that some super spy named after a nutty Baron who wanted to conquer the world is trying to capture the Clipper and bring her back to Japan where they would build heavy bombers to help them enslave all of us. Now, if I sound somewhat paranoid by all of this, you'll have to grant me that what we have been through the last few days isn't exactly on page one in the Pan Am pilots manual. So what are we really sure of? In a few hours, the sun will rise and it will be tomorrow. That is it. Where the goofy Commodore is I quite frankly don't give a damn. I'm tired of Tanaka memorials, smelly tennis shoes, little people running around in stinking sweat suits and, pardon me Kathleen, finding out that

Washington knew but couldn't tell for fear of hurting the feelings of the Japanese," Ford stated. Pausing, he looked at the rest.

"All I want is to be alone. So John and John, get to bed. Kathleen, thank you for all your help but I don't think there is anything further you can do. I'm going to fly for awhile and look at the stars and try to figure where we go from Trincomalee, assuming we get there," Ford turned and slid into his chair as the other three looked at him and left.

0530 hours-22 December 1941-Aboard the Pacific Clipper

Mack was worried. The sun was rising and he tried to shield his eyes as he looked for land. Nothing. He knew they were on the right course but Ceylon was an island and he was flying blind and getting goddamn fed up with the radio silence that Pan Am had imposed. "What the fuck do they know in New York about what we were going through? Who in hell would care if we radioed ahead to find out where in the Christ we are!" the First Officer asked himself. His checked his instruments again and waited for Ford to come up and take the controls. But it was John Steers who came out first from his navigator's cabin. Neither spoke. They looked out the cockpit windows and quietly enjoyed the magnificent sunrise over the Bay of Bengal. Like their crewmates, the two of them had never been in this part of the world. Even at this early hour, both were excited. A new day was about to begin, in an exotic land they had only vaguely heard about and it was impossible not to sense that combination of fear and curiosity that men feel when entering the unknown. And they had one other factor to figure in, they didn't have the vaguest idea of where in the hell they really were! Then Bob Ford came out of his tiny room onto the bridge. The two Johns just nodded to the Captain and he smiled back as he checked the instruments and stretched. He leaned against the back of his chair and as John Mack began to rise, Ford put his hand on the shoulder of his First Officer, telling him he still had the con. Ford just wanted to enjoy the sunrise. The three flyers enjoyed the spectacle in front of them, each with his own thoughts. Below, on the passenger level, the rest of the Pan Am crew also began to awake but in truth, the few hours any of them slept were fitful, all were tired. Ford finally stirred himself from the sunrise and touched John Steers on the shoulder. As the navigator turned, Ford spoke.

"John, I want no more surprises like we had coming into Surabaja. From now on, you or whomever you want will be in your little nook back there, scanning both the skies and the seas. Go below and get some breakfast and then line up your replacements so that at all times there is someone telling us what they see. It will be boring as hell, I know, but we're almost flying blind now and we need anything that will tip us to a problem, ahead or behind. Though I haven't the foggiest idea of what I'd do if you told me there were a bunch of Zero's on our tail!" Ford joked.

The three laughed and as Steers rose to go below for breakfast, Mack shifted seats and Ford moved into his pilot's chair. Like any good pilot, he assumed nothing and checked all the instruments. His only concern was their fuel supply and he knew, unless they had missed Ceylon by a thousand miles, they were in good shape. Soon they should pick up its shoreline, then follow it north to Trincomalee. They had used about two thirds of Oberfeldt's fuel Ford, checking their altitude saw that Mack had maintained their level at the usual 8000 feet. Ford decided to bring her down on the deck, not in the hope of saving fuel but just in case they missed the island!

"Wouldn't that be something!" Ford thought. "We jump over a sampan to get out of Surabaja, beat up the Jap commandos then run out of gas in the middle of the Indian Ocean," Ford thought to himself. Then he laughed out loud and he noticed John Mack's look. He was about to explain but he knew Mack already understood. So he pushed forward on the yoke and the Pacific Clipper responded easily as he gradually brought the plane down towards the water. In his mind he rationalized the lowering of their altitude as trying to save on gasoline but he realized that the lower they were to the water, the tougher it would be for the enemy to find them. And he knew, with six Japanese soldiers below, that the enemy was out there, looking for him and his plane. And he also understood, that from now on, the enemy wasn't just the commandos below, but everyone, no matter where they went. He thought of Sir Reginald Leach and realized again that the Pacific Clipper had become a "Golden Fleece." Wherever they landed, there would be people and governments that would try to capture her. Ford's naivete was ending. It was the Pacific Clipper against the world. Then he again laughed, knowing he was giving himself a pep talk, like a guy whistling in the dark as he walked past a dark alleyway. "And I'm just as afraid as that whistler," Ford admitted to himself.

Ford leveled off at fifteen hundred feet. The powerful Wrights purred as the Boeing sped at 160 knots, and to the crew, Shamus, Kathleen and Thu, they were literally skimming across the waves. It was exciting but most felt they had had their fill of such exhilaration.

John Steers climbed back up to the flight deck and entered his navigator's cabin. In a few seconds he came out with the binoculars around his neck. "Who have you lined up to spell you in the bubble?" Ford asked.

"Shamus asked if he could help and I told him I'd check with you. OK?" Steers responded. "I also asked Henny to lend a hand."

"Fine. You take the first hour, then Shamus and Henricksen can finish up," Ford answered. Steers nodded and went back into his room and began his scanning of the sky and the sea. About an hour had gone by and Steers was bored to death. He had seen nothing. The Bay of Bengal was empty; not a tanker, not a sampan, not even an outrigger canoe. He was about to go out of the room but decided to scan the sky once more. He gave it a full 360 degree turn and there were no planes anywhere. He focused on the sea and again saw nothing. But just as he pulled the glasses away from his eyes, something registered in his brain. He had seen a speck on the horizon, directly ahead. Quickly, he brought the glasses to his eyes and slowly rolled the focus knob. Straight ahead he saw it, just a speck but there was something on the water. As the Clipper sped towards the dot, Steers kept the glasses on the spot on the horizon. Now the dot became larger and took on a form, the form of a boat! And then the boat got bigger and bigger and suddenly John Steers' blood froze. Bursting out of his door, Steers startled Ford and Mack.

"Captain. Straight ahead. Twelve O'Clock. A boat. Looks like a submarine!" he reported. Standing between the two pilots, he pointed and the two nodded. There it was and even with the naked eye, they could see the boat was a submarine. Now the only question was whose. There was a British naval base at Trincomalee so it could be a friend but even with the binoculars, Steers couldn't make out any flag or insignia. The two Johns looked at Ford and wondered what he would do. They were on the deck and closing fast on the sub. Though the Pacific Clipper was the best plane in the world, it wasn't a fighter plane and she couldn't climb fast enough to escape if the sub was unfriendly and tried to fire on them.

Steers, with the glasses trained on her, began a running commentary. "There are men on the deck, with their shirts off, like they are getting a sun tan. They don't see us or if they do, they don't seem concerned. Probably can't hear us. They have nets over the sides, and some of the men are swimming. Jesus Christ. They're Japs, Its a Jap sub!"

Ford listened and when Steers identified the sub, he push ahead on the steering column and put the Clipper right on the water, fifty feet off the deck. Pushing the throttles forward, the Clipper quickly gained more air speed as he headed her right for the sub. 1000 yards... 500 yards and suddenly she shot right over the sub. Men were jumping into the water and diving onto the deck of sub, covering their heads with their arms. And as they flashed over the sub, Steers ran into his room and kept up his running commentary.

"Captain, men coming out from below, onto the deck, running to the deck gun. Looks like a five millimeter. What are you going to do?" Steers yelled.

Ford knew. The reason he buzzed the sub was to frighten the men on the deck and he kept the Clipper on the water, not veering from the straight line he'd taken going over the Japs. As an old trap shooter, he knew the toughest shot was straight on. With no angle, the gunners would have to try to bring them down with a tail shot. Good for fighter planes, not for subs. He had pushed the throttle forward some more. Now the Clipper was speeding across the surface of the water at 180 knots and the sub was quickly behind them. But a five millimeter canon shell can close that distance very easily. He waited for Steers to yell when he saw the explosion from the deck gun. The sub was bobbing in the water from the air wake the Clipper had left as she shot over so unless that gunner was Hawkeye, there was no chance he'd hit the Clipper. But you never knew.

"They've fired, Captain... .and again... and another!" Steers reported. Ford looked ahead and waited for the shells to explode. He felt totally calm, as if he were sitting above it all, Zeus like.

"There! Off to the left... Way too high," John Mack commented, his voice low and the words unhurried. "Another. Over to the right. Way off! They are trying to bracket us," Ford knew that if that gunners were any good, that third shot would be the one that could blow the Clipper out of the sky! "On the left, close but no cigar," Mack reported. Ford could see the burst and he veered slightly to his right, still skimming over the water. He didn't think the Japs had the range to hit them with a fourth shot and when Steers was silent, he brought the Clipper back to its original heading. One minute went by, then another and finally Steers' returned. No one spoke. Then Ford slowly began to throttle back and brought her off the deck, climbing to a higher altitude. Reaching over, Ford picked up the intercom and spoke.

"Barney, think you could rustle up some coffee for us? By the way, we just buzzed a Jap sub. And if any of you noticed the fireworks outside, just their way of saying hello," Ford reported. Then he looked at the two John and grinned!

The rest of the trip was uneventful. A couple of hours after the incident with the sub, they spotted the shoreline of Ceylon, turned north and headed for Trincomalee. Steers' continued to scan the sky for planes as they neared their destination. Then he saw it. Ahead on the left. He leaned into the cabin to tell them but saw that Ford and John Mack had already seen their next landing site and Steers let out a sign of relief. John Poindexter looked up from his radio console and grinned. Steers gave him the thumbs up sign and three of the men on the bridge relaxed as Bob Ford brought the Pacific Clipper into position to begin her landing on the waters of the harbor at Trincomalee, Ceylon.

Ford went through his check list with Mack echoing each point. Slowly the big plane began her decent straight at the center of the harbor. They were still a couple of miles out and as Ford dropped the ships altitude from 5000 down towards the water, Mack would read off the altitude every 500 feet. At 500 feet, Ford went to full flaps down and lifted the nose of the Clipper slightly. Ahead, they could see some British ships, one a battleship. There was no activity on the water which Steers found weird. But with a war on, maybe the British Navy felt secure with her ships tied up to the docks, trusting to the anti-aircraft battalions he could see along both sides of the harbor. But they were unmanned.

Suddenly, a motor launch appeared from behind the battleship. It looked like a Harbor Pilot's craft and the men on the deck assumed she was racing towards them to lead them to their docking area. Ford put the Clipper on the deck and gradually pushed her nose forward, the Clipper smoothly broke the waters of Trincomalee harbor. Ford let the great plane bounce a little as she sped down the water runway and then she began to slow. As gravity and the friction of the water against her hull helped, Ford reversed the engines and the Clipper came to a slow stop, riding easily in the water. The launch approached and a man in a British navy uniform was standing on its bow, a megaphone in hand, yelling something at the plane. Ford cut the port side engines and then pushed back the side of his cockpit window, leaning out to hear what the man was saying.

"Welcome to Trincomalee. Follow me. You have just landed in a mine field!"

Chapter 10

Trincomalee

The tension on the flight deck was palpable. No one spoke as the Pacific Clipper bobbed in the water. The back of Ford's neck was bright red and Steers and Poindexter could see it clearly from their seats behind the pilot. It took all of John Mack's self control to keep from sneaking a quick peer at the Captain. He knew if he did he'd break up laughing. Then he heard Ford muttering to himself and he could imagine what he was saying. Suddenly, Ford began laughing and the three breathed a sigh of relief and joined in. Even those below on the passenger level knew what had happened and hadn't said a word, also holding their breaths. When Ford's laughter was heard by them, they all broke into big grins. They had landed at Trincomalee, 3500 plus miles from Surabaja and hadn't hit a mine, yet!

"It's not funny so why am I laughing?" Ford thought. He tried to bring himself under control but when he looked at John Mack's face, he broke out laughing again. Mack's face was as white as his was red! Then Mack joined in and the two of them sounded like kids that had just raced through a graveyard and hopped the fence to the safety of the street.

"Can you believe this?" Ford began, addressing no one in particular. "Landing in a mine field! After what has already happened. What next? I wouldn't be surprised if that old battleship opened fire on us!" Taking a deep breath to regain his composure, Ford then leaned out the port window and yelled down to the man on the launch.

"Thanks for the warning. We'll follow you," The British officer saluted and climbed back into the cabin of the boat. Slowly the launch turned in front of the Clipper and moved cautiously back towards the battleship. Ford eased the throttle forward, using only the two outside engines, having cut the power to the port side ones. Gradually he maneuvered the Clipper so she was about fifty yards behind the stern of the British boat. They were proceeding very slowly when John Steers decided to give them a running commentary of where the mines were as he spotted them. "There's one at ten o'clock... pretty close, Captain. And another just ahead but further away... and another... Christ, their everywhere!" Mack turned in his chair and Steers got the message and shut up, It seemed like forever as they slowly maneuvered out of danger. Finally, a British sailor came out of the cabin back to the stern and waved, signaling they had cleared the minefield. As the launch picked up speed, Ford pushed the throttles forwards and the Clipper kept pace. Just past the stern of the battleship, Ford noticed a smaller harbor and the launch headed that way. Ford, the flight crew and those below relaxed for the first time in 22 hours!

As the Clipper came into the small cove, Ford could see that the launch was leading them towards a large buoy in the center of the water. He reduced the speed of the plane and she slowly came upon the buoy, a large red one sticking up about eight feet above the water. He leaned back and looked at John Steers and the navigator, without a word, turned and walked down the stairs to the anchor room. Once in, he popped open the hatch and grabbed the ten foot pole with the steel hook on the end. Leaning out the hatch, he swung the hook at the top of the buoy.

"Shit!" Steers' muttered to himself as he missed. Reaching again, he hooked the top of the buoy but as he pulled on the pole to bring the nose of the Clipper close, the steel hook came loose and hung on the buoy's nose. As the Clipper bobbed, the hook came free of the wooden pole, fell off the buoy and sank into the black water of the cove. "Goddamn it!" Steers' exploded. Now the Clipper was drifting away from the buoy and he had to do something quick. "Fuck it" he thought as he reached for the rope on the anchor room floor, grabbing the top of the hawser and climbed out of the hatch onto the Clipper's nose, Steers saw he was too far away to reach over and grab the buoy's top. "Oh, the hell with it," he thought as he jumped off the Clipper's nose onto the buoy. Grabbing the buoy around the neck with his left arm, he pulled the rope through the open hole and tied it to the bouncing buoy. As the buoy swayed hard to the left, then spun to the right, Steers' hung on and grabbed the rope with his right hand. But the buoy was wet and his body began to slide down. He pulled on the rope but that just brought the huge prow of the Clipper right at him. "Shit" the navigator yelled as he jumped into the water. As his head broke water and he sputtered, he saw John Parish securing the rope inside the anchor room and roaring with laughter. Steers was wet and embarrassed but the Clipper was docked and secured.

When Ford saw Steers' body flash out of the anchor room and land on the buoy, he just shook his head. When Steers' fell into the water. John Mack, standing and looking out Ford's port side window began laughing. But when Parish signaled that the Clipper was secure, Ford just heaved a sigh that could mean anything. Mack correctly interpreted it as a "what else can happen" gasp.

Below, the crew was busy preparing the ship for deplaneing and all, above and below, began to wonder what they were going to do with six Japanese commandos. The British launch had turned and come up to the nose of the Clipper and the officer in command had walked out to the bow and was hailing Ford.

"Captain, welcome to Trincomalee. Sorry it was a bit hairy. We didn't know you were coming or we would have warned you about the mines!" he yelled. Ford, leaning out the window, just nodded in understanding. He had cut the engines and the propellers on the two starboard engines were just ending their spinning so he waited until they completely stopped so he was sure the British commander could hear him. Now he spoke.

"Thank you, Lt. You were suppose to have been notified by the Dutch on Java or by your Ambassador in Batavia. No matter. We are here and delighted to be," Ford answered.

"How many are there of you?" the Englishman asked and his eyes opened wide as he saw John Steers pull himself out of the water and climb onto the port sponson. He peered at the navigator and then back at Ford and was about to ask what happened but thought better of it. "Yanks," he muttered to himself.

"Ten crew members, three passengers and six Japanese commandos." Ford answered casually. The British officer looked at him and shook his head. The American in the white uniform climbing out of the water had shaken him and he was sure he didn't hear the pilot's answer correctly. Something about Japanese commandos. He knew how the Americans enjoyed a good practical joke and he didn't want to be the butt of one.

"I'm sorry, Captain. I misunderstood you. I thought you said you had six Japanese commandos on board," the officer laughed, nervously. "You did not say Japanese commandos, did you?" he asked, hopefully and somewhat incredulously.

Ford laughed. "Its a long story Captain. Yes, we do have six prisoners, Japanese commandos. I'll tell you all about it when we get to shore. How do you want to handle this?" the pilot asked.

The Captain of the launch just shook his head again and, putting his hand up to signal Ford to wait, he climbed back into the cabin, picked up radio mike and began talking to someone. Ford turned to John Mack and smiled.

"If I know that cat, he's calling his commanding officer telling them that some crazy Americans are pulling his leg about some Japanese commandos aboard their plane. I'd think that way myself!" Ford commented. "I'd like you to stay on board. I'll go in with the others to begin making arrangements for gasoline and maybe hotel rooms for all of us. Keep the engineers with you. Give her a major inspection. The Clipper has done her job, beautifully," Ford instructed

"Ok, Bob. We'll give the bird a good going over," the Second Officer responded. "You staying on the Clipper tonight?"

"Probably unless the hotel is something special, which I doubt." Ford answered. "Maybe Shamus has connections here and he'll put something together for the crew,"

As Mack was about to respond, the British officer came out onto the deck and hailed the Clipper.

"Captain, The Port Commander requests that no one leave until he can send out a prison boat to take the prisoners. Do you need any help with the Japanese?" the officer asked?

Ford thought for a moment and decided no. "Let's wait until the guards arrive and we'll do everything at once. How does that sound to you?" Ford asked.

"Makes sense, Sir. I'll move the launch up by the passenger door when you signal for us," he answered and saluted. John Mack went below to the passenger level to organize the departure of those that would leave the Clipper first.

After Mack told them to gather their things to spend the night off the Clipper, the group split up and the men picked up their shaving kits and extra basics like shorts and undershirts while only Kathleen Elmes had decisions to make, which she did quickly, bringing just slacks, a blouse and flats to change into. She doubted they'd be going out to any place where more formal attire would be required. Then she had second thoughts. In Surabaja, while Ford and John Mack had visited with Shamus, she'd been given a ride into the downtown area by one of his drivers and bought some dresses, native clothes she wanted to have just to remind her of their adventure. One was a "Dragon Lady" silk dress, black with crimson trimming and the slit up the side that ran up to her thighs. She was tempted to take it and wear it, if just to shake up the crew. Hanging next to it was a lovely sari, gold lame with a matching sheer silk shawl that looked more than suitable for a Rani. Depending on where they were going tonight, she'd either be casual in slacks or native in the sari. Leaving the Master Suite with her clothes in her small carrying case, she glanced at Major Thu tied into his seat. Suddenly it dawned on her that he was probably going to spend the rest of the war in prison. And the thought did not disquiet her for a moment! Smiling, she looked at the Major and in a mocking manner, bowed. Then standing erect, she flipped her head so her blond hair swirled about her neck and, throwing her shoulders back, walked away down the aisle towards the rest of the group. She could feel the eyes of Thu burning into her back and it felt great!

To Ford's surprise, and probably the British, the departure from the Clipper went smoothly and the prison boat from the Revenge easily handled the transfer of the Japanese prisoners. Ford took special delight standing at the exit as Major Thu walked past him, in handcuffs. Thu did not look at him and Ford was about to say something, like "nice try" but he held his tongue, feeling no comment was more of a put down than anything he could say. And as the Japanese left his ship, Ford felt almost the same relief as he did when he pulled the Clipper out of her death dive.

"Good grief! We're are only a few days out of Auckland and already we've been in a barroom brawl, almost shot down in Java, attacked by Japanese commandos and land in a mine field. And there is still some twenty thousand miles to go! What can happen next?" the pilot though to himself. "And now I've got to find 4000 gallons of high octane and figure how we'll get to Karachi without any goddamn maps or charts or radio," he groaned to himself. With a sigh, he moved away from the exit as the British captain had come on board and introduced himself as Lt. Smythe. He smiled a wicked grin as he shook Ford's hand, both of them thinking about the Clipper's landing in the mine field. Then the Lt.'s eyes caught sight of Kathleen Elmes and as his jaw dropped, Bob Ford began to laugh to himself.

"Lt. Smythe, may I introduce Lt. Kathleen Elmes of the United States Navy. Although she is in mufti, she is a member of Naval Intelligence. The Lt. was a passenger with us flying to Auckland when we got the news about Pearl Harbor. Kathleen, Lt. Smythe of His Majesty's Royal Navy," Ford smiled as he introduced the two. He was thoroughly enjoying the British officer's perplexed state but felt a sudden twinge of jealousy and he wondered why.

Recovering quickly, Lt. Smythe saluted Kathleen then offered his hand. Kathleen took it hand, and smiled. Smythe knew his mouth was open but he couldn't close it. Kathleen, enjoying his distress but not wanting to embarrass him further, smile and released his hand as she swept by him towards the door and out to the sponson, where Barney stood to take her by the elbow and escort her onto the British launch. He beamed a very proud, fatherly smile and as Lt. Smythe followed, Barney's grin quickly changed and the young British officer understood that he better behave when with the beautiful Intelligence Officer or he'd have to answer to the very formidable looking steward, and probably the rest of the plane's crew.

1330 hours-22 December 1941-Tanaka to Tokyo

The plane left the runway at Okinawa, headed for Tokyo. The pilot was bored to death. He glanced over at his co-pilot, Lt. Ohura and envied him his youth and enthusiasm. It wasn't often that a junior officer had the opportunity to be part of what they both knew to be an important assignment. To a transport pilot like Captain Elko, the first part of the journey was exciting. Flying to Kota Bharu from Guam with all those ranking officers aboard was the stuff of what junior officers dreamed. Then the unexpected, sudden realization that there was no American super plane waiting, the quick departure by the brass, the order to return to Kota and pick up Commodore Tanaka and now, here he was with only the Commodore aboard. Elko was far too low in the pecking order of ranking officers to have what was happening explained to him but it didn't take four stripes on your sleeve to know the illustrious Tanaka screwed up. If that were so, then Tanaka could only be reporting to the High Command and that probably meant Admiral Yamamota... maybe even General Tojo! The Commodore was the nephew of Baron Giichi Tanaka and the son of Count Tanaka, the Emperor's closest friend and in Japan, the Tanakas talked only to the Hirohitos who talk only to Buddha! Elko smiled at his small joke. He had no idea how close he was to the reality of Japanese life at that level.

Commodore Tanaka sat in the passenger part of the ten seat, twin engine Mitsubishi transport, a lone crewman sitting in the back. And Isodecki Tanaka was alone with his thoughts. He had ignored the fake pleasantries of his fellow officers on the trip to Guam. He knew they were delighted in his apparent failure and although not one word issued from any of their lips on the trip, he knew. Now his idea of striking the Pacific Clipper down when she landed in New York had to be solidified before he saw Tojo. He was well aware that when he had his audience, all the negatives about the failed mission would have been given to the Prime Minister. Some enemies of his uncle still existed and they would do what ever they could to discredit him, and through him, the memory of Baron Tanaka.

The hours in flight from Guam to Okinawa were some of the most frustrating he'd ever known. When the smirking ship captains had left him in Guam, he knew that their reports would be on the way to Tokyo and he also knew that Ford and the Pacific Clipper were far ahead of him. He had prepared a plan for the Prime Minister and the key was simple... to beat Ford to New York. If he could show Tojo that destroying the Pacific Clipper in the very shadow of the Statue of Liberty would shake the Americans as Pearl Harbor had done, he'd get the necessary support to have a plane ready to help him fly across Alaska, Canada and into New York.

The thought of New York suddenly brought back memories of his favorite city in the world. The museums, the restaurants--the finest in the world, Fifth Avenue, the women--the most glamorous anywhere. Nowhere in the world was there a city of such variety and excellence. "And what a place to send the message... that we in Japan can destroy anything you have, no matter where or when!"

The Commodore's excitement stimulated him. He stretched in his chair. For the first time, he noticed the crewman sitting in the rear and nodded for him to come forward. Tanaka told the young airman he'd eat now and the man scurried back to the small galley up in back of the plane. "Ok, Isodecki. Enough of what will happen in New York. You've had one shot at capturing the Pacific Clipper. And that failed. Now you better come up with something that will make that history," The big man sat back and began to plot his approach that he would use to sell the Prime Minister and the others that he needed to back him in his continuing pursuit of the Pacific Clipper.

1400 hours-22 December, 1941-the Royal Arms Hotel-Trincomalee, Ceylon.

The morning was behind him and Ford, sitting with Shamus and John Mack in the cool of the lobby hotel enjoyed these few quiet moments. After checking in and taking ten rooms for the crew and Kathleen, Ford began to relax. The place was a flea bag but according to Lt. Smythe, the best hotel in Trincomalee. Ford had already decided he'd stay on the Clipper but Shamus was working on getting them a special evening of dinner and partying at a most interesting house of a friend. Ford didn't care. His concern was fuel. The British attache that had greeted them when the launch docked assured him that there was 100 octane gas available for the Clipper. The problem was getting it into the Clipper's tanks. There were no docking facilities where she could berth and there were no gasoline pumps anywhere close enough where they could fill her up. And although the gas or petrol as the British called it was available, it was in cans. Four gallon cans!

"John, I think the best way to fill up the Clipper is to have a Chinese fire drill, the barge with the gas cans moved out to the ship and we load her just like they put out fires in those Westerns where the barn is burning and the school marm is trapped. With the cans being passed from hand to hand up to the fuel tanks and poured in!" Ford stated.

"That's one thousand cans of gas, Bob. Christ. That could take a day. Can it be done?" John Mack asked.

"Doesn't make any difference. We have to do it. And unless someone can come up with a pumping system that will get the job done, I can't see how we can refuel her without the Chinese fire drill!" Ford responded. The other two looked at the pilot and finally both nodded.

A waiter came over to where they were sitting to see if they wanted a drink but Shamus signaled with a shake of his head that they would pass. As the waiter turned to go, movement on the stairs leading down from the mezzanine level caught their eyes and coming down them was Kathleen Elmes. She had changed into her slacks and blouse and looked unbelievably cool, even in the equatorial heat of Ceylon. The three men stood as she approached and John Mack stood behind one of the chairs, holding it for her. When she sat, the other three did the same and the waiter came back to see if she wanted anything. Kathleen ordered a ginger ale and the three men decided to join her. As the waiter left, she smiled at them and announced that her room was surprisingly clean and comfortable. It should have been. Shamus had made arrangements for her to have what passed in Trincomalee for the Presidential Suite.

The small talk continued. As the waiter brought them the drinks, a British officer came into the lounge. Looking around, he spotted the Americans and approached. Saluting, he addressed Bob Ford.

"Captain Ford. Captain Loud of His Majesty's ship Revenge requests the presence of you, Lt. Elmes, First Officer Mr. Mack and Mr. Ginsberg as his dinner guests tonight aboard the Revenge. I'm Lt. Skates and I'll be your escort to the Revenge if you can join the Captain," the young officer stated.

"Thank you, Lt. Please join us," Ford said standing. The British officer nodded his thanks to Ford and sat.

"That is very considerate of your Captain. What time would he expect us? We have some work ahead of us getting our plane refueled but if we can, speaking for all of us, I'm sure we'd be delighted to join him aboard the Revenge," Ford responded to the invitation. The other three nodded their agreement.

"Captain Loud told me to leave the time for dinner open, knowing of your refueling schedule. By the way, the petrol you requested is waiting on the docks. The men wish to know how you want it delivered to your plane," the officer asked.

"We need it brought out to the plane on a barge or a boat that can be anchored next to the Clipper," Ford asked.

"We can make arrangements to get you a barge that can tie up to your plane and be big enough to carry the cans of petrol," Lt. Skates answered. "By the way, am I correct in stating that you need 4000 gallons of petrol?"

"That's right, Lt. 4000 gallons! And since the petrol we need is only available in your four gallon cans, if my math is any good, that means we need one thousand cans of it!" Ford explained. "We want to leave Trincomalee tomorrow morning so that means we have to do it this afternoon. We can't do it at night, not without lighting the area around the plane and that would mean a perfect target for the Japs. By the way, we flew over a Jap sub earlier this morning coming into Trincomalee," Ford stated. Lt. Skates almost spit out the ginger ale he had in his mouth when Ford mentioned the Jap sub.

"What did you say? A Japanese sub, here, near Trincomalee? My God, I better report this to headquarters! The Captain should know about this. He might want to weigh anchor and go find her. He's itching to get the Revenge out to sea and go after the enemy. This might be a good enough reason. Where did you see the sub?" Lt. Skates asked, excitedly.

"About three hours from here. She was steering the same course we were towards Trincomalee but we have no idea of where she went when we left her behind us.' John Mack answered. "We buzzed her and she fired three rounds at us but where she is now, I have no idea."

"A Japanese sub in the Bay of Bengal. His Highness will love to hear of this," the British officer responded excitedly. Looking at the surprised expression on the faces of the Americans when he said, "His Highness" the British officer explained. "Oh, I'm sorry. Sometimes we refer to Captain Loud that way. You understand. It is done with affection. I'll want to report this information right away. I have no idea how he'll react but I'm guessing the Captain will want to weigh anchor right away and dinner on the Revenge might be canceled."

Rising, the British officer saluted and began to move towards the door. John Mack followed and the two talked about the refueling arrangements as Kathleen and Ford headed for the dock at the hotel where Lt. Smythe and his launch waited to return them to the Clipper. Shamus excused himself to call a friend. A few minutes later he came to the launch with news that should they wish, his friend would love to have the whole crew out to his house for dinner. Shamus assured Ford and Kathleen it would be an evening they would long remember.

John Mack had gone with Lt. Skates to arrange for the 100 octane to be taken to the Clipper. Walking past the loading area, he spotted huge, empty oil drums back of a shed. Mack picked out four of the 500 gallon size and some British soldiers cleaned them out for him. Putting them on the barge, the soldiers filled them from the petrol pumps near a small loading area, far too confined for the Clipper to be able to approach. Then he and Lt. Skates went over to where the Base fire trucks were and talked to one of the men on duty. When Mack explained what he wanted to do, the man quickly got four long rubber hoses, fifty feet in length, about two inches in diameter, unscrewed the nozzles on each and placed the hoses on the barge. Then riding out to the Clipper with Mack, the soldier from the fire department, named Charlie, supervised the refueling of the Pacific Clipper. Mack, Swede Rothe, John Parish and Mr. Brown opened up the mouths of the four gas tanks for the four engines. Charlie put the open end of one hose in each of the 500 gallon drums and climbing up on the wing of the Clipper, began the siphoning process from each of the drums to each of the engines. Twenty minutes later, the Pacific Clipper was refueled!

Now Ford could leave at any time. Jim Henricksen had been taken to the British hospital on the base and had his head sewn up with 22 stitches. The doctor pronounced him fit to fly. So everyone was on board but it was nearing evening time and if they left now, they would be flying at night all the way to Karachi. Or they could spend the night at anchor. Going to Shamus' friends home in Trincomalee for a special dinner was one option. They had seen the Revenge weigh anchor to search for the Jap sub, so dinner aboard her was out. They had been under tremendous pressure since leaving Auckland and deserved a night of relaxation. So he told the crew they would spend the night in Trincomalee. The news was most welcomed.

He hadn't decided on whether to stay aboard the Clipper or join the rest at Shamus' friends house. The experience with Thu made him lean towards staying on the plane but he decided to at least enjoy the visit to this "special" house. Kathleen Elmes smiled when informed the Captain would be joining them. Although he was fit to fly, Jim Henricksen decided to stay aboard. John Poindexter also passed so those two would guard the Clipper. Captain Loud of the Revenge had detailed two British Tommies to be on board for protection. Lt. Smythe's launch brought out the soldiers and took the rest back to the hotel to change and get ready for the evening. All of the men had taken a clean set of their whites into the hotel earlier so after getting there, a quick shave and changing, they all assembled in the lobby to see what their beautiful passenger had decided to wear for the evening.

As they were having drinks and seated around a couple of tables in the lobby, Kathleen swept down the ornate staircase in her gold and yellow sari to join them. She did indeed look like royalty. The few guests sitting in the lobby of the hotel nodded approvingly and smiled as her traveling companions applauded her entrance. With broad grins on the faces of the men and Kathleen smiling in enjoyment, the Pacific Clipper group headed for the waiting taxis to go out to Shamus' friend's establishment. The two Johns, Mack and Steers joined Ford, Kathleen and Shamus in one cab while the other six piled into the second. The cars were similar to the large, comfortable cabs that Londoners used and both groups had ample room. The Americans settled back to enjoy the ride. It was evening time and the late rays of the sun bounced off the Bay of Bengal to illuminated the beautiful tea plantations that rimmed both sides of the river they followed towards their destination. No one spoke and the few minutes of quiet left each with their own thoughts. Finally, John Steers broke the respite, asking the driver the name of the river they were paralleling.

"The Mahaweli, Sir," the driver replied. "It is one of our major rivers and flows from the mountains hundreds of miles away to the harbor here. In the rainy season, the river floods all the lands you see but the way we plant and grow our tea and other crops, they are all are safe when the monsoons she attack."

No one commented and they sat back and enjoyed the view of a part of the world that none had ever seen. The land was lush with dark rich soil, the low hills gradually rising from the river in layered levels of small green shrubs and black dirt, showing that the planters were very aware of soil conservation. John Mack asked the driver where the name Ceylon came from. The driver just shrugged his shoulders and shook his head.

Shamus Ginsberg did. "From what I've been told, the Portuguese came here four centuries ago and they called the land Ceilao. Then the Dutch a century later put their flag over the land and called it Ceilon. Then when the British took over, they just changed the pronunciation to what we call it today," the innkeeper commented.

"I remember reading something about Ceylon in an Asian history course I took in college," John Steers interjected. "The only reason I recall it was that the professor said that King Solomon sent his people here to some fabled city called the City of Gems to get jewels for the Queen of Sheba. Can you believe that?"

"Come on, John. Solomon and Sheba? Sounds like a C.B. DeMille movie," Ford interjected. "Please, Ceylon has to be 5000 miles from Palestine. How in the world would Solomon's people get here?"

"Actually, Captain Ford," Kathleen Elmes joined in. "What we call Ceylon today was known by both the Greeks and Romans as the island of Taprobone. It was noted on maps of Alexander the Great's when he moved into Asia Minor to continue his conquest of the world. Later, Roman emperors from Octavius to Caesar Augustus even to Constantine knew of the island and had their galleys visit here. So there is no doubt that if King Solomon wanted gems for the Queen of Sheba, he could have sent his ships here. Didn't they teach you anything at Wisconsin?" the Lt. explained, laughing and silencing the Captain. The rest sat back and watched the sundown.

Finally, Shamus spoke. "For centuries, the Arabs mariners have sailed to Ceylon and they called the land Serendip, meaning Land of Delights. In Hindu, it is Sri Lanka, meaning Resplendent Land. And sometime past, an English writer sailing to Ceylon heard of the Indian name for the land, Serendip and instead calling it the Land of Delights, he named it "unexpected delights" and coined the phrase "serendipity."

"Isn't the word serendipity derived from the Persian fairy tale "The Three Princes of Serendip?" Ford asked, much to the surprise of Kathleen Elmes and the rest of the riders. And as they looked at him, he responded. "Yes, Lt. Elmes. At Wisconsin they did teach us more than Engineering, Physics and Math. We were also schooled in the Liberal Arts," the Captain of the Pacific Clipper intoned. Then he sat back in the taxi.

As they all looked at each other and nodded that they were impressed, Ford laughed. "I have to admit that I did sleep through some of those courses and if the truth be told, my father is a history buff, especially about ancient civilizations, so growing up, I often heard he and his colleagues talking about Asia, the Middle East and Africa. In fact, when I looked at the atlases Bill Mullahey stole for us, many of the names of the countries and cities were already very familiar to me. So deciding to come this way wasn't all that difficult since I felt as if I already knew something about the geography and history of this part of the world. Unfortunately, Dad's group never talked about winds, weather and the tides in the countries out here. Or where we'd find 100 plus octane."

"What did your father teach at Wisconsin?" John Mack asked.

"Political Science. Still does," Ford answered.

"How did you get into flying, Captain?" Shamus asked.

Ford shook his head and demurred. "Lets just enjoy the time we have on the land and this lovely evening."

But Kathleen Elmes wasn't going to be put off. Even as John Steers shook his head in warning, knowing what a private person the Captain was, she plunged in.

"Please Captain. I'm dying to know. Please tell us," she begged. Ford was embarrassed and reluctant but he figured that she'd keep after him all night so he relented.

"Waldo Pepper," Ford said.

They all waited for more and finally he explained.

"He was barnstorming throughout the midwest and came to Wisconsin. I took off from school to see him when his show came to Madison. That was it. From that day on, all I ever wanted to be was a pilot," Ford stated in typical brevity. But Kathleen Elmes wasn't finished and peppered him with questions until Ford laughed and answered her questions, and as it seemed, she was speaking for the other three as well.

"The University's Engineering school was one of the few in the country to begin courses in Aeronautical Engineering. And because my father was a member of the faculty, by the time I had finished high school, I knew the whole Engineering school's staff. After graduating, I was tempted to join the Army and become a pilot. Billy Mitchell was a hero of mine. The travesty of his court marshall made him a hero to all of us that loved flying. The General is a Wisconsinite and the Dean of Engineering knew him well so he set me up to visit him at his offices in Milwaukee. He talked me out of the military, saying with my education, I should go into commercial flying where the real research and development in aviation was taking place. He arranged for an interview with Pan Am in Chicago and they hired me. That's it," Ford concluded and as Kathleen began to ask for more details, Ford was saved when the driver told them they had arrived.

Looking out the cab windows, they saw that Shamus' friend's place was a one story house, sitting on a knoll over looking the river. As they stepped out of the taxis, the door opened and a huge man, well over six foot, weighing at least 250 pounds stepped out. He was dressed in the soft white pants and shirt of the natives but his bejeweled vest and the jewels on his fingers indicated he was more than just a local home owner. He walked over to them, smiling in greeting and then, picking up Shamus in his arms, kissed him on both cheeks. Putting the innkeeper down, he bowed to Kathleen, taking her left hand and kissed it. Straightening and walking over to Ford, he introduced himself.

"I am A.B.E. Winjaym. Abe to my friends. Welcome to Jafa, my humble establishment. Captain Ford, you do me a great honor to come to my home. It is indeed a memorable moment in my life to have as guests the pilot and crew of the world's most glamorous plane, the Pacific Clipper. And Miss Elmes!" their host paused, and looking at Shamus, he shook his head in mild rebuke.

"Shamus Ginsberg, my old friend, why did you tell me she was only beautiful! Roses are beautiful. Sunsets are beautiful. But beautiful is almost banal to describe Miss Elmes. She is exquisite!" the giant man proclaimed. Smiling, he turned and placed Kathleen's right arm on his left one and the two led the group into the house.

And what a house! From the outside there seemed to be just one level but upon entering, the Americans saw that the house stretched far back and there were stairways that led down to lower levels. The floors were of dark wood, mahogany and the ceiling was beamed, each bean at least two feet wide and the edges tipped in ivory. Throw rugs of obvious Persian quality were strewn across the shining floors and the furniture in what was the living room matched the beamed ceiling only this time, the wood edged ivory chairs. Huge sofas, with silk cushions for backs and seats bracketed a seven foot throw run, the skin of a leopard with the head facing out towards the room. A fireplace to the left was wide and tall enough so the whole crew could have stood inside it and not touched either side. A fire roared in it and over the mantle was mounted the pelt of a tiger, so large that the great cat had to have been ten feet long when alive and stalking in his forest. The steps and banisters of the twin stairways were also of ivory, without any carpeting and they led down to a dining room of stunning richness. More ivory, gold appointments and a grandfather clock whose face was studded with sapphires, emeralds and rubies. And as the Americans reached the floor, waiters surrounded them with hors de overs and drinks. There were no other guests in the house and it was apparent that Shamus' friends establishment was his home!

The evening was a treat for the crew and their host seemed to enjoy himself even more than his guests. After a few minutes of small talk, the crew members began to wander around the house, marveling at the jeweled plates and trays, the gold and silver services and vases that probably would rival anything from the Ming dynasty. Abe had told them he was a jewel dealer and collector. And the accumulation he had in his home led them to believe he must be the wealthiest man in Ceylon. The dinner was spectacular and afterwards, he led them all out through tall French doors to a terrace lit by blazing torches spaced around the periphery of the patio. Waiters brought around a wide selection of after dinner drinks, cigars and cigarettes. While the front of his house faced the river, from the veranda, the crew of the Clipper could see Trincomalee down in the distance and the Bay of Bengal. Although it was just a few days before Christmas and the evening was late, the temperature was mild and very comfortable.

Ford stood near the patio, looking down at Trincomalee while talking to Swede Rothe and John Parish. It was shop talk. As Shamus and Abe approached, the two engineers excused themselves.

"A magnificent view, don't you agree Captain Ford?" the big man stated. "I never tire of it and will often take my dinner out here alone, just to enjoy Allah's handiwork," The three of them just gazed out at the water and the city below. Then Kathleen Elmes and John Mack walked over to join them. As they arrived, she heard Ford telling their host he wanted to leave early tomorrow.

"Why do you want to leave so early, Captain Ford?" Kathleen asked. "After visiting this beautiful home, I'd love to have the time to see the mines where these fabulous gems came from."

"Actually, Kathleen, our stones come from pits, not mines. The workers stand in the mud holes with baskets, dip them in the mud and then sift by swirling the baskets until the mud runs out. Then, hopefully, some raw gems will be there. If there are, the worker calls the supervisor over and he takes the minerals to the office. Then when enough are accumulated, they are brought to a processing room where they are cleaned, buffed and cut. Then people like me come and buy at auction those stone we want," the jewel merchant explained. "In his travels, Marco Polo came to Ceylon. He wrote in his journal about "from muddy waters comes incredible beauty... 'rubies, sapphires, topazes, amethysts, garnets," The recovery process is basically the same today as it was 700 years ago when the great voyager came this way."

Winjaym's story had captured at attention of all his guests and there was a moment of silence before conversations began again. Ford, looking at his watch decided it was time to go. Thanking their host for his kindness, Ford shook hands with the jewel merchant and the rest of the crew did the same. Kathleen kissed the giant on his cheek to express her appreciation for a fabulous evening. Shamus came over and shook hands and whispered something in his ear. The big man laughed and put his arm around the innkeeper's shoulder. He and Shamus went around the side of the house while the members of the Clipper and Kathleen walked back through the villa for one last look at his marvelous home. The crew got into their cab while Ford, the two Johns and Kathleen waited for Shamus and Abe to join them. As they approached, Wijjy, Shamus's nickname for him, put out his hand again to Ford.

"I'm sorry you must leave so early. But from what Shamus has told me, it has been quite a busy day. So I'll wish you God's speed and his protection as you try for home. And Kathleen, maybe Allah in his infinite generosity will bring you back to Trincomalee so I can show you our lovely island," Taking her hand, he kissed it, ushered her into the cab, then turned and shook hands with Ford, the two John's and hugged Shamus. As the cabs rolled down the driveway, they looked back and waved goodby. The drive back to town was quick and quiet.

Entering the hotel lobby, some of the crew headed for the bar and a nightcap while others went to their rooms. Ford still hadn't made up his mind about spending the night on the Clipper and when the others asked him to join them for a drink, he passed. He saw Kathleen walk out the door that led to the garden in back of the hotel and decided it was time to set things right between them. Watching her walk out into the garden, alone, gave Ford the chance to speak to her. He walked out the same door and saw her about twenty yards ahead, on a stone path that led towards a gate at the back. When his leather soled shoes crunched on the stones, she turned and seeing it was him, smiled. She waited for him and when he reached her side, neither spoke. Looking out, they could see the harbor and the empty dock area where the Revenge usually berthed. The moon shone bright on the harbor and the Bay and the fragrance of the flowers and shrubs around them lent an almost enchanted feeling to the evening. There was no movement of anything in the harbor and they could see the Clipper in her cove, resting easily. And Ford began to laugh.

"What is so funny?" Kathleen asked.

"Looking at the Clipper at her mooring reminded me of John Steers and his problems trying to hook up the Clipper to that buoy. Did you see him?" Ford asked.

"Well I wondered why he was dripping wet when I saw him before we deplaned. What happened?" she asked.

Ford recounted the foibles of his Second Officer trying to secure the Clipper and they both had a good laugh. Ford nodded at the path that led out towards a wide grass field and they walked in silence along it until they came to field. The moonlight lit the area and as the two stood there, Ford commented.

"Looks like a couple of football fields but it is laid out like a baseball diamond," he said.

"Probably a cricket field or polo. The British are big on both," Kathleen commented.

"You're probably right. I'll bet that on Saturday, with their tea and crumpets, they gather for a jolly good time watching the games," Ford commented, continuing with the small talk. Then taking a breath, wondering why he felt nervous, the Captain of the Clipper continued.

"Look, I've wanted to talk to you to tell you that I'm sorry about the way I've been towards you. I mean, when you tried to explain about Pearl Harbor... although, I guess no one could explain about that, and then at the Ambassador's in Auckland, and... what I'm trying to say is that... " and he stopped as Kathleen put her finger over his lips and silenced him. He looked at her in the midnight moonlight and seconded Wijjy's comment that 'she was exquisite.'

"There is no need for that, Bob Ford. I understand. Is there a Mrs. Bob Ford domiciled somewhere back home? A fiance? Or concubines stashed across the Pacific in all your ports of call?" Kathleen asked, laughingly.

"No to the first two questions and I see that you have been listening to the two Johns and probably Mullahey about the parties in New Zealand," Ford laughed. "Errol Flynn couldn't live up to the stories about me but I can assure you, while I'm no monk, I do enjoy the company of bright, articulate women and if they happen to be pleasing to the eye, so much the better. And since we are asking, is there a Mister Kathleen Elmes back home?"

"Yes," And Bob Ford's heart sank.

"His name is Cliff and he teaches Math at UVA... the University of Virginia. Like your father, a professor," Kathleen commented. "It was his interest in word games like crossword puzzles and theories of probability that got me into cryptography. Even as a little girl, I couldn't wait for him to come home so we could work on the Sunday New York Times's puzzles," Kathleen explained, smiling at Ford.

His total befuddlement made her laugh out loud.

"Cliff is my Father," she explained. And Ford felt great! He didn't say a word but looked at her, relaxing a little. Kathleen looked at him, smiled and then put her hand in his and turned back towards the path to the hotel. Entering the gate, they turned to look back at the Bay and the Clipper at her anchorage. But Ford only glanced at his plane. He couldn't keep his eyes off Kathleen. He wanted to refocus, to clear his mind and get control of his feeling. He looked out at his ship and tried mightily to concentrate on the problems that still faced him trying to get home but suddenly, he knew it was useless. Kathleen seemed to sense his quandary and laughed. Ford looked down at her and grinned. Leaning her head against his chest, she squeezed his hand and together they walked back to the hotel and Bob Ford knew he wouldn't be spending this night aboard the Pacific Clipper.

0555-23 December, 1941- the harbor at Trincomalee

Lt. Smythe arrived with the patrol boat at the small dock in back of the hotel to pick up the rest of the members of the crew, Kathleen and Shamus. A half hour earlier, he had delivered Bob Ford, John Mack and Barney Swacki to the Clipper. The sun was just rising and the crew felt the cold as the boat sped across the water towards the waiting plane. As the pilot slowed, one of the British seamen climbed out and walked to the prow, holding a rope. Standing on the boarding sponson was John Poindexter and he caught the rope the seaman tossed to him. The boat pilot cut his motor and the craft slowly drifted towards the Clipper. Another seaman stood on the port side and as the boat neared the Clipper, he pushed against the nose of the plane so the two didn't touch. Poindexter secured the rope to the hook on the sponson and assisted Kathleen off the boat and into the plane. Shamus and the rest followed. John Parish relieved Poindexter and unhooked the rope and held it as the two British soldiers left the Clipper and boarded the boat, turning and saluting the ship. Parish tossed the rope back to the seaman. He then secured the door and now the Clipper could leave whenever Bob Ford wanted to. Barney had coffee ready and was taking breakfast orders, which he'd serve after they reached cruising altitude. Danish and donuts were available.

Ford was in his chair as John Steers climbed up the stairs to the flight deck, Poindexter behind him. Kathleen and Shamus checked on the condition of Jim Henricksen who told them he was fine. Giles

Brown, the Boeing Tech Rep, came by to see how his patient was doing and both Kathleen and Shamus commented that they hadn't seen much of him at the party or the hotel. He just smiled and went forward to the galley to get some coffee. Shamus and Kathleen looked at each other and shrugged. G. Brown was a quiet person, kept pretty much to himself. But Kathleen had noticed whenever she was ashore he would always seem to be in the neighborhood. She was glad he wasn't around last night! Or was he?

Shamus did not like the Boeing man and he was hard put to explain why. He had a queasy feeling that G. Brown was not what he professed to be. But it wasn't any of his business and as long as he didn't bother him, he'd not bother the Tech Rep.

Ford looked out his port side window down at Lt. Smythe standing on the deck of his boat. The sun had risen and another beautiful day for flying was theirs. Ford was ready. It was now 0630 AM and he wanted to be on his way to Karachi. The flight check had been completed and now he started the engines of the great plane. As Engine One roared to life, the British officer saluted Ford and moved back into the cabin. His boat turned and sped ahead about one hundred yards and waited. Engine Three kicked in, then Number Two and finally Number Four. Ford allowed the Wrights to idle before pushing the throttles forward to rev them up. The Clipper rocked easily in the water and John Mack looked at Ford, awaiting his nod to lower the flaps. Ford nodded and the huge plane slowly inched forward towards the patrol boat and maintaining their interval, Lt. Smythe led the Clipper out of the cove and across the mouth of the harbor, headed for the area where the Revenge had been docked. Then turning to the starboard, she moved more rapidly, parallel to the mine field. Ford followed in the wake until Lt. Smythe turned hard to port and stopped. The waters were clear and ahead lay the opening into the Bay of Bengal.

Pushing forward on the throttles, Ford poured the high octane gas to the four Cyclones and the Clipper shot down her watery runway. As they passed the British launch, Ford saw Lt. Smythe and his crew standing at attention, saluting the Clipper and wishing her safe passage. John Mack returned his salute for the whole crew and Ford, pulling back in the yoke, brought the Clipper free of the grasp of the water. The plane roared slowly off the surface and Ford waggled the wing in salute to their hosts. Pulling back on the stick, he pointed the Clipper's nose towards the sky and banking the plane slightly to the port side, they raced out over the Bay of Bengal towards India and across the subcontinent, 1000 miles away, Karachi. "India," Ford thought. "Gunga

Din, tiger hunts, mysterious, unknown India. Wish we could see her. Maybe Gary Cooper would go boar hunting with us. Wow, what fun!"

John Mack reached over and tapped Ford on the arm and pointed out ahead, about 1300 hours. Ford, leaning forward, spotted the Revenge and her corvette escort steaming back to Trincomalee. It was a majestic sight, the old battlewagon moving towards her anchorage as the smaller ship trailed behind, then quickly racing ahead, watching for danger from below. Ford adjusted his course and turned so the Clipper would fly directly over the battleship. As he brought the Clipper over the Revenge, he again dipped his wings then brought the plane back on course and headed for India.

When Ford had her at 4000 feet, he signaled Barney to begin serving breakfast. The Chief Steward was ready. He and Vern Edwards had eggs, bacon, sausage and even waffles ready for the crew. Vern prepared the trays for the bridge and took them up. Barney filled the serving trays and brought out the hot food for the rest. The Japanese were in the hands of the British, the tanks of the Clipper were filled and it was a beautiful morning for flying. Then it happened.

"Wham!" "Wham!" "Wham!" The Clipper shook as if she had crashed into a wall! Ford quickly looked at his instruments and knew that the problem was in Engine Number Three. He cut power to it and feathered propeller and then yelled over the intercom for Swede Rothe to get up to the flight deck. He hadn't got the last word out when the big man's head appeared at the top of the stairs, John Parish right behind him. Rothe threw opened the door leading to the engines on the starboard side and black smoke billowed out of the wing. Going inside, the two shut the door to keep it contained. Inside the wing, Swede flipped on a light and immediately saw the problem. Three of the sixteen cylinder hold downs had ripped away from the engine block on Number 3 engine. The rotating cylinders of the engine had stopped when Ford had cut power to the engine and the two could see through the smoke that somehow the number 10 can had blown. There was no choice but to return to Trincomalee to fix it. But Rothe knew that there were no replacement studs on the Clipper. He'd have to find one and he knew there wouldn't be any back in Ceylon. In hindsight, Ford's decision to leave the extra engine back in Auckland looked bad.

Walking along the catwalk to the damaged engine, Rothe was relieved that there was no fire. When he had flipped on the light, a ventilating fan automatically cut in and it was quickly dispersing the smoke out the wing. To the passengers, seeing the smoke pouring from the starboard wing meant the Clipper was on fire. But it wasn't. A fast scan by Rothe showed that the engine was safe for now and there wasn't a thing to do but get back to Trincomalee and repair it. And there lay the big problem. The tool he would need to reattach the new cylinder holds was also in Auckland so he'd have to make one. As he crawled back to the door and the flight deck, in his mind he was making an inventory of things he'd need to make the holds. He'd have to see the British maintenance people to get his tools and equipment. And with luck, he'd have the Clipper in the air in two days. With luck.

Ford took Rothe's report without reaction. The Clipper had been checked and double checked in Auckland and although he knew that if he'd kept the extra engine in the hold, Swede could cannibalize it for the parts, he wouldn't second guess himself. He'd made the decision and nothing could change that. But Ford was sure that some time ahead on this trip, he'd be glad he rid the Clipper of the thousand plus pounds of weight from the extra engine. As Rothe had explained, the big problem was the special tool he had to have. The Wright people had designed it. And although each Pan Am maintenance depot had them, it wasn't a regular tool that an engineer like Rothe would have as part of the Clipper's on-board supplies. The Swede assured Ford that all he'd need was some rolled steel and he could fashion the implement he needed.

Even with Number 3 engine out, Ford and the flight crew had no difficulty bringing the plane back to Trincomalee. This time as he brought the plane down towards its landing, he kept the Clipper close to the waterway he'd used when leaving and the mine field far to their left. Splashdown brought Lt. Smythe and his patrol boat racing towards them and when the Clipper slowed to just bobbing in the water, he pulled up by Ford's port side window and hailed them.

"Captain Ford. I trust the trouble isn't serious. How can we be of help?" the British officer asked.

When Ford explained their predicament, Smythe returned to his cabin and talked to his dock people. He came back and told Ford to follow him. The Clipper did, slowly passing the Revenge. But instead of turning into the small cove, Lt. Smythe took them towards the end of the Revenge's dock. Ahead, Ford could see a couple of British sailors waiting to help berth the Clipper. They secured the plane and Lt. Smythe came aboard.

"Captain, our people aboard think they can help," the British launch officer explained. He assured Ford that when Rothe was ready, he'd escort him aboard the big ship where help waited for the Swede. He asked Ford if the crew wanted transportation to the hotel. Or would they be staying on the plane. Ford looked at his watch to see that only an hour had elapsed since they left the waters of the harbor for Karachi. It was just mid-morning. Ford decided to table any decision about that until Rothe reported. Rothe's schedule would determine what they did in Trincomalee.

What they did was stay two more days in the Ceylon city. It took Rothe, working with the British engineers and maintenance people that long to fashion the tool from the rolled steel available in the ship's supply room. While Rothe was supervising that chore, John Parish and Giles Brown made sure the broken studs were removed and the engine ready for Rothe's hand made replacements. For the rest of the crew, it was more leave time. Lt. Smythe came to visit on Christmas Eve to see if the Yanks wanted to party. They found a willing group among the Clipper's crew and John Steers led their contingent. Wijjy's car came to pick up Ford, Kathleen, Shamus and John Mack but only Shamus could join him. Captain Loud of the Revenge had requested the presence of the other three at his mess to celebrate Christmas Eve. Of course, Ford accepted. So on the evening of 24 December, 1941, members of the Pacific Clipper, joined their British allies, to celebrate the birth of the Prince of Peace while most of the world was burning.

The return of the Pacific Clipper to Trincomalee was of interest to more than just the jeweler, the British and the Clipper's crew. Agents of Japanese Intelligence, charged to report all activities of the British in Ceylon, routinely reported the landing of a flying boat in the harbor at Trincomalee. The report of its initial landing was transmitted through regular channels to Tokyo where Naval Intelligence received the news. The report was filed with normal intelligence traffic and since an American commercial plane was of no importance to anyone at headquarters, no one paid any attention to the message. But the next day, when another message from Ceylon arrived telling that the American plane had departed and then suddenly returned, the officer in charge noted the report and remembered that Commodore Tanaka was in the building and had requested that their agents be alert for the movements of an American flying boat. He had the information decoded and sent upstairs to the office of the Commander of Naval Intelligence and had it marked for the attention of Commodore Tanaka. He went on to other business, no longer concerned. To Isodecki Tanaka, the message was more than important, it was life saving!

Chapter 11

Tanaka's Second Chance

0800 24 December, 1941, Captain Teshio's office

When he had entered Teshio's office yesterday he had no idea of what kind of reception he would receive from the Captain. Because of his standing in Japanese society and rank in the Navy, he knew he would be treated respectfully. He was. What surprised him was the brevity of the meeting. Teshio rose from behind his desk and bowed. Tanaka did the same. Then he indicated a chair for Tanaka to sit. He opened a folder, briefly scanned it and closed it. Expressionless, he looked at Tanaka and spoke.

"We have made arrangements for you to stay here tonight in the Visiting Officers Quarters. Tomorrow morning, at 0800, we will discuss where you think you might be of greatest service to the Emperor. By then, we should have more details on the happenings at Surabaja. A report from one of our submarines in the Bay of Bengal indicates that the plane was spotted earlier yesterday morning and as of now, we know she is resting at anchor in the harbor at Trincomalee in Ceylon. Our agents reported the plane landed in a mine field! The American pilot seems to have great Karma," the Captain said.

Tanaka's heart jumped into his throat while his eyes and face did not change expression. He waited for Teshio to continue but he did not, just sitting there as expressionless as Tanaka. Then he rose as did Tanaka, and the two exchanged bows. Tanaka rose to his full height and saluted smartly. Teshio, about a foot shorter, did the same.

Now, this morning as the Commodore looked out upon the scene of scurrying people but not seeing them, he again reviewed for the umpteenth time what might await him and how his plan to continue his quest for the Pacific Clipper would play with Teshio and consequently, with Tojo. As he waited to appear before Teshio, he suddenly became quite phlegmatic about his future. He felt no need to call upon any deity to aid his cause. What would happen would.

"Commodore Tanaka," Teshio's secretary spoke, breaking the tall man's reverie. Turning, he looked at her and for the first time noticed that she was an older woman. "You would think someone as ranking as Teshio would have a much more attractive woman for his secretary," Tanaka thought as he nodded to the woman and followed her into Captain Teshio's office. "What a strange thought, Isodecki! Here you are walking into a room where your future is to be decided and you're thinking about some old secretary. Wake up. Your life is at stake!"

Entering and bowing to the Chief of Naval Intelligence, Tanaka waited for him to be invited to be seated. The Captain had risen and bowed and returning to his chair, sat and then motioned the Commodore to his chair.

"Commodore Tanaka, I asked you yesterday to think how you can best be of service to the Emperor. What are your thoughts?" the Captain began. He had no idea what this egotistical bastard would have to present but whatever it was, he hoped he could support it, no matter how screwy as long as it got Tanaka out of Tokyo and away from him! When he first heard of the failure to capture the American Clipper ship, Teshio thought that the Commodore would do the honorable thing and commit Hara Kiri. When orders came down for him to be flown back to Headquarters, Teshio knew that he would be stuck with the arrogant son-of-a-bitch. Tojo wanted nothing to do with anything that would bring disgrace to the Tanaka name. Tojo told him to solve the problem himself but if the Emperor ever heard anything that would diminish his friend, Count Tanaka's son in his eyes, it would be Captain Teshio with the knife stuck in his intestines. Nodding to the nephew of Baron Tanaka, Captain Teshio waited.

The tall one was ready. He knew that even though he had failed to deliver the Boeing as promised, he was well aware of how much the ruling military party feared his father. Teshio was a solid military man, and although for the last few years involved in the clandestine world of Intelligence, still a practical man. He had to have facts, rational analysis of how his plan could succeed, not wishes and pipe dreams.

"Captain Teshio. Thank you for your consideration and the time you have allowed me to go over my thoughts with you this morning," the big man began. " When I first presented my plan for the capture of the American flying boat to General Tojo and Admiral Yamamoto, the basic assumption was that the Boeing would give us the long range bombers we needed to project our military strength across the Pacific.

But with the success we have enjoyed thus far and the sureness that when the Philippines fall, the Americans will sue for peace, the need to spend all those resources to build the bombers may not be necessary. However, as you know, even if the Americans started the peace process, it will take months before they totally capitulate. What is needed is another demonstration of our power, of our ingenuity, our resolve and our invincibility. We must make the American people know that there is nothing that can keep us from our destiny!"

Rising so quickly that he startled the Captain, Tanaka's long stride took him to a polar projection map of the world, hanging from the far wall in Teshio's office. Opening his huge right hand, he put his thumb on Tokyo and stretched his middle finger out, placing in on New York. Turning, he looked at Captain Teshio and began what he knew would be the greatest bullshit job he'd ever undertaken!

"There, Captain Teshio. That is the capital of the United States. New York City. Not Washington," he almost shouted. "This is where America lives. This is where the newspapers are, the magazines, the radio stations and Wall Street. New York is the heart and the guts of the country. We may think here in Japan that Roosevelt and the Congress run America but it is here. This is where public opinion for the Americans is shaped. New York, not Washington," Tanaka dramatically stated.

"Very good, Commodore. I was told you had a great knack for the dramatic. That was very entertaining," Teshio thought beginning to feel a slight appreciation for the tall man. Teshio didn't know where Tanaka was headed but the opening that "New York is the capital of America" got his attention. As the Commodore walked back to his chair, he stopped to pick up a map he had spotted earlier, sitting atop others on a table near the Captain's desk. Spreading it out on Teshio's desk, the Captain looked down and saw it was of the United States. He then sat while Teshio looked at the map of the enemy's homeland. Teshio nodded for him to continue.

He had Teshio's attention and now he had to get his support. Leaning forward, he spoke softly so the Captain had to move closer to hear him, making the Captain subconsciously think they were in this together. "The attack on Pearl Harbor sent most of the American Seventh Fleet to the bottom. Seven of their great battleship lie in or under the waters of the harbor. But Hawaii in not part of the United States. Many Americans know little about the islands except they think the people run around in grass skirts. It is just a protectorate and while a few thousand sailors died there, it is not as if it had happened in San

Diego or Los Angeles. Had we sunk those seven ships in New York harbor, then they really would be frightened of Japan. But Hawaii is four thousand miles from Los Angeles and eight thousand from New York. In other words Captain Teshio, while we have delivered a great blow against the American Navy at Pearl harbor and are conquering the Philippines, we haven't frightened the Americans. Made them angry yes, but frightened, no. The war is too far away. I want to take it right to them. Here!" Suddenly standing and again giving Teshio a start, he thumped his forefinger on the map, hitting New York.

Teshio got excited. He had no reason for feeling like he did but there was something in the way the big man spoke that was electric and the Chief of North American Intelligence anxiously waited for more. He nodded at Tanaka to continue.

"I do not exaggerate the importance of New York when it comes to influencing public opinion in the States. It is in New York that we must strike. But why and how? Obviously, if we had the striking power in the Atlantic that we have out here, that would have been the place to attack. But we don't," Tanaka began. He knew from the way Teshio leaned forward in his chair that the old sea dog was interested. Now he warmed to his plan. He was winging it and had no definite point by point plan but he had always dealt in selling the concept and let others work out the logistics.

"Captain Teshio. The Pacific Clipper is headed for New York. And it is there that we will destroy her, right in front of the Statue of Liberty! When the news of the destruction of America's symbol of aviation superiority is broadcast over the airways and through the press services, the American people will know that the Empire of Japan can, whenever it wishes, reach right into the heart of their homeland."

Teshio sat there and looked at Commodore Tanaka. He clenched his jaw to make sure his mouth hadn't dropped open in complete surprise at this totally idiotic suggestion that Tanaka had just lay before him. "By Buddha's balls! What in the world is he thinking of. Blow up the American plane in New York harbor! In front of the Statue of Liberty! This guy is crazy!" the Captain thought to himself. He had to will himself not to laugh. Taking a deep breath to both compose himself and form an answer to Tanaka's plan, he sat back and looked at the man. He hoped his face remained noncommittal but he decided a brief smile might get the big man to relax and think he had impressed him. And he had but not the way Tanaka thought.

"Before I reject this out of hand, let me look at what he is saying to see if there is the germ of possibility there, something I can seriously take to Tojo. But this! How in the world would he ever catch the Americans, even if we had a plane that could fly to New York! Maybe that is it. Let him explain to me the logistics of getting his ass now in Tokyo to New York and just how he plans to destroy the plane. Make the Americans cower with fear by blowing up a plane! My ass." Teshio thought. He nodded to the Commodore, not trusting himself to speak. "If there was just a semblance of rationality to the plan, I'd support it for no other reason than to get the Count's son away from Tokyo. Even Tojo would appreciate that. But this!"

"Captain, I know you think this idea is inane. So did I when I first thought of it. It wasn't until I had thought through all the reasons why this wouldn't work that I came to the conclusion that it could. Remember Ford has to have aviation fuel to fly the Boeing and after he left Trincomalee, it is likely that he'll never find any high octane gasoline for his plane," As Tanaka looked at the Naval Intelligence Head, he still couldn't read the man. But the fact that he hadn't tossed him out of the office gave the tall man hope that some of this made sense to Teshio. It hardly made sense to him but that didn't matter. Destroying the Pacific Clipper in the shadow of the Statue of Liberty was his best shot at staying alive and he had to harp on that. Tanaka knew the whole plan was a house of cards because of Ford's long lead. But he wasn't about to admit defeat. So he plunged ahead.

"As you know, a few years ago, we purchased, with the Germans, three cargo ships from Uruguay. They are manned by South Americans with some of our intelligence people aboard. Right now, they are sailing up and down the Atlantic Coact as merchant ships but spying on the Americans. And in each of those ships, there are two man subs. I plan to meet one of them in Nova Scotia, at Halifax," Tanaka began. Taking a deep breath, he knew the Achilles' heel of his plan was about to be exposed. If he were to get Teshio's support, it would be because of what he said now. And he knew it would blow the old sea dog's mind. "I can see him laughing as he explains to Tojo my scheme. Even Yamamoto would grin," Tanaka thought as he charged on.

"I plan to fly the Polar route. My first stop will be at Attu, in the Aleutians. Our soldiers already have a foothold on the island and the Americans haven't done anything about it. So I can safely refuel there and fly on to Alaska. As you know, certain Inuit tribes have been well paid by our government for their information and they will help me across Alaska. The longest part of the flight will be across Canada. I can land on the frozen lakes and at most of them, there are small trading posts. Most of these posts are operated by native Canadians, the Cree and Inuit Indians who have little love for their white masters. Plus, the money I'll pay will keep them warm for many winters to come. Our people in Alaska can alert those in Canada and they will have gasoline and supplies waiting for us when we land at the stations I'll select. Once across Hudson Bay, I'll stay far to the north of any sizable Canadian cities until I reach the Gulf of St. Lawrence. Then, down to Nova Scotia. There is a huge national park not to far from Halifax. We'll land there. At this time of the year, everything in Canada is frozen and there is no fear of anyone spotting me landing, especially at night. Members of the crew of the trawler will meet me and take me to the docks and the ship. From Halifax, we'll cross the Bay of Fundy, down the coast of Maine, past Boston and into New York," Tanaka summed up, making a twenty thousand mile trip sound like a Sunday stroll along the Ginza in cherry blossom time.

Teshio was very impressed. He hadn't heard such a tale of fantasy since his father read him stories from the Arabian Nights. "Tanaka, you are a match for Sinbad the Sailor. What an imagination," he thought.

"Commodore, I am most impressed with your knowledge of the Polar route and as you easily fly across the top of the world, one would think there was nothing to it," Teshio began. He had had enough of this egotistical bastard and no matter what Tojo would think, he was going to shoot Tanaka's idea down here and now. Then the nephew of Baron Tanaka could explain to the Prime Minister himself how he failed to capture the American plane in Surabaja.

"But I too have a flirting knowledge of other parts of the world and unless I'm mistaken, the Americans are now halfway across India. And granting your hope that they will have to use automobile gasoline to get home, they have such a lead that there is no possible way to beat them to New York. Not only do we not possess a plane with the speed and range to do what you suggest, everything in your plans is predicated upon the American being held up because of lack of aviation gasoline. Why? They will be in Arabia and there is oil and gasoline there. The Pacific Clipper has the range to fly non-stop from Africa to South America. I'm sorry Commodore. The Americans have too great a lead for you to catch them, even if your wonderful dream of flying the Polar route was feasible. I agree that there is great propaganda value with the blowing up the American plane in New York but there is no way you can beat him to New York," Teshio said.

Tanaka just sat there. He had tried to steel himself against the anticipated refusal by Teshio to support his scheme but he could feel the color rise in his face by the embarrassment of being put down by a desk

Captain. The taste in his mouth was one of anger and frustration at being blocked from his plan by this nobody. The blood of his ancestors flowed through him and as he was about to respond angrily that Teshio was an ass, he could hear his father and his uncle both telling him that anger was for fools. They both taught that there was always another solution, be patient and he would find it. "Yes, Father and Uncle, but you were not chasing a man and a plane that was already half way around the world and each hour getting further away," the Commodore thought to himself. "Well, I'm still here and he is still listening. So let's see how he handles this one."

"Captain Teshio. Your point about fuel and the American's lead is well taken. What would you recommend we do?" Tanaka asked.

"We do? You smart ass. This screw up isn't my doing. It is yours!" Teshio thought to himself as he secretly admired the brashness of the man across the desk. "Let me end this charade and send this egomaniac off to what he deserves. But I can't. Tojo would have my balls if anything negative about Count Tanaka's son was ever to reach the bastard's father. Now he's got me mixing metaphors! Take a deep breath, Teshio and suffer this fool a little longer."

Just as the Captain was about to respond to the total idiocy of the Tanaka's plan, there was a soft tapping at his door. The reprieve was most welcomed. Telling his secretary to come in, she entered, bowed and brought a message to the Captain. Bowing again, she turned and left the office. Teshio didn't look at her but opened the message and read it. Then read it again. And again. He sat back, his face totally void of any expression and quietly screamed "Banzai" to himself! He would indeed support this halfassed plan of the Commodore! There was no way he could pull it off but Teshio didn't care. The message in his hand gave him his reason to back Tanaka and give Tojo and himself a way to be rid of the son of Count Tanaka and the nephew of the Baron. If the tall man failed, he would die a hero and never return to Japan. If by some wild stroke of luck, he pulled it off, glory for the Emperor, General Tojo and himself!

"Commodore Tanaka. It seems that Captain Ford's karma has somewhat deserted him. This message just came in from our people in Ceylon. You may have a new life after all," the Intelligence officer spoke. Leaning across, he passed over the message to the tall man.

Tanaka took it and leaning back in his chair, he read the transmission. "American plane returned to Trincomalee. Number three engine out. Will keep advised," Tanaka reread the message and he found it hard to keep his emotions under control. He wanted to jump up and rush to the door and but he sat there, not looking at Teshio, allowing his stomach to return to normal. "Ah, Captain Ford. You are not so far ahead of me as I thought. This delay gives me one, maybe two days to catch up to you. And I'll not waste it. But I need a plane. The submarine driver will be on board one of the tankers. But I will need a copilot. The two of us will fly the plane, one sleeping while the other pilots so we only have to stop for gas. I need a two engine plane. Range is more important than speed. A Mitsubishi bomber, stripped of armament, will suffice. And all insignias have to be taken off."

"Captain Teshio, this news from your men in Ceylon is indeed a most welcomed turn of events. If the Americans have to stay in Ceylon for a few days, I can beat them to New York. The word from you to General Tojo would clear the way for me to leave immediately. Now that Ford is stuck in Trincomalee, every minute counts if I'm to fulfill my mission for the glory of the Emperor. We have no idea when the Pacific Clipper will be repaired and take off for India," Tanaka stressed.

Teshio looked at the nephew of the Baron and was almost as happy as he was with the news. "Young Tanaka. How lucky you are! With the message from Ceylon, I have enough to go to Tojo and get his permission for your crazy scheme to continue. In fact, I already have Tojo's tacit assurance that I can do anything I want with you as long as your away from Tokyo and the Emperor! Yes, my young friend, you will be on your way shortly with the blessings of all of us, especially the Prime Minister," the Intelligence officer thought to himself.

"Commodore, it is my great pleasure to take your plans for the destruction of the American plane to the Prime Minister. While I schedule a meeting with him, please use my secretary and together make a list of your needs; type of plane, personnel to accompany you, codes to notify our people of your arrival. She will contact the different departments to make sure you have the proper maps, charts, and other necessary materials you'll need to guide you from here to New York," Teshio instructed as he stood and extended his hand to Tanaka. The Commodore took it, bowed and then standing as erect as possible saluted and executed a perfect about face and walked to the door. Had he turned he would have caught Captain Teshio shaking his head and grinning from ear to ear.

1150 hours-24 December, 1941-runway at Assiti Naval Base-Tokyo

Commodore Tanaka taxied the two engine Mitsubishi to the end of the runway and awaited take off instructions. His co-pilot, a young Army pilot quite familiar with their craft, sat next to him completing the check list. When clearance came from the tower, Tanaka pushed the throttles forward and the plane moved smartly down the runway. When reaching take-off speed, the Commodore pulled back slowly on the yoke and the Mitsubishi easily left the earth. Lt. Oho was impressed by the smoothness of the takeoff and how easily the Commodore banked to plane away from the airport and headed north, north to the Aleutians, to the island of Attu and hopefully, USA.

1830 hours-24 December, 1941-Aboard HMS Revenge-Trincomalee, Ceylon

The Honorable Captain Brewster M. Loud, commander of the HMS Revenge was pleased. The dinner had been magnificent. His chef had prepared fillets of Dover sole, saute meuniere, small whole potatoes, grilled, with peas and a tossed green salad. And they had enjoyed an exquisite Chardonnay that the Captain told them he had set aside for a particular moment. And this was that moment. The three Americans were flattered and when the chef came in with the baked Alaska dessert, they applauded! The chef bowed and the Captain smiled. Coffee and after dinner drinks were served, brandy for Kathleen and Scotch for the two Captains and John Mack. The three men lit their cigars, Cuban, and John Mack lit Kathleen's Chesterfield.

Captain Loud stood and raised his glass."Captain Ford, Lt. Mack and Lt. Elmes. The King" The two men rose and touched their glasses to Captain Loud's. He remained standing as Ford and Mack sat down. Raising his glass again, he nodded to Kathleen and spoke.

"And may I toast the lovely Lt. Kathleen Elmes. What a pleasure to have you grace our ship! And on behalf of the men of the Revenge, let me wish the three of you, Merry Christmas. And may this damn war end soon with our side victorious."

The others answered "Amen" and raised their glasses to the Captain. He sat and picked up his cigar, drawing on it and exhaling a large puff of white smoke. Sitting back, he surveyed his three guests and began to speak.

"I thought you would like the latest intelligence I have on the state of things across the world. Simply put, they stink. The Russians and their winter have stalled the Germans at Stalingrad, Leningrad and Moscow. Hitler overreached and his troops are freezing to death. So almost a century and a half later, history repeats itself. But the news isn't good around the rest of the world."

Rising, cigar in his left hand and a snifter of Scotch in his right, he walked over to a large map of the world hanging against the starboard wall. Taking a sip of the Scotch, he began his briefing.

"Here in the Pacific we have nothing but disasters. If that donkey's head, Tom Phillips hadn't gone searching for the Japanese fleet off Singapore, without air support, Repulse and Prince of Wales would still be with us and the Japs probably still be tied up above Shanghai. As it is now, Singapore will fall soon. And where you just were, in Java, the Japs can take that with ease. Australia lies totally exposed but my guess is that the Japs won't go there. When they take Java they'll have all the oil and rubber they need. A couple of their heavy cruisers of the Nati class can isolate Australia. Unfortunately, I have some immediate bad news," the Captain stated.

"Wake Island fell yesterday," Admiral Loud said softly.

"Any details, Sir?" Ford asked.

"None Captain. We picked up the dispatch from our people at Singapore. Your people put up one hell of a fight. And I guess your Major Davenport got his wish," Captain Loud summed up.

When the three Americans looked quizzically at him, he smiled and nodded.

"Yes, we heard of the Major's request to "send him more Japs," Brave man. And brave men. Let us raise our glasses in tribute to these courageous men and the rest of our fighters across the world," the Captain proposed. The three Americans, each with their private thoughts, raised their glasses. After a few seconds of silence, the Captain continued his update on the state of the war across the world. "The Japanese will have most of the South China Sea under their control in a matter of weeks. Until your Navy recovers, the whole Pacific is again Hirohito's lake. In Europe, Hitler is in total control but the Russians are making him pay dearly," Taking a sip of his Scotch, he continued. "I know you have to maintain radio silence, Captain Ford. You wouldn't have landed in my mine field had you not been under such orders! So let me offer to send coded messages ahead to the places where you'll be going. Our consulates there will be of assistance to you. We will, of course, after you leave Trincomalee, alert them of your coming and tell them to extend every courtesy. But I don't know if there is aviation fuel for your plane. I'll instruct our people to find out and you'll know before you leave here," the Captain offered.

"Much obliged, Captain Loud," Ford responded as John Mack and Kathleen Elmes nodded their thanks.

"Don't thank me. I thank you. That news about the Japanese sub in the Bay of Bengal gave me the excuse to get this old sweetheart's boilers pumping and the crew some action. I thoroughly enjoyed the search even though we didn't find the bugger," Loud responded.

" Now, I'll finish my report so we can enjoy our visit. As I stated earlier, the Germans control Europe and much of North Africa. And it is there that I see your greatest danger. For it would be nothing for Rommel to send a couple of Messerschmitts down from Tobruk and intercept you at Bahrain or Khartoum. That is if the Germans knew how valuable the Clipper could be to them in the war. Those four Wright engines of yours on their bombers could give them the range to pound the Russians and England from inside Germany. Hitler could put a lid over all of Europe, most of Africa, and reach India, if he had your plane. And the convoys carrying supplies to us from America would never get halfway across the Atlantic before being sunk by his bombers," the Captain summarized for his guests. Then he rose and walked over to his desk. Picking up a manila envelop, he brought it back to the table, opened it and passed it on to Ford. As the pilot of the Pacific Clipper began to read, he looked at the Captain of the Revenge and smiled. The letter spoke of how important the American plane was for the winning of the war and that England should have the plane. It urged all British commanders and representatives to try and secure the Boeing. The letter was signed by Sir Reginald Leach.

Ford looked at Captain Loud and raised his eyebrows. And he laughed. "Never fear, Captain Ford. I have no intention of commandeering the Pacific Clipper. Sir Reginald's letter was forwarded to Whitehall and they have recalled him. However, I don't know how many of these letters Leach sent out. Did he know where you were flying?" Captain Loud asked as he eased Ford's concerns.

"He did indeed. Do you think Ambassador Leach sent the same letter on to others?"

"Probably, Captain Ford. But I doubt anyone would support Leach and interfere with you," Loud smiled at his guests. He reached over and, picking up the small copper bell, shook it. The steward entered.

"As you Americans say, one for the road," the Captain instructed the steward who left and returned almost immediately with fresh glasses, filled. Serving the four, he departed and Ford proposed a toast.

"Captain Loud, on behalf of the crew of the Pacific Clipper and the three of us, let me thank you for a wonderful evening and the help your people are giving us in repairing our engine. You are a superb host. Hopefully, someday when all this is over and you'll allow us to entertain you. But I doubt we can match the grace and style of this evening," Ford said lifting his glass in toast. The other three raised theirs and all sipped their drinks.

"Thank you, Captain Ford. Now, one last duty. You and your crew need protection from the malarial mosquitos here and the diseases and filth where you'll landing as you fly to Karachi and the other ports in Arabia and Africa. Our ship's doctor is waiting for you three to inoculate you and tomorrow, we'll do the rest of the crew. Lt. Smyth will clear the pick up time with you Captain when he takes you back to your ship," Captain Loud informed them.

Standing, he walked over and kissed Kathleen Elmes on her cheek, shook hands with John Mack and saluted Bob Ford. "Only God knows what the future holds but I have a very strong feeling that you will make it back to America. And that the Pacific Clipper will be of great help in winning this war. God Bless all of you."

The three had planned to meet the crew at the Orange Hotel after dinner with Captain Loud. And Bob Ford was looking forward to being alone with Kathleen Elmes again. And in a way, he was.

They got their shots for Dysentery, Malaria, Typhus and the other diseases that would threaten their health along the route across the subcontinent. When Lt. Smythe dropped them at the Clipper so Kathleen could get out of her uniform and into something more casual, Bob Ford was already feeling queazy. He thought it was the Scotch but as he walked up the stairs to the flight deck, he was in agony. Sweat poured down his face and his knees wobbled. He opened the small john on the bridge and tried to throw up but all he could do was wretch. Splashing his face with water brought only a second of relief. He lay down on his bed and his stomach was in knots. His body was hot then cold and he knew he was having a reaction to the shots he'd just taken from the Revenge's doctor. Midnight strolls with Kathleen Elmes became the furthest thing from his mind. Sleep was the only antidote.

The crew, led by John Steers, thoroughly enjoyed a major league Christmas Eve party with their British friends at the Orange Hotel. Christmas Day, the crew recovered as did Bob Ford.

On the day after Christmas, after three days in Ceylon, Bob Ford again took the Pacific Clipper off the waters of the harbor at Trincomalee, past the mine field and pointed her west towards Karachi, India. He was now three days behind his planned schedule and although he was irritated by the delays, he knew it really didn't matter. The rest of the trip should be a milk run.

Chapter 12

Across the Underbelly of the World-Trincomalee to Khartoum.

0800 hours, 26 December, 1941-Attu Island, the Aleutians.

Zero. Commodore. The temperature outside is zero," Lt. Oho reported. The tall man glared at him as if it were his fault but Oho ignored him. In the two days since they left Tokyo, he'd already become impervious to the icy stares of the famed Tanaka. He was freezing his ass off and all because this crazy bastard wanted to sink an American plane in New York harbor. And a commercial plane at that! They were inside a small hut, warmed by a pot bellied stove that the soldiers here kept fully supplied with coal and wood. Their commanding officer made sure the two pilots had the fuel, while the rest of his small command of 100 soldiers suffered in the cold.

The euphoria of their departure from Tokyo on the great quest had left both men as they spent the second day in the icy cold of the Aleutians. The swirling snow and knifelike winds that greeted them when they landed hadn't abated. And if the foul weather didn't lift in another day, when it finally did, they would just turn around and fly back to Japan. The American's lead would be far too great. Just then, the door of their hut opened and Lt. Shouro entered. He was in command of the detachment charged with helping Tanaka and Oho continue on to Alaska.

"Commodore. I have good news. Our weather is beginning to lift and in a few hours, if the present pattern continues, you will be able to leave. I've got my men checking the plane and everything seems ready. You are fully fueled," Shouro reported. Tanaka's smile made the hut 50 degrees warmer and Oho knew that no matter what, they were going! Next stop, Kayak Island. Oho wasn't worried. On Kayak, Naval

Intelligence had assured them they would be greeted by friendly natives when they landed. Now, all they had to do was wait until the skies cleared. Two hours later, the Mitsubishi rolled down the snow covered rocky runway, lifted off and headed out up the coast of the Aleutian Islands then across the Bay of Alaska into Kayak, landing at twilight on a small field, covered with snow but usable. Gas was waiting. Oho supervised the filling of the tanks of the Mitsubishi and Tanaka, who had studied the maps of Alaska and British Columbia in Canada decided against a night flight to Dease Lake in British Columbia. Supplies awaited and he wanted to be sure they didn't miss their rendezvous.

1200 hours 26 December 1941, aboard the Pacific Clipper

Barney Swacki and Verne Edwards were serving lunch to the crew and guests and everyone was quite relaxed. The hangover some of the men suffered from the Christman Eve party with the British had dissipated and those that had bad reactions to the vaccines were in one way or another, healthy. When Ford left the harbor at Trincomalee he headed briefly up the Bay of Bengal paralleling the shore of Ceylon until John Steers told him that Madras was coming up on the left. Using that as his dead reckoning turn to port, Ford banked the great plane and headed across India for Karachi. Much of the flight would be over land and the crew split up into groups to look at the few atlases aboard to follow the route the Captain said he was going to fly. At 8000 feet it wasn't too hard to see the villages and lands beneath them. At first, it was exciting... tiger hunts... Bengal Lancers charging against the heathens... hidden treasures... Rudyard Kipling and Gunga Din. But after awhile, the topography was so similar that they became bored and went back to reading or their duties. No tigers or panthers or Rajah's.

To Ford and the flight deck crew, it was ideal. The big plane was flying along with all engines purring. For the first time since they left Darwin, they were relaxed. No Dutch fighters threatening to shoot them down, no Japs trying to steal their plane and hopefully, no mine field to land on! All they had to do was make it to Karachi and with the tanks full and clear skies ahead of them, maybe they could pull this thing off. In their minds, they and the Pacific Clipper had overcome the worst part of their trek and now it was just flying, the most boring but happiest time for pilots and crews. There was a brief stir of excitement when Oscar Hendrickson, the Second Radio Officer spotted Bombay ahead and everyone pressed their faces to the port holes and looked as the Clipper approached the fabled city. Five minutes later, water, the Arabian Sea. Three hours later, without incident, Bob Ford pointed the nose of the Pacific Clipper down towards the Gulf of Kutch and landed easily on the waters of Karachi, India. They were now about a third of the way home.

The local people were running down a long pier that jutted out into the water, yelling and pointing at the Clipper. Some were jumping and waiving their arms as Ford taxied the plane across the water towards the dock. They couldn't see anyone that looked like an official to welcome them and no boat came towards them. The pier became even more crowded as word of the strange plane that floated like a boat quickly circulated. Ford stopped the Clipper about fifty yards from the dock and kept the engines idling, almost as if he was ready to turn her around and head out to sea if problems developed. Then, a man in a light weight suit came running from behind one of the low buildings and ran towards the Clipper. He stopped when he was near enough to the Clipper to yell at her, and taking a deep breath, he called out to them. Ford cut the two starboard engines and the inside port so they could hear him. John Mack's window was opened and he leaned out to get the man's words.

"Captain Ford. Welcome to Karachi. I'm White of the BOAC. We received the message from the Revenge and have been waiting for you. We'll help you get docked. A few of my men will be here in seconds so you can bring your ship closer and toss us your lines," the BOAC man stated. Just as he finished, four other men, not natives, hurried through the crowds to join White. John Parish had opened the starboard passenger door and Barney had opened the anchor room and was standing ready to toss the line to the dock hands. In next to no time, the Clipper was safely tied up to the dock. They were in India.

But it wasn't the India of Kipling or Cary Grant or Gary Cooper. Only Shamus of the Clipper's compliment wasn't shocked by the filth, the stench and the poverty that greeted them as they went into Karachi. Cattle and camel dung filled the gutters of the streets and raw sewage was everywhere. Every time the horse drawn coaches stopped, beggars surrounded the open carriages, yelling and pawing at them, racing behind in chase down the streets until the Clipper's crew and their buggies reached the grounds of the hotel where they were staying, the Carlton. Once inside the iron fence, the beggars stood outside and watched as the two cabs pulled up to the entrance. Liveried men in blue and red uniforms opened the small step doors and the crew stepped onto the red bricks of the driveway and walked up the steps into the hotel lobby. Inside, overhead fans swirled, trying to bring some of the cooler evening air to the room and the guests.

The Americans checked in and went to their rooms to freshen up. John Steers took a bath and found the soap smelled as bad as the streets and when he got out and pulled the plug, the water ran out all over the floor! He ordered a cold beer from room service and they brought him a glass of water. He sent out his laundry and after a few minutes resting, he looked out his window and saw his clothes being beaten against rocks in the dirty water of a small stream in back of the hotel!

Ford met with the BOAC's White to get whatever maps and charts they could pass on and to make arrangements for refueling. White advised Ford that while there was 100 octane available, the mixture was half leaded and half unleaded. And White told Ford that there was no charge for the gas! It seems that the letters Sir Reginald Leach had sent had just the opposite effect from what he had hoped. People from the BOAC reacted with great anger. They knew what Ford and the crew of the Clipper were trying to do and as part of this very small fraternity the men at BOAC wanted to see the Clipper reach the United States. After all arrangements were made, Mack, Swede Rothe and John Parish supervised the refueling of the Clipper. As darkness fell over the dock, Ford decided to stay the night on his plane. He wanted to be with Kathleen Elmes but he was tired and knew the last thing he needed was to come down with malaria. Ford realized he hadn't completely recovered from the bad reaction he'd had from the shots he'd received aboard the Revenge. He didn't want to go ashore in a town as filthy as Karachi and risk catching something. So when John Mack and the Swede left, he stayed aboard the Clipper.

At the hotel, most of the crew assembled in the lounge and discussed what to do that night. Shamus had no contacts in Karachi but had talked to the hotel's manager about recommended places to visit and to have dinner. The manager, in all modesty, advised the innkeeper that he was standing in the lobby of the best that Karachi had to offer. When this intelligence was passed on to the men of Pan Am and Kathleen, a group decided to see for themselves what the town had to offer. Kathleen hid her disappointment that Ford had decided to stay on the Clipper and accepted Shamus' invitation to join him for dinner in the hotel dining room. John Mack and Norm Brown joined them while the two engineers, Rothe and Parish as well as the Tech Rep G. Brown took a table across the room. The rest of the crew left and got into the horse drawn cabs and headed out into the evening for a tour of Karachi. They were back in less than an hour and John Steers' joined Shamus, Kathleen and the flight officers to report on their jaunt into the Indian city. Signaling the waiter, he ordered a Scotch on the rocks and shaking his head, began.

"For the first time in my short, sweet life, words fail me. There is no way for me to describe what we saw. That trip from the dock to the hotel this afternoon, well, that is the best part of Karachi! The second we left the gates, the hansom was surrounded by beggars, even women carrying their children on their back or in their arms. And they would grab your arm, hard and you'd hit their hands to get them off you and they still wouldn't let go! And the noise and the smells. It was scary. And of course we didn't speak the language and the driver didn't speak English, just kept grinning at us and nodding as we all tried to get him to move faster away from the beggars. Finally, Oscar put his fingers in his mouth and blew a whistle that finally got the damn driver's attention and we all signaled to get us back here. At first he seemed to draw a blank but with all of yelling "Carlton Hotel" he understood we wanted to come back here!"

As Steers was talking, the waiter brought him his drink and the other crewmen in the room, nodding their agreement to what Steers was saying. They repeated the story to Swede and the other two. So the first and only evening in Karachi for the men of the Pacific Clipper ended with dinner in the hotel dining room and an early wake up calls for the next day. There was nothing exciting for John Steers to enter in the Clipper's log about their day in Karachi.

0415 hours-27 December, 1941-Kayak Island, The Aleutians

The two Japanese pilots had slipped into their heavy flying suits. They had eaten, answered nature's call and were ready to leave on the next leg of their journey to Dease Lake. This was the longest and most dangerous part of the trip. They would push the Mitubisi to the edge of the range of her two engines and any kind of strong headwinds would leave them stranded in the bitter winter of the northern British Columbia. Neither had any idea of where their prey was but they knew wherever the Pacific Clipper was, her crew was a hell of a lot warmer than they were. The two moved out of the small cabin and walked towards their plane, now uncovered and sitting quietly on the snowy runway in the below zero weather. Tanaka climbed in, snuggled against the cold and looked down at his co-pilot, standing near the engines with the small fire extinguisher in his hands. Tanaka turned the switch on and let the electrical charges of the plane circulate before trying to turn on the port engine. Then he pushed in the starter and said a quiet prayer to Buddha. After what seemed an eternity, the left engine slowly began to move the propeller and in a second, the explosion of sound and the ball of white smoke coming from the engine told him it had kicked in. He slowly moved the throttle forward and watched as the blades pick up speed until he could no longer see them. Then pulled back on the throttle to idle as he repeated the routine with the starboard engine. Finally, Oho saluted and pulling the safety cocks from the front of the wheels, he threw then into the open side door of the plane, climbed in and joined the Commodore. He'd barely sat down and strapped himself in before Tanaka revved the engines and they headed for the western edge of Canada and one thousand miles closer to the Pacific Clipper. If it was still flying!

0800 hours-27 December 1941-aboard the Pacific Clipper

The Clipper and crew gladly left Karachi and were now climbing to altitude over the Arabian Sea, headed for the Persian Gulf and the island nation of Bahrein. This was one of the shorter parts of their journey, just under 1000 miles and the group on the passenger level discussed their next landing, Baherin. Some had heard of it, none knew anything about it. Except Shamus Ginsberg.

"Gentlemen, and Kathleen. If you think India was strange, we'll soon be landing in a land directly out of The Arabian Nights. Bahrein is a British protectorate, but run by Arab sheiks. And how would I describe an Arab sheik so that you can understand their power? Well, imagine if you will Al Capone being told by Washington that he could run Chicago as he wanted, as long as he didn't embarrass the Federal government!" Shamus began as the crew laughed at the analogy. "Bahrein is oil rich, as are most of the lands of Arabia. But because they are a British protectorate and have had the benefit of English and American technology to develop their asset, they are far richer than any nation of Islam. And their oil is vital to the British. However, we know Rommel's Afrika Corps is headed across the Sahara to Egypt, to take the Suez Canal. If they do, the oil here stays in Baherin," he reiterated.

"Let me try to give you a quick look at life in an Arab land. If you steal an apple from a fruit stand and get caught, they chop off your hand! If a woman is found outside on the street without her face covered, she is stoned, and I don't mean with pebbles, rocks, aimed to kill. And if you protest in public any treatment you think unfair, the sheik can, and probably will have your tongue cut out," the Irish/Jew began. Kathleen Elmes was standing on the edge of the group listening, a wry smile on her lips.

"Ah, Lt. Elmes. Your expression indicates that you think I exaggerate. You might be right. But you are coming into a part of the world where a woman is less valued than a camel," the innkeeper commented.

Kathleen, knowing Shamus was trying to bait her, smiled and calmly answered. "Shamus, this may surprise you but I'm sure that the lot of women in Arabian lands isn't quite as bad as you paint it. I know that the Koran protects their rights and all Arabs that follow the dictates of their religion treat their women with respect,"

"We'll see, Lt., how you react in Bahrein when you see first hand how Arab women are treated," Shamus answered laughingly. "But I'm more anxious to see how the towelheads react when they see you!" That brought a big laugh from the rest of the crew.

"Do you think the Germans pose any threat to us?" Oscar Hendrickson asked. "I mean, we're heading towards Africa and they're headed towards Egypt. What do you think?" The rest of the crew and Kathleen awaited to Shamus's answer and for some reason, they seemed to feel that he would know!

The financial backer of the Clipper's flight home just looked at them and shrugged. He shook his head and smiled. "I have no idea. Look, you almost were shot down coming into Java, the Japs tried to shanghai us when we left Surabaja, we landed in a mine field in Ceylon, so what possible problem could someone like Field Marshall Erwin Rommel pose to the Pacific Clipper!"

The crew laughed at the innkeeper's dark humor but as they broke up to tend to their duties, the idea that they were coming close to the lair of the Desert Fox gave them all pause. However, none of this bothered the flight crew and the Captain. As far as they were concerned, the next stop brought them another thousand miles closer to home and other than toping off the tanks, Bahrein would be just an overnight stopover.

It was an overnight stop but not as they had envisioned. Ford landed the Clipper on the smooth waters of the Gulf of Bahrain and taxied towards the docks of Al Manamah, the capital city of Bahrein. Ahead he could see the docking crew waiting for them and standing off to the side, near the edge, a man wearing a Palm Beach suit. Ford guessed he was the man from BOAC. He was and when the Clipper's docking had been completed and the big bird was safely secured, Mr. Stuart Shaw came on board to greet the Americans. Climbing up to the bridge, he shook hands with Ford and invited everyone on board to spend the night at their headquarters, assuring them that in this land of heat and sand, they would sleep in air conditioned comfort! Needless to say, his generous offer was quickly accepted. As Ford and he left the flight deck and came down the stairs, Shaw saw Kathleen Elmes, dressed in her Navy uniform and he stopped on the steps, his mouth wide open, his eyes wide. Ford just laughed then did the honors.

"Mr. Shaw, this is Lt. Kathleen Elmes of the United States Navy. Lt., Mr. Stuart Shaw of BOAC. And this is Shamus Ginsberg, late of The Black Swan in Surabaja, accompanying us back to America," Ford said introducing them to the BOAC man. "Mr. Shaw has invited us to spend the night at their quarters and enjoy an air conditioned slumber. I accepted on behalf of all of us."

Shaw smiled and nodded affirming what Ford had said but he couldn't take his eyes off Kathleen. And it wasn't her beauty although he would agree that she was as beautiful as any woman he'd seen in years. It was that Shaw knew a woman, any woman, flying with men would get the Islamic fundamentalists causing more trouble. And this one wore a man's uniform!

Before Shaw could comment, the civilian, Shamus, asked a question. "Mr. Shaw, an old friend of mine, Sheik Abu el Shar lives in Bahrein. Is he still alive?"

"Indeed he is!" Shaw answered, ecstatic. Here was someone that knew the ruler of the land. What a godsend. When Shaw saw Kathleen, he didn't see beauty but problems. Now this Shamus said he knew the Sheik and if he did, maybe there would be no problems! "And I'm sure he will be delighted to know you are here, Mr. Ginsberg. If you wish, when we have gotten you settled at the rest house, I'll have a runner take any message you wish to the Sheik's palace. I know he is in residence," Shaw answered. The Englishman's natural reticence kept him from asking an innkeeper from Java how he knew the most powerful man in Bahrein. He was sure he'd find out later.

An hour after the Americans had settled in their rooms at the BOAC's inn and relaxed in the comfort of this oasis, Ginsberg sitting with Ford at a table in the lounge, wrote a short note for Shaw's man to deliver to the Sheik. Ford had already made arrangements with Shaw to top off his tanks with 87% octane. That's the only kind they had in Baherin so he arranged to take on 800 pounds since Shaw assured him that the BOAC base at Khartoum had 100 octane. Now Shamus looked at the BOAC man and spoke.

"Is the Sheik still in the white slave business?" Ginsberg asked Shaw, who almost swallowed his tongue. He looked at the innkeeper and realized that Ginsberg probably knew more about what the Sheik did than he. Taking a deep breath, Shaw answered.

"The governor has made known to the Sheik the strong distaste the Empire feels to any slave trade. However, he has little power to do anything about it. But as far as we know, the Sheik is clean," Shaw answered.

Ford knew that across the Middle East, the selling of humans was more than a cottage industry. It was a way of life. The Arabs were the biggest slave traders in ancient times and as late as the 17th century, it was the Arab tribes that captured the Negroes in Africa that were shipped to the Caribbean and the American South in chains. But from what Shaw was saying, it was still going on, right here in Bahrein! He looked at Shamus and again was struck by how little he knew about this man that he was bringing to America. Shamus seemed to know the movers and shakers everywhere they landed.

"I know my old friend had a young son. Tell me about the boy, Ali," Shamus asked the BOAC man.

"The boy is now a man. He is also an enigma. Sometimes, to use an American phrase, Ali el Shar can be first class ass hole. Depending on his mood, he can be cruel, vindictive and act like a spoiled brat. Or he can be generous, thoughtful, supportive and creative. He is very well educated. You never know what face he'll be wearing and his moods can change like the weather. His father dotes on him. However, to answer your direct question, Mr. Ginsberg, no, the Sheik is no longer a 'white slaver.' Why?"

"Mr. Shaw, you know that by now, the Sheik knows Lt. Elmes landed with us. I'm sure he'll invite us to the palace and he'll be affronted if we show up without her," Ginsberg stated. "My question is simple. Will she be safe?" Shaw looked at both men and all he could do was shrug. But Ford wouldn't accept that.

"Stuart, Lt. Elmes is an officer in the United States Navy. If the Sheik's invites those of us aboard the Pacific Clipper to come to his home, Lt. Elmes will come with us. But this is your country and we are your guests. Should you decide that her safety is at risk and diplomatically prudent for Lt. Elmes not to attend, I will respect your wishes. However, the crew of the Pacific Clipper will decline the Sheik's invitation. Mr. Ginsberg is a passenger. He'll make his own decision," the Captain of the Pacific Clipper stated.

Just then, the Governor of Bahrein, the Honorable Chauncy McCloud arrived and Shaw went to greet him. Escorting him to the table where Ford and Ginsberg sat, the BOAC man did the honors. The

Governor was a most engaging man, a ready smile on his face and his red nose indicating that he enjoyed sipping Scotland's most admired export. Sitting, he winked at Ford.

"Captain, you have no idea of the troubles you and your plane have caused the British diplomatic corps. But I can report that as far as this post is concerned, Ambassador Leach's request has been filed where it belongs, in the garbage can," The feisty McCloud announced. And before Ford could respond, the waiter brought the Governor his drink. Taking a sip, he looked at Shamus Ginsberg.

"Shamus Ginsberg. How do I address you? River rat... gun runner... hustler... tavern owner... confident of paupers... and princes! Yes, Mr. Ginsberg, Whitehall has a dossier about you, as does Scotland Yard. You are very well known to us. And I must say, I'm thunder-struck to find you back here, in Bahrein... in Arabia, knowing that there are still some 'due bills' from us as well as the French and the Egyptians. I am here at the request of the Sheik to come with you and the crew of the Pacific Clipper to his house this evening so you are under the umbrella of protection of Sheik Abu el Shar and I'm in no mood to spoil what promises to be a splendid evening. Personally, I find it refreshing to meet someone who has tweaked the noses of such respected governments. And, in case you didn't know it, but I'm sure you do, you're also under the protection of the American government," the Governor stated, neither with malice or threat. It was a statement of facts and off-handed admiration.

Shamus just nodded and looking at the Governor, smiled. "Your Excellency, thank you for the thumbnail sketch of my work history. I'm most impressed. I had no idea my career was of such interest to your government as well as Scotland Yard," Ginsberg commented. The Governor just laughed and then turned to Ford.

"Mr. Shaw tells me that you are worried about the safety of Lt. Elmes. Believe me, there is no reason. While the Arab way of treating women is somewhat foreign to what we of the West expect, there will be no trouble tonight when Lt. Elmes joins us. I assure you of that," the Governor stated as forcefully as possible. Ford sat back and looked at the Governor, then nodded, without comment. Inside, he was anything but reassured. Something bothered him and he didn't know what it was except it all revolved around Kathleen Elmes. That irritated him, not only because it had nothing to do with flying home but because his feelings for her had become much stronger that he would like to admit.

The cause of Ford's concern knew none of this. Kathleen had gone to her room, excited about the coming evening. "Imagine, attending a party in the palace of a Sheik... Rudolph Valintino... Beau Geste... The Desert Song... wee! But what will I wear?" She had brought with her only the summer dress she wore on the day they found out about Pearl Harbor and the gold sari she wore to Wijjy's. Kicking off the regulation shoes, she again surveyed her small selection and then it hit her. "Navy. The United States Navy! That's it. I'll wear my uniform. The Sheik and his people know I'm aboard. So no matter what Shamus says they can't stone me when I arrive smartly dressed in this uniform. I just wish the shoes didn't look like sandhog boots," And that was how she was dressed when she entered the small lobby of the BOAC rest house.

When Chauncey McCloud saw Kathleen Elmes as she entered the reception room, he understood Ford's fears. All of a sudden, he quickly weighed the assets he had to protect her against what the Sheik's son Ali had. For he knew immediately, when the young Sheik saw her, he'd try everything to get her. Then he relaxed. The old Sheik still ran things and he'd never let anything happen to the American Naval officer. And Ali had a way of being the perfect Arab sheik's son when he wanted to be. So Chauncey McCloud put aside his concerns and the whole contingent rode to Sheik Abu el Shar's palace in the BOAC bus. As they drove up the long road, the Sheik's palace was indeed something right out of the Arabian Nights. Emerald green and white minarets about twenty feet high stood on the four corners of the building while a marble archway welcomed them to a courtyard of trees, flowering plants and a small waterfall that cascaded down from behind a wall, spilling into a pool, kidney shaped that flowed into small beds, watering the foliage and lending a sense of tranquility to the whole scene. It was beautiful. And standing on the marble steps that led up to the entrance of his palace was their host, Sheik Abu el Shar.

Stepping off the bus, the Governor led the contingent towards the Sheik but he came forward to greet them. It was a mark of his regard for his old friend Shamus Ginsberg and the Governor understood. The Sheik's somber face broke into a huge grin as Shamus walked towards him. The two embraced and looking at each other, they began to laugh as old friend do when they haven't seen each other in years. Clasping Shamus across the shoulders, the Sheik led the way into his home. Just as the group reached the stairs to enter, eight horsemen raced into the courtyard, yelling and laughing. The leader, riding a magnificent black Arabian, sped to the steps, and reigning hard, pulled up so the horse reared, flashing its hooves at the assembled guests. Ford knew immediately the rider was Ali el Shar. And he didn't like him.

But his father did! Laughing and waving at his son, he shouted that his old friend Shamus Ginsberg had come to visit on the wings of a flying boat! And he brought his fiends along! The son, calming the black, bowed from his saddle, looking at Kathleen and then to Ford. His expression didn't change but Ford noticed a tightening around the eyes as they looked at each other. Ford felt the young Ali was measuring him, ready to test him. So the two looked at each other and in a second, it was over.

The worries about the Sheik and Kathleen faded the second he took her hand, kissed it and taking her arm, led the party inside and brought her to the pillows on the other side of the low table to sit at his left hand. Shamus sat on the right. The Governor sat next to Kathleen and Ford by Shamus. The crew spread out on either side and they were joined by the Sheik's men. Since Bahrein is an Islamic nation, there were no acholic beverage served for the guests. However, what was served their taste buds told them it was either gasoline mixed with motor oil or good old West Virginia moonshine. A nod from Shamus told them to be very careful. Then Ali and his friends joined them. Off his horse, Ford could see that the young Sheik was a handsome man, slender and wiry, of average height, with dark hair, brown eyes that seemed angry. He moved with an athletic grace and it was easy for the crew of the Clipper to understand that the young man could be a formidable opponent.

Ali's friends sat at the end of the semi circle as he moved up towards his father, who smiled benignly at him. Ali stood between Ford and Shamus and waited as both slid over to make room for him. Then he sat, looked at Kathleen Elmes and grinned. Kathleen smiled back at him.

It was memorable evening. The food was excellent and the Americans ate native, using their fingers. Emulating their host, they rolled the rice pilaf between the thumb and forefinger into small bite-size lumps and then popped them into their mouths. Shish kabob was brought in on flaming spits then served onto gold plates to each of the guests. After that, the main course was brought in by four servants and placed in front of the Sheik. A young sheep that had been cooked over an open pit and the aroma of the burnt flesh that had been seasoned by the cooks filled the room with a most pleasant odor. The Sheik did the honors as he took the prime parts from the slain sheep, lungs, brain and kidneys and cutting them up, served the guests. The Governor hoped the Americans knew what an honor the Sheik was showing them, actually serving his guests. Finally, after the dishes had been removed and everyone had eaten their fill, coffee, spiced with cardamom was served in thimble size cups.

As is traditional at Arab banquets, while dinner is served, almost no conversation takes place as the guests dine. And, after they have eaten, a sizable belch from the guests indicates to the host that the meal was special. It was and the crew showed its appreciation with loud belches. Now the Sheik sat back and smiling, reached into the pocket of his tunic and pulled out a pack of cigarettes. Using a small gold lighter to ignite his smoke, the Sheik took a deep drag and smiled his guests. Those that wished also lit up and now the talk began in earnest. The Sheik and Shamus began to get caught up on the years while Ali and Ford talked about the Clipper.

"Captain, needles to say, the arrival of the flying boat has our people agog. The harbor area is swarming with people trying to see her. And I am just as curious as they," the young Sheik stated. Ford was very impressed by his English and his expression must have shown it because Ali began to laugh. "Two years at the university in Cairo, then two more at the Sorbonne in Paris, Captain Ford. My father said I had to learn to speak impeccable English," Ali explained. And looking at the Governor, Ali continued. "Sir, I hope you won't take offense but my father's reasoning is that someday America will replace the European countries as the dominate economic power in the world and I had better be able to speak English. And no matter how bad things seem now, he and I and our people are confident that now that the United States is in the war, victory for the Allies is a certainty," The young ruler-to-be looked at Ford for his assurance that what he said was true.

"I wish I were as confident, Sheik Ali. But in the few weeks we have been in the war, the Japanese rule in the Pacific and it seems the Germans aren't doing so badly in Europe. And if Rommel gets to the Suez, well, the picture is pretty bleak, as of now," Ford answered. And before young Shar could answer, Kathleen Elmes spoke. And when she did, all other conversation ceased.

"Sheik Ali, what is the latest intelligence on Rommel? We haven't heard much about him because we were running from the Japanese. Now that we are in Arabia I guess I better get caught up on the Germans, right, Captain Ford?" Kathleen stated as she looked both Ford and Ali.

The room was silent. The Americans were waiting for young Ali's answer to a reasonable question while the Arabs were stunned that a woman spoke directly to a prince! And then the tension on the Arab side was broken by Sheik Abu's laughter. Reaching over to slap Shamus on the back, he continued laughing. The Arabs understood as did the two Englishmen while the Americans wondered what was so funny. Seeing the quizzical look on his guests' faces, he nodded to Shamus to explain. But before the innkeeper could speak, Ali did.

"My American friends, please try to understand. As my father wanted me to speak English, he also wanted me to become aware of the customs in other lands. In Arabia, women do not usually join the men for dinner. In America, that of course is quite the opposite," The Americans laughed, some ruefully. "And when Lt. Elmes spoke directly to me, my friends were surprised. Not me. I expected it," Ali explained, to the satisfaction of his father and the others. "And forgive me Lt. Elmes, I think your question about Field Marshall Rommel's movements should be addressed to the Governor. Don't you agree?" Ali asked, nodding his head slightly towards McCloud.

"Indeed, Sheik Ali, I stand corrected. But since you were talking to the Captain about the war and I'm suppose to be the Intelligence specialist, I thought you might have the latest information on the Desert Fox. Governor, my apologies. Can you enlighten us on what is happening in the Sahara?" Kathleen asked, hoping to ease whatever tensions she had brought.

McCloud smiled. The American officer was not only attractive but smart. He guessed that she had planned that opening to the young Sheik to catch him off balance and immediately put herself, in Ali's mind, on his level. And as of now, it seemed to have worked. So McCloud gave Kathleen, Ford and the rest of the guests the bad news.

"Before I speak of Rommel, I have some bad news that I'm sure you didn't hear. Hong Kong has surrendered. Happened Christmas night," the Governor stated, quietly but the news sobered everyone. No one spoke for a minute then McCloud spoke again. "Some better news. It seems the Desert Fox is stalled at Tobruk. Not that we had anything to do with it. Hitler decided to send more supplies to the Russian front and Rommel has to do with what he has. So the fate of the Suez hasn't been decided. Yet. Captain Ford, with you flying to Khartoum tomorrow I'll make sure Mr. Shaw and the BOAC personnel will be ready to fill your tanks so you can be on your way quickly. Even with a semi-standoff in the Sahara, Rommel's planes still dominate the air from Tunis to Egypt and as far south as Lake Victoria. So get in and out of Khartoum as fast as you can."

The talk of the war brought Ford and the crew back to the reality of their situation and the old Sheik guessed that they were anxious to get back to the BOAC house. He rose and so did all the others.

Escorting the guests to their bus, the Sheik again kissed Kathleen's hand, shook hands with Ford and offered his hopes to the rest for a safe return to America. Shamus was going to spend the night as his guest and the Sheik promised Ford he'd have the innkeeper at the docks well before Ford's planned takeoff. With that, the crew and the British contingent boarded the bus back to their digs.

It was still fairly early, just past 2100 hours so Steers and a few of the others decided to enjoy a nightcap. John Mack, Swede Rothe and John Parish walked down the ramp to the dock area and along the wharf to the Clipper. John Poindexter and Jim Henricksen were on board, standing watch. They had volunteered for the duty and so when the other three came aboard, the two pumped them for information about the Sheik and his palace. It wasn't anywhere as near as exciting as the two had hoped. The three left and returned to the BOAC house and also had a nightcap.

Ford and Kathleen were standing by the garden area as the three came by and passed on their invitation to join them. They stood on the edge of the patio and looked out at the moon. The night was warm and the little breeze that came off the Bay of Bahrein was comfortable. Kathleen had taken off her heavier Navy blue blouse and the two just stood and made small talk.

"What did you think of the evening?" Ford asked. Kathleen laughed. "When we walked into the Black Swan that afternoon did you ever think we'd have someone on board that seems to know every important person in the subcontinent? I wonder whom he knows in Khartoum!" she asked. Then Ford told her about Governor McCloud's description of Shamus and they both enjoyed a good laugh at Shamus' expense.

"And young Sheik Ali?" Ford asked.

Looking at Ford, she suddenly realized that there was a trace of jealousy in Ford's voice. And she was very pleased. But she passed on the chance to tweak him.

"Very attractive... has an air of mystery about him... smart, probably dangerous if crossed... no Hollywood sheik... his eyes... they were very, how shall I say, arresting. A very interesting man, one I'd not want as an enemy. You?" she summarized then asked.

"Cold. Very calculating. Good looking but if there is any fire in that heart, I didn't see it or feel it. Shamus is worried... thinks Ali will try to abduct you tonight and sell you into some "white slavery' ring! And watching him look at you this evening, I think our host's son might consider the odds and try something," Ford stated.

Kathleen looked at him and as she was about to laugh, someone coughed behind them and when they turned, there stood Sheik Ali el Shar. Alone. He was dressed as he had been at dinner, riding boots, jodhpurs, a small jeweled dagger in his belt, with only a maroon silk cloak over his shoulders that changed his appearance. He bowed to both and smiling, walked towards them. Ford felt no fear and neither did Kathleen. They both smiled back.

"Sheik Ali. What a pleasant surprise. I'm sorry we didn't get a chance to say good by at your father's palace," Ford stated.

"Thank you Captain. And I apologize if I startled you Lt. Elmes. When you left, I met with my friends to decide how to enjoy this pleasant evening and I found myself wanting to talk with both of you, if for no other reason than to enjoy your company," he began. "As I said at dinner, my Father and I agree that when this war ends, the United States will be the most powerful nation in the world. And in a few years, the mantle of leadership of Bahrein will fall on my shoulders. So I told my friends I'd look in on you and if you hadn't gone to bed, see if you'd indulge me with some conversation about America. I know it is getting late and you have much to do tomorrow and if this is inconvenient I'll understand. But it isn't often that one meets a pilot of the most famous airline in the world as well as a beautiful American woman, and one that is an officer in her government's Navy, to boot."

They talked unto almost midnight. When it became too cool on the patio, they went inside. John Mack joined them as the Swede and John Parish had a nightcap. The young sheik confessed that the first time he saw Kathleen, thoughts of abduction flashed into his mind! She laughed and he assured them it was just a brief, fanciful idea. "After all, isn't Valentino revered around the world for kidnapping beautiful women?" the sheik laughed and the others joined in.

The give and take between the four was all that Ali could have hoped for. They discussed the war, America coming out of its isolationism, where the wealth of the Arab world would could lead them, flying and the Clipper's trip, woman's rights, slavery and the Germans. The Sheik shocked them when he listed all the Arab countries that were pro German and how they respected Hitler and German might and he told them that it extended across Africa. He gave them a thumbnail history of the rise of Islam, surprising them with stories of how vast the Arab conquests had been, larger than the Romans and rivaling those of Genghis Khan. Finally, it was time to go to bed.

Sheik Ali kissed Kathleen's hand shook hands with John Mack and promised to come to the dock tomorrow to see them off. It was obvious he had something he wanted to say to Ford so as the other two left, he and Ford sat.

"Captain, you need not fear me or my people. But fear your friends. I warn you. Khartoum is very dangerous. I can't be more specific because all I have are rumors about certain people there and an instinctive feeling that while you may have escaped the Japanese, be ever on the alert. After you leave Khartoum, you know you'll be flying into places that are sympathetic to the Germans, as is the Shah of Iran and not very fond of Americans. So be careful. That is all I can say," Young Ali said and rising, he shook the pilot's hand. Bowing, he swept out of the door of the BOAC house mounted his horse, waved to Ford standing in the doorway and began to canter up the street back to the Sheik's palace. Ford went to bed.

The next day, the Arabs struck. Word had gone out in Al Manamah of the infidels who landed in a flying boat, of a woman who walked about without her face covered, wearing a uniform and talking as an equal to men, Arab men. And they heard that their Sheik had even had them as his guests for dinner. The news was welcomed by Ben Adrisi, the Imam of Bahrein who was consumed with hatred for their jailers, the British and especially the family of Sheik Abu el-Shar. When he heard of the Americans and the woman, he knew here was at last a chance to embarrass the Sheik and the British by raising protests against the infidel Americans. Ben Idrisi knew nothing would come of this other than a brief showing of his power to the Sheik, who would immediately dismiss it. But to the masses, he knew that any humbling of the foreigners would only strengthen his influence. So early the next morning, Ben Adrisi led a screaming mob to the dock where the strange plane sat and they invaded the Operation center, demanding the infidel's craft not be allowed to fly across the land of Mohammed and that for permission to leave Bahrein and to atone for their sins against Allah, they must pay tribute. The BOAC man behind the counter was himself an Arab and as he tried to reason with the Imams, their wrath turned on him and he hastily beat a retreat to the headquarters, bringing Mr. Shaw to the Ops center.

What greeted the Englishman reminded him of what it must have been like at the Tower of Babel. The room was jammed with shouting Arabs, and the noise made his head pound. He couldn't understand what they wanted until Ben Adrisi quieted the crowd. Demanding that the Americans not be allowed to fly across the kingdom of Saudi Arabia because they are infidels, they have a woman among them and she didn't have on a vail, Shaw finally was able to understand what was happening. The Imams had no way of forcing the English to obey their laws but they could create a major problem for the Americans, embarrass the British and the Sheik at the same time. Shaw agreed and went to the BOAC house to talk to Ford. As he hurried there, he saw the Americans walking towards him. And there was Kathleen Elmes. Ben Adrisi and some of the other Imams had followed Shaw from a distance and when they saw her, they began screaming, pointing and then rushing towards her. Shaw tried to explain to Ford and the crew what had happened but he couldn't make himself heard. Just as he was about to led a retreat to the house, the Sheik arrived with Shamus Ginsberg, his son Ali riding his horse besides the Sheik's car.

The Arabs raced to the Sheik's car and screaming at him, the Imams demanding that the woman be made to wear Arab dress, be veiled and the Americans agree to change their flight plan so they did not cross Saudi Arabia. And they should pay a heavy fine or not be allowed to leave. The Sheik looked at Shaw, then at his son. He got out of the car and faced the Imams. Before the mob knew what happened, Ali's horse began moving quickly through the crowd and the Americans followed behind, while the Sheik's driver brought the car up behind Ali's horse, with Shamus still inside. Going around the Ops building, Ali led them down the dock towards the Clipper. The passenger doors had been opened earlier by Henricksen and the crew quickly jumped in, Kathleen with them. Ford stayed outside as Ali dismounted and Shamus got out of the car. The three quickly decided that there was no way to reason with that mob, some of whom were already inching down the dock towards the plane. Ford knew it was time to say goodby. He signaled Mack to start the engines and as one of the BOAC men at the stern untied the hawser from it cleat and Barney opened the hatch and pulled the anchor into its room. Ali had already begun to untie the bow rope and Shamus ran over, grabbed it from him, shook his hand and ran for the door. Ford waved to Ali, jumped aboard and as he slammed tight the passenger door, he heard the port engine rev up and felt the Clipper moved away from the dock and slide towards the channel. The mob had stopped near Sheik Ali whose stance told them that they would have to get by him if they wanted to get to the Clipper. Quickly, Sheik Abu and Shaw and some BOAC men joined Ali at the dock area as the Pacific Clipper slowly moved out into the channel. Ben Adrisi, the Imams and the mob stopped. The crowd began to quiet and as the engines of the Clipper roared to life, the noise seemed to take the anger from the crowd. That and the sight of their ruler and his son standing in their paths. It was over. The people began to move off the dock as the BOAC guards gently prodded them. Sheik Abu, young Ali and Shaw stood there watching the Clipper taxi towards the center of the Bay and begin her run towards a watery takeoff. Ali looked at his father and both smiled. Now the Clipper raced down the water and lifted off, headed south down the Persian Gulf. Shaw wondered if Ford would fly the extra thousand miles around Saudi Arabia. He laughed, knowing the American wasn't intimidated and would take the shortest way to Khartoum, over Saudi Arabia. The elder Sheik knew after last night's long talk with Shamus he'd never see his old friend again. And Ali watched the Clipper climb into the sky, laughing to himself. "I wonder what Ford or Kathleen would say if they knew my men were hidden outside, ready to take her! Well, good luck you two. Allah be with you. I have a feeling you'll make it."

Ford had taken the controls after John Mack had gotten the Clipper airborne. The crew had returned to the few duties they had after the confrontation with the Arabs. Shamus was trying to explain what had happened on the ground but the more they asked him the more he confused them. Repeating what little he had gotten out of Shaw, "the Arabs were pissed because we infidels were walking around with a woman who didn't have her face covered and we planned to fly over Saudi Arabia, home of Mohammed," The others looked at him and when he had nothing further to add, they dispersed.

The weather was clear and as he climbed to 10,000 feet, higher than usual because of the heat emanating from desert air, Ford had Steers plot the course from Bahrein to Khartoum via the Persian Gulf, over the Gulf of Oman, then southwest down the Arabian Sea to the Gulf of Aden then across Ethiopia into Anglo-Egyptian Sudan and on to Khartoum. He also had Steers plot a course directly across Saudi Arabia, to the Red Sea. across her to the Nile and the Sudan, following the Blue Nile till it met the White Nile at Khartoum. It didn't take Sterns long and as he moved from his navigator's table to report to Ford, there was a sudden explosion!

They all looked at each other but Ford knew immediately what had happened. There was no problem that they couldn't handle. Part of one of the exhaust stacks on number four engine had blown off. It made noise but in no way endangered the flight. They'd fix it in Khartoum. But after what had happened to Number Three leaving Trincomalee, Ford was determined that he devote one full day giving the engines as complete breakdown as they could. They didn't have any dry dock to put the Clipper on but they would wash her down good, getting all the saltwater off her wings, spontons, and exhausts. And he'd have Swede check the engines as throughly as possible. The exhaust stack should be no problem.

Steers report didn't surprise Ford. If they went the way the Imams in Bahrein wanted, they'd be adding an extra 1000 miles to the trip. So Ford gradually put the Clipper into an easy banking turn to starboard and they headed for Saudi Arabia. There were mountains ahead and Steers gave him a course that took them between the ranges. There was no cause for alarm. But in another two hours, the clouds got thicker and Ford gradually brought the plane lower. About three thousand feet, they came clear of the overcast. The lands below them were desolate. Steers had gone into his observation bubble, looking for something that would give him a clue to where they were. Only rock and sand and emptiness. Then, ahead he saw something rising off the desert floor and the Clipper was headed right at it. Coming out he saw that Mack was pointing at the same thing. It was a town, no a city and at 180 knots, her exhaust belching hideous noises, the Pacific Clipper zoomed over Mecca, whizzing over the great lodestone of the Islamic world, the black Kabba of the Great Mosque. Everywhere on the ground the worshippers ran, pointing to the sky and screaming or covering their heads as they ran towards the safety of the walls. As quickly as the Clipper had destroyed the tranquility of Islam's most revered shrine, she was gone, only her burping exhaust leaving the awe struck Moslems wondering what Allah had wrought.

It happened so fast that only those on the flight deck knew exactly what took place. When Steers explained everything to the rest, there were some laughs and after what they had gone through in Bahrein, some heard Norm Brown mumble "serves the towelheads right."

The afternoon sun was directly above them when the Clipper crossed over the Red Sea and in another hour, Bob Ford saw the Blue Nile ahead. Banking to the left, he followed the ribbon of water to where she joined her sister, the White Nile at Khartoum. As Ford brought the giant plane down towards the water, the few small Arab craft on the river scattered. Putting her hull on the broadest part, almost a quarter of a mile across, the Pacific Clipper landed on the river of Cleopatra and Ramses, the Mahti and Chinese Gordon. The Nile was not Blue or White but yellow.

Chapter 13

Germany Joins the Chase

0645 Hours-29 December, 1941-Dease Lake, British Columbia, Canada

Tanaka was asleep. They had left Kayak Island at night, using the stars to guide them from the Aleutians to Canada and their next landing site, Dease Lake. He had flown most of the way from Alaska. Oho had taken over an hour ago and the sun was just coming over the Rocky Mountains as he brought the Mitsubishi down towards the frozen lake. Somewhere along the eastern shoreline he expected to see a signal from the Cree Indians that had the fuel for their plane. The lake was located in the dense woods between the Coast Mountains and the towering Rockies. There were two small towns located at either end of the lake and their contact on Kayak Island assured them that there was little to fear from anyone seeing or hearing them. The lake was a narrow, finger like body of water, about 30 miles long, The land was covered with snow and the lake itself frozen solid. Oho needed all his considerable skills to bring the plane down on the deck and skim along the lake's surface until he saw the signal. He had just dipped his wings and began his decent when he saw a few miles ahead the flash of light reflecting from a mirror on the west side of the lake. Looking into the still darken area directly across from where he spotted the mirrored signal, he saw the dot-dash-dot-dash-dot-dash signal from a flashlight on the shore. Cutting back on the power, he brought the small plane down and as her wheels touched down on the frozen water, he could feel and hear the ice crunching under the tires. Not wanting to take any chances that someone might hear them, he did not reverse the engines to slow the fighter plane but trusted to his foot breaks and the natural friction of the ice on the tires to stop them. He knew the place where he saw the coded message flashed was a mile ahead and he'd stop in plenty of time.

Tanaka had awakened when the plane touched down and stretching, he looked at Oho and nodded. They would refuel here and hopefully there would be a message waiting from Tokyo on Ford's location. He suddenly felt very thirsty and reaching behind him, brought out the thermos and poured himself a drink. Refilling the cup, he offered it to Oho, who in shock at Tanaka's thoughtfulness, almost shoved down on the breaks and spun the plane on the icy surface.

As they approached the spot where the Indians should be waiting, the trees parted and three men came forward from the shore dragging two sleds piled high with gas cans. Oho came within twenty feet of the men and cut the engines. A fourth man stood on the shore holding knapsacks filled with food and a piece of paper. Tanaka pushed open the cockpit door and eschewing the step ladder, climbed out and walked over to the man with the supplies and the paper. Tanaka took the sacks and the paper from the Cree and passed over to him the belt filled with gold. The Indian didn't look at what the belt held, knowing full well what was inside made he and his friends rich beyond their dreams. He told Tanaka that their next stop was at a place called Lake Athabasca, about 600 miles as the crow flies. There was a Chipewyan Indian reservation there near the base of the lake and the Japanese were expected by early evening. They would be refueled, fed and given directions to their next rendezvous. He took Tanaka's map and pointed where they were now and where they had to go. The tall man turned and walked back towards his plane. Oho had followed Tanaka out of the plane and walked to its front and opened the gas tanks on each engine. The three men pushed the sled up close and began to fill the tanks. Not one word was spoken. When the tanks were filled, the extra cans were loaded in the rear of the plane, lashed down and covered. Oho figured that they had an another 500 pounds of gas back there and looking down the length of the lake, he knew they would need that long runway to get airborne. He was so busy he didn't notice the cold. But when he took off one of his gloves to shake hands with their suppliers, in seconds he realized his mistake and quickly put them back on! Now Tanaka returned and the two climbed in, closed the door and Oho took the pilot's seat, started the engines and staying close to the shore line, the pair began the next and most dangerous part of their trip, over the Rocky Mountains and onto Lake Athabasca. Both looked out ahead on the ice to make sure there were no hidden hazards. When the plane had reached lift off speed, Oho kept it on the ice for another minute. The extra 500 pounds on board dictated such caution. Finally, he pulled back and they were airborne. Glancing over at his co-pilot, he saw the Commodore smiling. The news of Ford must be good.

It was. Tokyo had wired that the Americans had left Ceylon, landed in Bahrein and were headed for the Sudan and Khartoum. Tanaka was delighted. It would take them another 10-12 hours to reach their landing at the Chipewyan reservation. From there, they would still have three quarters of Canada to cover but Tanaka felt good. In his mind he could visualize where Ford was in Africa and knew that with the Clipper's great range, he could reach America in another four or five days. Tanaka needed another miracle like the one at Trincomalee but now he was closer to New York than Ford. He knew the Boeing would easily make that up. His range was 1000 miles maximum, Ford's five times that. But he was still in the hunt and that's all that counted. Looking out the cabin windows, as far as he could see, everything was white, except far ahead. As they climbed to altitude, he could see the first of the mountain ranges they had to cross. On the map they were called the Cassiar Mountains. But ever above them in the distance, the dark shadows of the wall that was the Rocky Mountains loomed. They didn't have the power to fly over its highest points so they would fly through, around and wherever possible, over the smaller peaks. The white desolation below and mountains ahead of them filled Tanaka with a fatalism about their flight and his goal. Although Oho was seated next to him, he felt alone and in someway, free of any concerns about Ford and the mission. It would be as it would be and there was nothing he or Ford could do about it. Reaching for one of the knapsacks, he opened it and brought out some food, meat of a kind. Smelling it, he realized it was elk. He had had venison once and thought that's what it was. Chewy and very tangy. He pulled off a piece from the bone and handed it to Oho, then took one for himself. Settling in, the Japanese posse continued their chase.

1545 hours-31 December, 1941-Khartoum, Anglo Egyptian Sudan

Ford was relaxed. He sat in the tub in his room at the Grand Hotel, the hot water finally coming from the bearers after an hour's wait and he was going to enjoy every minute of this bath. All things considered, even counting the problems two days ago at Bahrein with those nutty Imams, the trip here had been almost perfect. The crew took yesterday to fix up the Clipper, giving her a good shake down, checking all four engines, making sure all wires were connected and secured, changing the plugs, oil and cleaning out the sand that seemed to infiltrate every part of the ship. Last night, he and Kathleen had a chance to walk together in the exquisite gardens of the hotel and stand looking over the Nile in a moonlight that would have made Bing Crosby begin to croon. Today, the crew repaired the loose exhaust pipe on Number 3 and John Steers had taken the small boat the RAF had lent them and extended the runway markings on the Nile by 500 feet each. As he left the Clipper to fulfill his assignment, the crew kidded Steers about not falling into the water and to beware of the crocodiles. When the RAF people delivered the 100 octane for the engines, all was ready for the Clipper to leave early tomorrow morning for Leopoldville. Sliding deeper into the tub, unable to stretch out his long legs so his knees stuck up above the water, Ford suddenly thought about the young Sheik, Ali and his warning. In a way, it was similar to what Shamus had said before they went to the VanGelder party in Surabaja. "Watch out for your friends,"

"What did he mean?" Ford thought. "Friends? The British in Bahrein? Well, we're here in Khartoum. Could Ali have meant here? And Shamus suspected him of having designs on Kathleen. White slaver! What a laugh. But he wouldn't have warned me unless he knew something. What? Maybe it's was just a feeling but somehow I think he heard or saw something that made him tell me to watch out. But what?" Ford wondered and as he noticed the water was getting more tepid, he decided he'd had enough and rising, he reached for his towel and dried himself off. He looked into the mirror that barely reflected back his image and knew he needed a shave. The only warm water was in the tub so he reached into it with his right hand, splashed his face and taking his shaving cup and brush, tried to raise a lather. It wasn't much but it was good enough that he rid his face of its growth. Dressing in a clean set of whites, he surveyed his looks in the mirror in the room and nodded his approval. As he headed for the door and the lobby, he wondered what Kathleen was planning for tonight. He knew she was shopping in some of the bazaars with some of the officer's wives from the RAF group that came when they had landed the other evening. Last night had been great and although they hadn't made any definite plans, he was hoping they'd be together again tonight, preferably alone. Opening the door to his room, Ford walked from it towards the stairs that would take him to the lobby and his crew. What he found was trouble.

As Ford came down the stairs, he scanned the lobby and saw it was crowded with as eclectic a gathering of individuals as he'd ever seen before. Arabs in long flowing robes, Englishmen in uniforms or business suits, Negroes in colorful tribal costumes, other Arabs wearing fezes and white linen suits, and others, Occidentals, obviously refugees from Europe, hoping to find in Khartoum a way to some part of the world where there was no war. The occasional American stood out like a sore thumb, totally lost in the sea of foreigners and the language of the Middle East. Ford felt empathy for those few. He saw John Mack talking to Squadron Leader John Wild, the man that had greeted them when they landed and who had been so helpful since then. Ford like the Englishman. Mack, looking up and spotting Ford, nodded and he and Lt. Wild moved towards his Captain.

"Captain, Mr. Wild has come over to pick you up. It seems the Governor here, a Mr. Edward Heath, wishes to see you. Squadron Leader, maybe you should explain to the Captain," Mack stated, turning things over to the British officer.

Ford laughed at the concern he saw on Mack's face. "Look, Squadron Leader, I know I broke protocol by not presenting myself to the Governor when we landed the other day. But it was late and we were dirty and tired. Yesterday, with so much to do to get the Clipper ready for tomorrow, I couldn't get away. And today was more of the same. I'm afraid I forgot my diplomatic obligations. John, you'll have to give Norm Brown a demerit for not reminding me of the proper responsibilities of a Pan Am Captain when visiting a foreign government," Ford said in an amused fashion. The other two didn't seem to think it funny.

"Captain, perhaps we should retire to the lounge so we can sit and talk in private," the British pilot suggested. Ford nodded and the three went into the lounge. The room was dark and cool and Wild led them to a corner table, signaling to a waiter to come over for an order. When seated, they ordered Scotches and while the waiter went to fill their requests, Wild looked at Bob Ford and began.

"Captain, my apologies. I too am at fault. I should have told you when you landed that you had to see the Governor but things happened so fast"... and with that Lt. Wild shrugged his shoulders. "But this has nothing to do with diplomatic niceties. Sometime earlier today, probably this morning, an urgent request, no, more of an order, came down from Cairo to the Governor to hold your plane so you can take some very important passengers back to the States. He wants to see you personally to make sure you understand the orders," the flyer began and even in the semi darkness of the lounge, John Wild could see Ford's jaw harden. Holding up his hand to try and calm the American, he continued. "The governor's aide called me at headquarters and asked that I personally see you as soon as possible and escort you to the palace. The Governor can be a trifle stiff, somewhat of a martinet, you might say. Governor Heath has no direct authority over my detachment but we always try to cooperate with the people running the colonies."

Ford snorted and Wild totally understood. If he were trying to accomplish the impossible and someone told him to wait because some VIP's were coming, he'd blow his stack. Ford's self control impressed him. Even though he and the Americans had hit it off and had kidded about the problems they had faced to get to Khartoum, it was only now he began to appreciate what Ford and his crew had faced since leaving Auckland. They were always at the mercies of the local government and its people wherever they landed. They had no friends. Not here or anywhere. Not only the flying across uncharted lands and waters but landing in places controlled by colonial powers as foreign to the Americans as the Pacific Clipper was to the natives. Even here in Khartoum, it was the British Governor, not the Germans causing the problem. And Squadron Leader Wild did not for a moment believe that any VIP's of such importance were coming to this insect filled backwater that the American plane should be held. As a pilot, he was well aware what a tremendous asset those powerful Wright Cyclone engines would be on the wings of British bombers. With those engines, they could take the war right to Hitler's backyard, probably even dominate Rommel up there in Tobruk. Maybe that was the reason for the urgent message to Heath. He hoped not.

"John, thank you for bringing me the message but who knows we are here and who is it that is ordering us to stay?" Ford asked and as soon as the words left his mouth he began to laugh. It was as if the whole world knew where they were and Trippe's "radio silence" command was a great joke.

"Captain Ford, I'm sorry. I'm flying blind on this. Governor Heath will explain all of this when we meet him. And we better get a move on. He is quite the stickler about being on time and while I don't want to convey any impression that he is a difficult man, he is! So let us be off," the Squadron Officer summed up as he sipped the last of his Scotch and rose. Ford did the same and looking at John Mack, just shrugged. Mack shrugged back and watched as the two made their way from the lounge, through the lobby and out the door to Lt. Wild's lorry waiting with a driver at the front of the hotel.

They drove through the crowded main street of Khartoum from the hotel towards the Governor's residence and both were silent with their own thoughts. For Ford, this idea that he'd have to wait an extra day in Khartoum for some people that he didn't know or care about was idiotic. For Wild, he only hoped that the Governor had a very strong reason for holding the Americans. He wished that Mr. Heath would understand that Ford and Pan Am were far too important to the overall scheme of things to screw around with them. Looking over to the American, whom he greatly admired as a fellow pilot as well as personally liked, Wild saw an iciness about Ford that was even more frightening than the anger he'd seen earlier.

"Look, Bob. I know you understand that I have no idea of what is going on. But Governor Heath said... and the Squadron Leader stopped. Ford had held up his hand and smiled. He nodded to Wild, sat back and seemed to relax. The car turned and ran along a narrow road that paralleled the Nile and just ahead Ford saw the palace of the Governor.

"Who is that?" Ford asked Lt. Wild, nodding to a bronze statue of a uniformed man sitting atop a camel, gazing across the Nile.

"Lord Kitchner. The Honorable General Horatio Herbert Kitchner, conqueror of the Sudan, revenger of the murder of General Charles "Chinese" Gordon, and later, the man who led the British forces that defeated the Boers and garnered South Africa for the Empire," the Squadron Leader answered.

"Churchill," Ford stated as the car slowly moved towards the palace gate. Wild looked at the American and smiled. "You mean Mr. Churchill, our PM?"

Ford laughed and nodded. "I remember reading that as a young man he was in the British Army that recaptured the Sudan and later wasn't he in the Boer War? Didn't he write about it, for one of your newspapers?" Ford asked.

"My compliments, Bob. I am amazed to find an American that has any knowledge of the early days of our Prime Minister. I don't mean to be disparaging but if you were to ask me about the early life of President Roosevelt, other than his contracting polio, I'd confess I know nothing. I am impressed," Squadron Officer Wild stated, looking at his American guest with further appreciation.

Ford shrugged and as the car came though the palace gate and stopped, the two stepped out into the early evening heat and began walking up the steps towards the palace entrance. Wild stopped Ford and pointed to a spot about half way above them. "Captain, since you know something about the history of the British conquest of Egypt, the Nile and the Sudan, about twenty feet ahead you can see a plaque. I'll tell you now that it marks the spot where Arab tribesmen, probably the

Fuzzy Wuzzies, killed General Gordon. Legend has it that Gordon had gone alone into the desert for a face to face meeting with the Mahdi to try and end the war. The Mahdi met him and told him to go back to England because Allah had promised that when Khartoum fell, he and Islam would rule all of Africa and the Middle East. But under no circumstances was Gordon to be harmed. When the Arabs broke through Khartoum's main gates, Gordon walked down these very steps to confront the invaders. They killed him, chopped off his head, stuck it on a lance and raced around Khartoum showing it off as the rest of their comrades destroyed the British garrison, including the women and children. When the Mahdi heard of Gordon's fate, he tore his clothes off and ran into the desert. Within six months, Kitchner had defeated the Mahdi's troops. No one ever found the body of the holy man," Mr. Wild illuminated as they reached the spot with the plaque. The two stood and looked at it and the inscription. Just then, they heard the steps of someone coming to greet them. As Ford and Wild turned to walk up the rest of the steps, Wild whispered to Ford. "Mr. Heath thinks he's "Chinese" Gordon," Ford couldn't comment as the Governor's man greeted them at the top of the steps.

Squadron Leader Wild introduced Ford to Martin Clark, the governor's aide. He led them into a huge anteroom with people working at different tasks, most of them Englishmen with a few Arabs sprinkled about. Overhead fans twirled and cooled the room. Turning right and walking towards the Nile, they headed for a pair of tall, ornate wooden doors with carved panels. A brief glance showed Ford that each panel seemed to depict different battles the English had fought to conquer this part of the world. Mr. Clark pushed the doors open and, as Ford and Wild entered, closed them behind the visitors and left the two alone to face Governor Edward Heath, the man responsible for the administration of the largest of the British colonies in Africa.

The room was magnificent. High beamed ceiling ran the length of the room and directly in front were a brace of tall French doors that led out to a balcony and a splendid view of the Nile. Four huge fans spun the air around the room, hoping to ease the heavy heat and humidity of Khartoum. To the right, a wall filled with oil paintings of war; soldiers, obviously British, in conflict with all sorts of enemies. And to the left, where Ford's eyes almost immediately focused was the Governor. He was seated behind a long desk and over his shoulders, Ford saw hanging a huge portrait of General Charles George Gordon, in his day, the most popular hero in the British Isles. He had crushed the Taiping Rebellion in China, hence the nickname "Chinese" Gordon

Gladstone to put down the power of the Mahdi. His death caused an uproar across England. His father had told him about Gordon years ago and these facts popped into his head as he strode to meet the man who seventy years later stood in "Chinese" Gordon's place.

Governor Edward Heath rose to greet them and again Ford was struck by how much almost every Englishman he had met so far in their odyssey looked like someone from the movies. First it was Sir Reginald, then Captain Loud and now Governor Heath. For as he stood and walked around the desk, the man was a ringer for the stuffy Colonel in "Lives of the Bengal Lancers," A light Khaki blouse, buttoned up with a dark brown tie against a white shirt, jodhpurs and dark brown riding boots, shined to reflection. All that was missing was his pith helmet and the riding crop. He was rather short, slim and his grey mustache perfectly trimmed and he wasn't smiling.

"Governor Heath, may I present Captain Robert Ford of Pan American Airways. Captain Ford, Governor Edward Heath, His Majesty's governor of Anglo Egyptian Sudan," Mr. Wild stated, completing the formalities. Mr. Heath put out his hand and Ford took it. Motioning to the two chairs in front of his desk for them to sit, he returned to his chair, sat and looked at the American.

"Captain, I observed your arrival earlier this week and I must say your plane is magnificent. I hope that Squadron Leader Wild has been able to assist you in making sure you and your men are quite comfortable," the Governor began. Ford noticed the 'earlier this week' comment, and knew it to be a mild rebuke for not presenting himself until now. Ford nodded and smiled and waited for the Governor to come to the point. He did immediately.

"I have received instructions to hold your plane here to await the arrival of two very important persons coming here from Egypt to take passage with you when you leave Khartoum. The orders from Cairo came this morning," the Governor stated. Then he sat back, smiling, and waited for Ford's reaction, sure that the American would respond as all Americans do when something interferes with their plans, exploding and shouting. But there was no rejoiner from Ford. The Governor looked at the pilot and thought to himself that this would be a lot easier than expected so he repeated himself.

"I received the orders this morning from my superiors in Cairo. Since I had not met you yet even after you landed here the other day, I instructed Mr. Wild to bring you here so I could give you the orders directly. Do you have any questions, Captain Ford?" Mr. Heath asked.

He sat back, quite comfortable with the knowledge of his power to hold the Americans. And he was anxious to see if Ford would now react.

"Sir, Mr. Wild explained to me the request that you received from Cairo," Ford began as he framed his reply. But he was interrupted by the Governor.

Governor Heath looked at Ford and spoke bluntly. "It was not a request, Captain Ford. It was a direct order from the Ambassador."

Ford could feel the hair on the back of his neck begin to rise and his face starting to redden so he took a deep breath, sat back and looked at the little Chinese Gordon. "He stressed 'the Ambassador' in Cairo. Could goofy Leach's letter have caused this?" Ford thought to himself, trying to remain calm. "Now don't blow up. He wants that. Put on your poker face and play this through and see what the man really has."

"Sir," Ford began, softly, using Shamus's trick to get the Governor to lean forward." Did the Ambassador tell you who will be riding with us, when they will arrive and where are we to take them?"

The Governor looked at the American and was surprised by the tone of Ford's voice and the question. It had never dawned on him to ask that from Cairo so he had no answer! He had his orders and the American would have to accept that. But as he thought about it, the Captain's questions were very logical and he felt somewhat non-plused. So he reacted as the Governor of a British Crown Colony would to an American. He dismissed Ford's question with the wave of his hand.

"Captain, I'm just a poor governor in the backwaters of His Majesty's Empire. When orders come from Cairo, I obey them. The orders are to hold your plane until these people arrive. When they do, you can leave and take them where they wish to go. Other than that, do you have any questions?" the Governor stated, emphatically. Mr. Wild's face had lost most of its color as he listened and waited for the explosion he knew was coming. When there was none, he looked across and saw the American pilot quietly observing the Governor.

Ford realized that he was looking at another British civil servant who probably progressed though the "old boys network" as have so many diplomats in so many countries. So Ford held his tongue. It was already evening and to storm out and try to take off in the darkness was stupid. Anyway, his crew wasn't ready so he'd sit here and let the Governor think he'd won this round. "When I'm ready, Governor, the Pacific Clipper will be gone, no matter what Cairo tells you. And without your very important people," Ford thought to himself. He nodded and was ready to leave. To Mr. Heath, Ford's head movement meant he agreed with the dictates of the Governor of Anglo Egyptian Sudan. Smiling, Governor Heath stood and indicated the interview was at an end. Putting out his hand, he shook Ford's, then Squadron Leader Wild's. The two smiled at the Governor and left the room, Mr. Heath, watching them, quite pleased with himself.

The two walked out the same way they came in and when they reached Wild's car, Ford stopped and looked back at the palace. He didn't say a word and Wild knew exactly what he was thinking. They climbed into the lorry and returned to the hotel. Entering the lobby, they walked into the lounge to have a drink. As they searched for an open table, Ford spotted Kathleen sitting with Shamus and John Mack and he and Wild joined them. Ford's news of the holdup disquieted all of them but they realized that there was nothing to be done but wait things out. It was New Years' Eve and Squadron Leader Wild again offered his invitation for them to join him and the other RAF personnel at their mess. Mack accepted on behalf of the Pacific Clipper's crew but Ford and Kathleen demurred. All understood.

The next morning, New Years Day, 1942, about 0730, Ford met with his men. He had decided they were going this day but he also knew that the Governor could make things very rough. Ford would see him again with the Squadron Leader and explain the facts of life to him. They were all seated around a couple of tables they'd pulled together as the hotel staff brought them pots of coffee and some dates covered with a red sauce that most of the men found far too sweet. Pocket bread, called "pita" by the natives was served with goat cheese. Butter was not available in this part of the world. Neither was cream. So Barney being a good First Steward and knowing what the Arabs would serve them, had earlier used the small RAF launch at the dock, and gone back to the Clipper and raided his own larder for those items!

Swede Rothe assured Ford that the Clipper was ready and that the loose exhaust stack was secure. Steers had lengthened the takeoff run and the tanks were filled with 100 octane gas. Now it was up to Ford to remove the one problem facing them, the Governor's orders to stay. Before he did, he had to make sure that everyone was on the Clipper when he met with Mr. Heath. He didn't want to hang around Khartoum looking for his crew after telling the Governor to stick it! He ordered them to quietly leave their rooms and as unobtrusively as possible, move to the wharf were the small RAF motor boat was docked. Shamus and John Mack would accompany Kathleen. He hoped the Governor's men would not pay any attention to some Americans going out to their plane.

The group broke up and as they went to get their few belongings from their rooms, John Wild came into the dinning room and smiling at the crew who a few hours earlier he was singing "Auld Lang Syne" with, walked over to Ford's table. Ford motioned Wild to a chair and poured the Englishman some coffee. He offered Wild a cigarette and the pilot took it. His smile of enjoyment led Ford to laugh and push his newly opened pack of Chesterfields over to Wild. As he was about to protest, Ford held up his hand. American cigarettes were a luxury so Wild stifled his objections and pocket the pack, nodding his thanks.

"I'm headed over to the Governor's palace as soon as possible," Ford asked. Wild looked at him and read Ford perfectly. And Wild knew very well that the Governor would not hesitate a second to place Ford and his people under arrest and commandeer the Clipper if Ford tried to leave. He also knew if Heath did that, it would eventually cost the Governor his career. Wild wanted the Americans to make it back to the States and not have a fight with Heath. In a way, he felt sympathy for the Governor. The poor man was totally overmatched in this job.

"Captain, I appreciate your feelings. Believe me, I do. But if you try to take off without the Governor's approval, he'll have you arrested. And don't think I am, as you Americans say, blowing smoke. The man hasn't the foggiest idea of what you Yanks mean to all of us in this war. He is from that school of English diplomatic thought that still is furious with the American Insurrection... excuse me, the American Revolution," Wild began and his reference to 'insurrection' brought a smile to Ford's lips. And he nodded as the face of Sir Reginald Leach popped into his mind. "To be blunt about it, Bob, his nibs in the palace would probably consider himself a bloomin' hero if he held you here. And he has the power to do so."

Ford nodded and then shrugged. "Any problems you coming with me, John? I'd appreciate you being there in case I need a champion at my hanging. I don't buy what he told us yesterday evening but I didn't push it because I needed time to think through all my options. I think I have a way out of this. Will you join me... at least as a neutral observer?" Ford asked and then he and Wild laughed. Finishing their coffee, Ford reached down and picked up his little overnight case and rising, they left to see the smaller version of "Chinese" Gordon.

By the time Wild's lorry brought he and Ford to the steps of the palace, the crew of the Clipper was aboard and the RAF launch was tied up at the dock about 100 yards from them. Ford could see nothing happening in the area that would tell him his people were in any trouble. Looking out at the Clipper, he saw John Mack step onto the port sponson acting like he was doing something important. "A spy you'll never make, John" Ford thought as he watched his First Officer signal, at least he thought it was a signal, that all was secure. Ford turned as he heard Jonathan Wild laugh at Mack's studied casualness. Knowing the Britisher was thinking the same as he, Ford snorted and headed up the stairs past the Gordon murder placque to the Governor's office.They were immediately ushered in and the Governor was waiting for Ford.

"Captain Ford, my people told me that you had arrived and although I'm quite busy, please tell me what I can do for you? I've been advised that most if not all of your people are aboard your plane so I assume you're here to try and convince me to let you leave Khartoum against the orders of my superiors," the Governor stated. He was standing in front of his desk, his face somewhat flushed, wearing a civilian suit. His anger was obvious.

"Governor, yesterday you told us that you had received orders from Cairo to hold my plane. Would you be so kind as to tell me who the orders came from, who the people are that I'm waiting for and where am I to take them?" Ford repeated his question of yesterday, in a very, for him, conciliatory manner.

The Governor wasn't being placated. He was angry. And how dare this man ask him those questions. Taking a breath to control himself, Governor Heath answered.

"Captain Ford. You are in no position to demand answers from me. This is British territory and you have landed on our waters. Mr. Wild has extended every courtesy to you but to come here and demand answers to questions that are none of your business means that you Americans still do not understand that as quests and depending on our benevolence, you can make no demands on me. I am incensed that you would barge into my office. My orders came from Cairo and they will be obeyed. So you can have your men leave the plane. You are not going anywhere until the people Cairo said would be here arrive!" And Governor Heath stuck his chin out at Ford to emphasize his point. Turning, he walked behind his desk and sat.

Shaking Wild's restraining hand off his arm, Ford moved to the front of the Governor's desk and asked one question. "Did you confirm that the message came from Cairo?" Heath looked at the American and was about to dismiss him when he thought about the sequence of events. He had received no notification that the American plane was coming to Khartoum. When he saw the Clipper land, he called the

Squadron Leader. Mr. Wild assured him he knew noting about it and would see what was happening. Then orders came to hold the plane. The notice from Cairo came as a complete surprise.

"Captain Ford, as I said, I follow orders. And they are explicit. Hold the American plane until the passengers arrive. And that is what I am doing," the Governor replied.

Ford kept his voice low as he again tried to get the Governor to look at the whole picture. And the whole began with the first part, the order to hold the Clipper. For Ford felt that the order was a phoney. In the back of his mind were the warnings of Ali and Shamus. Too many things were happening that could not be chalked off to coincidence. He needed the Governor to confirm the order from Cairo. In his gut he knew that it hadn't come from British headquarters. And if he was right, then from where?

"Governor, all I'm asking is that you confirm with your headquarters that such a message was sent by them, not only from their offices but by a responsible official of the British Embassy in Cairo. Is that too much to ask? If they can confirm the message and tell you whom we are waiting for, then you'll have no problem with us. Please, not only for me but for your own peace of mind, find out if such a message was sent from your people," Ford asked, with complete calmness. Which he didn't feel.

Heath looked at Ford and was about to call for his guards to arrest Ford when he looked at Squadron Leader Wild. And suddenly he knew that the American had set him up; he had a witness, a British officer who would testify that the American had made a very reasonable request, considering the circumstance. He looked at Ford and reaching over he picked up his phone and instructed one of his aides to contact Cairo, the office of the Ambassador. Sitting there, he looked at the two pilots and then spoke, quietly.

"Our coffee isn't as good as your American brands, Captain Ford, but would you care for a cup while we wait? You Mr.Wild?" the Governor asked as the two flyers nodded yes. The Governor pressed down one of the many buttons on his phone console and when a voice answered, he ordered coffee for the three of them. While they waited for their coffee and the return call from Cairo, Governor Heath began to talk about the war. It was a rambling discourse, filled with self criticism about being stationed in Khartoum, about the way the war was being fought against Rommel and his not being there. Ford felt embarrassed for the Governor and looking at the portrait of Gordon behind him, Ford understood. There were no Fuzzy Wuzzies to fight, no glory being in Khartoum, a place not even being important enough for the Germans to care that the British held the Sudan. If the enemy didn't care, how important can a post be!

The coffee arrived and the three were making small talk when the phone rang. The Governor looked at Ford and smiled. This was his vindication and he picked the phone off its cradle and spoke. "Ah, Mr. Ambassador. Governor Heath here. Yes, I'm fine and I hope you are as well. I have a rather sticky problem and maybe you can help me. Yesterday, I received a message, by phone, from your office, to hold an American plane flying into Khartoum so persons of importance coming from Cairo arriving here tomorrow and would leave Khartoum on the American plane. I'm just calling to confirm that the message came from your office."

Suddenly, Heath sat straight up in his chair and both pilots could hear the voice of the Ambassador in Cairo screaming at the Governor of Anglo Egyptian Sudan. A few seconds later, Mr. Heath placed the phone back on its cradle, his face was pale and his eyes almost vacant. He was in shock! Looking at Ford and then Wild, he shrugged and shook his head. "No. No one from his office knows anything about an American plane except they want American bombers. As for important people, the Ambassador said that there were none, other than Rommel! He said I had been fooled. And a few other things," The Governor just sat there, stunned, looking as if he'd just lost his family. As Ford began to say something, blasts from the air raid sirens startled all three.

They jumped to their feet as the Governor ran to the windows and Ford, taking a quick look at Wild, turned and raced for the door, the Squadron Leader right behind him. They heard the first bombs explode as they raced down the steps to Wild's car. His driver had the motor going as Ford raced by, headed for the dock and the launch. Wild jumped in his car and yelled something to Ford who kept running. Then more bombs exploded and as Ford arrived at the dock, and turning, looked back across the city. He could see plums of smoke from the explosions at what he guessed was the RAF field. Jumping on the boat, he saw Wild in his car as it raced towards his base, the driver holding Ford's overnight case in one hand, trying to throw it to Ford while he raced to take his commander back to the squadron. Ford waved to Wild and forgot about the bag.

In seconds, he was climbing out of the boat onto the sponson and saw that Mack had started the engines. Looking back at the city, he saw them. Three German bombers, two engines types turning left for another run at the RAF base. In seconds he was in his chair and taking the controls from Mack, began moving the Clipper forward, down the Nile and away from Khartoum. Slowly the giant plane picked up speed and Ford pushed all four throttles forward to get the maximum from the Wrights. Steers was reading off the markers as they flashed past each one and Ford barely heard him. If he came out of the river and climbed too high, the Germans would surely spot them and they had far too much speed to run from. They would blow the Clipper out of the sky. So he had to hide. But where? As the banks of the river began to level almost to the water's edge, he made up his mind. Pulling back on the yoke, he brought the Clipper free of the Nile and turning her hard to starboard, Ford left the river and skipped over its low banks, not more than fifty feet off the desert floor. He dared not climb, hoping here on the floor, the Germans might not spot them against the background of the desert sands and rocks, reflecting off the morning sun. Steers was back in his bubble, with his binoculars, giving them a running bomb by bomb commentary of what was happening in Khartoum.

"The Germans are making another run at Khartoum... they look like Junkers, the two engine types that bombed England. Now they are turning, coming over the city... three, four, now a fifth... and a sixth... explosions in the city. They' re using their machine guns... strafing the city. The bastards... there are no military targets there... they are just killing innocent people. No planes rising from the RAF base... I can't tell... yes I can, they are coming this way! Captain, they are about 10 miles behind us, beginning to climb but still headed at us!" Steers voice continued and it was getting more high pitched by the second.

Ford felt totally useless. They were doing 75 knots on the deck and he felt as if he were swimming against the tide with 500 pound boots on his feet. There was no way they could outrun the Germans and there was no place to land the Clipper. They were dead ducks. All he could do was run and he had no speed! Ford looked ahead and there was nothing but sand and rock. Total desolation. Then another fear struck him. The Wrights! With the propellers' fifteen foot spinning circumference, she had to be leaving a wake, a monstrous wake of sand on the desert floor! All the Germans had to do, once they saw the wake was follow it right to them.

"John," Ford quietly spoke to First Officer Mack. "Please go down to the passenger level and tell me if we are leaving a wake in the sand. OK?"

Mack nodded and rising from his chair he went down. He was back in less than a minute. He'd looked out both the starboard and port windows over the spontons and saw that indeed the Clipper was making a small sand storm as she raced along the floor of the desert. He knew that was what concerned the Captain and he now really understood the meaning of "between a rock and a hard place."

Taking his co-pilot's chair, he looked at Ford and nodded. "Bad. A blind man could follow our path."

Reaching over, he flipped on the plane's intercom and requested the presence of Lt. Elmes. When the Naval Intelligence office came up, Ford asked her to replace Poindexter and try to lock in on the German transmissions between the three planes. He knew she understood enough German translate the transmissions between their planes. Kathleen slipped into Poindexter's chair and putting on the radio officers' ears, she moved the dial towards Khartoum and listened. She could hear some British soldiers or airmen yelling, some terrified Arabs screaming in the background but it was all gibberish. But nothing in German. Changing frequencies, she searched and finally heard them talking, plane to plane.

Her German was a little rusty but good enough to follow their meaning. She began a free translation for everyone on the flight deck. "They're looking for us... one says they can't miss us... biggest plane flying... sun is blinding... can't see anything yet... one of them ordered back... he's breaking towards Khartoum... thinks we might have gone back down the Nile towards Cairo... others are climbing to altitude to get a better angle... headed South!... along the river... nothing more."

Just as Kathleen finished her summary, Steers came from the Navigator's bubble to report the same. Ford nodded and the navigator went back to search for the Germans. No one was jubilant, knowing that the German's had so much speed that if they turned back and headed east, they'd spot the Clipper. Ford decided to risk bringing the Clipper off the deck. He feared the Germans would spot their sand dust trail and follow it to them. Slowly he pulled back on the stick and brought the Clipper up... 200 feet... 300 feet and kept it there. Steers yelled down that there was still a trail so Ford took her to 500 feet and held it there. In a few seconds, Steers said he said couldn't see any dust trail or any German planes now.

Ford told Poindexter to replace Steers and look for the Germans. He ordered Steers to plot a course, a dead reckoning one for Leopoldville. They were committed. The only large body of water between the Sudan and the Belgian Congo that could handle a flying boat as big as the Clipper was Lake Victoria, due south of where they were flying, exactly where he figured the German Junkers were headed. Kathleen had confirmed this when she reported Germans flight leader ordering the one plane to search back along the White Nile towards Egypt while he and his wingman would go to Lake Victoria. Mimicking the German, Kathleen said in guttural English "de Americanski plane is a boot and da's no vater but dare," It brought a few smiles, for a very brief moment.

The huge plane hurtled along the floor of the desert and there was quiet throughout the Pacific Clipper. Those not on the flight deck were strapped into their seats on the passenger level. All were well aware of what was happening. There was nothing they could so they sat in silence, a few praying to themselves. The race from Khartoum as the German bombers hit the city had left them all exhausted. And just knowing the German planes were searching for them made all of them keep silent, as if talking would lead the Krauts to them. As the minutes crawled by, some of them envied those above on the flight deck. At least they were doing something other than sitting. Then after what seemed to be forever, they could feel the Clipper begin to climb off the desert floor and looking out the portholes, all they saw was more of the sand and rocks. Not one cared what desert this was, all they wanted was to hear the Germans were gone.

An eternity later, Kathleen confirmed that the German planes had decided to return to Tobruk. There was no "Americanski" plane on the waters of Lake Victoria! The sigh of relief that went through the Clipper could have been heard by the Germans. But Ford wasn't relaxing. He was very worried, almost frightened. They had flown without breaking radio silence from the day they left Auckland and yet, wherever they landed someone either knew they were coming or was looking for them. Ford's thoughts became a jumble of flashbacks as he reviewed their trip from the day they left Auckland. And it made no sense. He'd figured out the Japanese rationale and he could understand the Germans trying to shoot them down. That was war. But how in the world could they always pin point where the Clipper was going and landing?

"John Steers. What do you think? I've got us on a course moving directly east from Khartoum. Find me a route to Leopoldville. Am I correct that our atlases are not detailed enough about Africa to give us any specifics to help get us there?" he asked.

"Right, Sir. We know Leopoldville is on the Congo and I have it on the map. But that is the only river named. The rest are just waving lines with no names," the navigator responded.

Ford responded. "I know the Congo is southeast of us so would you agree that we have to find some vegetation... trees and shrubbery then look for a river and follow it to one that is bigger and then to one even bigger and that should be the Congo. And flying down that, we should find Leopoldville," Ford easily summed up an unbelievable navigational task, dead reckoning to find a river somewhere in the heart of a part of the world where few white men had ever gone.

"Africa, the Dark Continent... at least to this navigator," Steers mumbled to himself and got busy trying to plot a course without any visual sightings or radio signals to use as markers to guide the Clipper. Steers looked at his commander and was about to tell him he was daffy when he stopped, thought for a second, then realized he understood the Captain perfectly. Yes, they had to find the Congo to get to Leopoldville and although the maps in the books Mullahey had taken were sketchy at best, there were some rivers to look at. The only question was which one to follow. And that was Steers' challenge. He looked at the map spread before him and it showed very little. Some dots for what he guessed were villages or towns but no names. The waving lines he thought were the cartographer's representations of streams or rivers but again no names. And he had no way of judging the distance the Clipper had flown since escaping Khartoum. They were at least a half hour gone from the Sudan capital and he guessed the average air speed at 100 knots. So that would put them about fifty miles from the Nile. Looking out the cockpit window, all he could see was the desert. They had to head South southeast to find the river Captain Ford said was down there, the one that would lead them to a bigger one and that one to the Congo. "What a way to navigate; a thumb and forefinger to measure distances, looking for a river to follow to another. God!" The navigator almost threw up his hands in disgust but things could have been worse; the Germans might have found them!

With that sobering thought, he got back to work and laid out a course for Ford. Mac's atlas was a Hammond, published in 1937. It was only four years old so it should be fairly accurate. It showed Steers the Belgian Congo in green bordering the red of Anglo Egyptian Sudan and Khartoum about 500 miles from that border. There were no names for what seemed to be a few rivers running south from the Sudan and into a river that formed the border of the two countries. The atlas showed the Congo River beginning somewhere in Northern Rhodesia. But it isn't marked as the Congo. There it was called the Lualaba and it ran to a place called Stanley Falls. Then it becomes the Congo River and goes to Leopoldville!

Suddenly Steers, laughing, stands straight and walks over to John Mack, tapping on his shoulder. As the First Officer turns to look, Steers puts out his hand and states, "Dr. Livingston, I presume," Ford and Mack look at him likes he's crazy and then it hits them! Flipping on the automatic pilot, Ford and Mack join Steers' at his table and look at the atlas.

"There it is! The Congo River. Don't you remember... Stanley looking for Livingston, tromping through the jungle, the heart of Africa. Well, here is where it all happened. Until Lindbergh flew the Atlantic, this was probably the most exciting adventure story in the world. And those famous words when the two meet... "Dr. Livingston, I presume!" Wow. And the Congo brings us to Stanley's Pool, just above Leopoldville. I hope it is more than wide and deep enough for the Clipper!" Steers' elation capturing a big smile from the two pilots.

"Where is the Ubangi? Ford asks.

"This has to be it, Captain. If you bear South southeast, assuming we are about here, we should pick up the Ubangi in a couple of hours. Then follow the river to the big river then into Leopoldville," the navigator affirmed. Both Ford and Mack nod in agreement and Ford returns to his chair, flips off the autopilot and reaches over to turn on the intercom. Picking up his mike, he tells the rest of the crew what is happening.

"For all you movie buffs, we are going to fly over the lands explored by Dr. David Livingston and Sir Henry Stanley, better known as Sir Cedrick Hardwick and Spencer Tracy. This is the heart of darkest Africa and we'll be looking for the Ubangi River that will take us to the Congo and Stanley Pool where we'll land. So we'll be following the path of those two great explorers, Livingston and Stanley, not Tracy and Hardwick. We'll touch down near Leopoldville in mid-afternoon. We should be seeing some fauna soon and as we get deeper into the Belgian Congo, lots of jungle. Enjoy the nickel tour," Ford ended.

The excitement of Ford's announcement moved the rest to stare out the portholes and looked at legendary lands. All they saw was desert that gradually became mile after mile of bush, trees and thickening jungle and soon became a bore. With little to do, most of the crew grabbed some extra sack time. They found a dirty, brown colored body of water rolling sluggishly along and guessed it to be the Unbangi. Following it South by southeast, they would occasionally see a small village here and there along the river bank would break up the monotony and some crocodiles or hippos splashing about got their attention. But mainly it was just flying and as noon gave way to the early afternoon, the sun moved over them and Ford decided to get off the bridge and stretch. He turned things over to John Mack and walked down to the passenger level and saw that most of the crew relaxing, playing cards, reading or getting some sleep. He spotted Kathleen reading and when she looked up and smiled, he grinned back, feeling pretty good about things. She looked great, as always. They'd be landing at Leopoldville soon and unless there was a problem with the local government, they should be able to load up with 100 octane and leave tomorrow. But the nagging questions were no longer about fuel and navigation. It was his feeling that someone was trying to sabotage their flight! He could understand the Japs and even the Germans but this was something more. And he was very worried it wasn't over.

He took a cup of coffee from Barney, lit an Old Gold and walked down to where Kathleen sat. Shamus was resting near by. He sat on the arm rest at the edge of her seat. They were now very comfortable with each other and their closeness was obvious to all. The small talk Ford began didn't hide from Kathleen that something was bothering him.

"What's wrong, Bob?" she asked.

"I don't know. I have this feeling, something I can't seem to shake but it's nothing I can articulate. Earlier, after it was obvious that the Germans wouldn't find us, I began to recall all the problems we've had and with the exception of Number 3 engine in Trincomalee, the flight has been routine, as far as the actual flying goes. It is all the other things!" Ford began to explain and then he stopped. He didn't know why except something told him to stop. He looked away from Kathleen to see if anyone was listening to him. It shouldn't have made any difference but somehow it did. No one seemed to be but he didn't continue.

"You call almost being blown out of the skies over Surabaja, spinning the Clipper into a death dive over the Java Sea, the shelling by the Jap sub and landing in a mine field routine flying! What would you call exciting!" Kathleen kidded.

Ford laughed and relaxed. "As our resident historian, what do you know about Leopoldville?" Ford asked, hoping to put the concerns he felt behind him for a few minutes. Out of the corner of his eye he could see the crew beginning to move towards them and what was going to be a private visit between the two would soon become a full fledged bull session. In a way Ford was glad. He'd been doing too much thinking, looking for goblins under the bed, seeing spies lurking in each and every place they landed. Even thinking there was traitor aboard. He looked over his shoulder and signaled to Barney for coffee. The First Steward come down the aisleway with a fresh pot, a tray full of cups and cream and sugar. Nodding to Barney, Ford asked Kathleen if she wanted a cup. Smiling at him, she nodded and as he served her, the others that had gathered took their cups and Barney filled them. He went back to refill the pot and also to served the crew on the bridge. Ford decided to cut out and nodding to Kathleen, followed Barney and went up the stairs, leaving Kathleen and the others to talk about their next landing site. He took his chair and looked out the cockpit window. Things raced through his mind and he tried to sort them out, to see if there was any discernable patter that would tell him what was happening, if anything.

"Maybe I'm getting paranoid. But it is too much of a coincidence that everywhere we land, trouble arrives right behind us. The Dutch try to shoot us down in Surabaja. An honest mistake. I'll buy that. Then Sir Reginald Leach tries to get me to take him home so the British can copy the Clipper. That doesn't make sense. All Churchill has to do is ask the President and he'd have the plans and prototypes in London in days. So Leach was probably doing this on his own. The Dutchman, Oberveldt was trying to protect his ass. The money meant nothing. And it was Shamus that got us the gas! I'd love to know how. Then Thu and his men, on orders from some nut named Tanaka try to shanghai us. But we whipped their ass and also figured out why they tried," the pilot mulled to himself. He hadn't taken the controls and Norm Brown was flying from John Mack's seat. The First Officer was taking a nap.

"Nothing happened in Trincomalee, except blowing those three struts and then getting sick. Kathleen, Shamus and those of the crew that weren't ill enjoyed the two days there. Nothing happened at Karachi and in Bahrein, other than the crazy Imams, nothing," Ford thought. Then his mind brought up the picture of young Ali and he remembered his warning. "Watch out for your friends."

"What did he mean? And who! We land at Khartoum and are told we have to wait for some important people. No names and no information other than an order... from Cairo. But Cairo denies sending the message... then the Germans show up and blow hell out of the town. Wild said that Khartoum is of no importance and hadn't been bothered... until we arrive. Coincidence... no way."

Brown looks over to see if Ford wanted the controls but the Captain smiles and shakes his head. Brown feels good that he is getting in some real flying time and even though the terrain is dull and uninteresting, being at the controls meant a great deal to him. And he is pleased that Captain Ford is showing so much confidence in him. Ford on the other hand wasn't thinking about his Second Officer's psyche. The more he thought about it, the more confused he became. Nothing made any sense.

Getting up, Ford went into his small room and lit a cigarette. Walking back onto the flight deck he moves over to the atlas and looks at the map of Africa. But he doesn't really see it. His mind is on what has happened in the past since they left New Zealand, knowing that everywhere they have gone there are spies... for the Japanese, the Germans, the English and probably even one or two for America. He knows you can't hide a plane like the Clipper especially when touching down in harbors where they have never seen a flying boat. So it is natural that the Clipper's movements have been followed and reported. Then he thought of Trippe's orders... "Maintain radio silence at all costs... what a joke... it looks like everyone in the world knows where we are!" and turns back towards his chair. As he is about to tap Norm Brown on the shoulder to take over, he stops and looks back at the atlas.

"There... that's the reason... Rommel!" Ford states loudly, moving Brown, Poindexter and John Mack just emerging from his cubby hole to look at him.

"Captain?" Mack asks for himself and the flight crew.

"Tobruk. The same thing the Japs had in mind at Surabaja. Capture the Clipper. Look," Ford states and Mack joins him at Steer's table. Without a word, Ford puts his thumb on Khartoum, then his middle finger on Tobruk, Rommel's stronghold in North Africa.

"The German planes aren't wasting bombs on Khartoum. It has no military value and hasn't been involved in the war... until we get there. Then the next day... they come here and bomb a small, inoffensive RAF base. Why?" Ford asks and looks at Mack and the others. They look back at him and as Poindexter shrugs his shoulders, John Mack smiles and nods. He understands.

"To get us in the air! They're not bombing Khartoum because of the war... they want to force us into the air... and once we're off the Nile, it is either crashing on the desert floor or flying... to Tobruk," and the First Officer emphasizing his point buy stabbing the atlas with his forefinger right on Rommel's headquarters. He nods his agreement with Ford's analysis. "You're right Captain. We'd have to fly to Tobruk or crash. Once there, then they'd just fly the Clipper to Germany. But how did they know we'd be in Khartoum?" Mack asked.

Ford just smiles at him. "That's easy. German agents or sympathizers in Khartoum told them. The original flight plan we filed in Bahrein called for us to go to Khartoum but the Imams forced us to change it... making us fly down the Persian Gulf, past Saudis Arabia, towards Lake Victoria. Spies in Bahrein would know the change in the flight plan and notify whomever that we were probably headed for Lake Victoria. That would be logical. But we went directly to Khartoum. Our landing is reported and the next day, orders are received by the British Governor that we are to be held for some important people... and it turns out they were the pilots of the Junkers," Ford began as he details his analysis of what had happened back in Khartoum. There is silence on the flight deck as the other three thought about what Ford had said.

"Captain, they screwed up!" Mack states. "They bombed Khartoum to get us airborne. Then they blew it. They went the wrong way! They never thought you'd cut across the desert! To them, Lake Victoria was the logical move for us. And that's what Kathleen heard. They went to Lake Victoria!" The other three smiled at Ford and waited for his reaction, forgetting in their elation that the question was still unanswered. Ford hadn't.

"Yes, they fucked up. But assume German agents told someone somewhere we had landed in Khartoum. Now, who sent the phoney orders from Cairo? Where and when was this plan concocted? In Bahrein?... Karachi? Cairo? Or Tobruk. Would Rommel take the time to get involved in capturing the Clipper when the Suez Canal awaits him? I doubt it. But someone did... someone so clever and so high up that he knows how to get the British Governor in Khartoum to blindly obey a phoney order from an imposter in Cairo and also have the authority to send three German Junker planes in the middle of a war to capture us. In other words gentlemen, somewhere out there is someone or some group that wants the Pacific Clipper and has the knowledge of everything we are doing. Who? I don't know. How? I don't give a damn as to the how. It's already happened. But we do know the why... to get the Clipper," Ford stated, tossing a little rain on their parade. "And I have no answers, so don't think I'm playing mind games with you. I want you to think about everything that has happened since we left Auckland. Maybe there is something you've heard or seen and it didn't mean anything then. It might now. And keep what we have discussed up here to yourselves. I will cover this with the other officers, privately.

Brown had been looking at Ford and turned back to his duties. Ahead the Ubangi was still rolling sluggishly towards the Congo and Brown, from their altitude of 5000 feet could see a widening of the river and he thought they had reached the confluence of the Ubangi and Congo rivers. They had.

0600 hours-1 January 1942-Hudson Bay, Canada

The Inuit Indians they were to meet on the western shore of Hudson Bay had yet to showed up. When they landed last evening on the ice near a village named Eskimo Point, Commodore Tanaka had gotten a big laugh that here he was just miles above the Canadian town of Churchill. That was last night. Their flight from Lake Athabaska had been routine as had everything up to now. But Lt. Oho could easily understand why their co-conspirators hadn't arrived. The winds outside had to be blowing at 50 knots or better and the snow was coming down so hard it didn't fall but came at angles to their ice covered hiding place. They still had fuel in the tanks but flying was out of the question until the storm ended. They had made such good time flying here that they could have continued on to their alternate rendezvous across Hudson Bay near the Belcher Islands. But Tanaka didn't want to fly at night. Once they crossed the Rocky Mountains, the tail winds across Canada had given them a strong push to Hudson Bay. But both knew that trying to cross this huge body of ice at night could spell disaster. Now they were snowed in and the Commodore was ready to kill!

They were hidden beneath overhanging branches of pine trees 30 feet above them and then a second cover of birch branches on top of their own tarp. They were safe from discovery. Their security didn't concern Tanaka. What did was that they were grounded and he was beginning to feel the pinch of time. For the tenth time in the last two hours, Tanaka pulled out the map of Canada and began his ritual of 'ifs and what about or should this or that happen.' At first Oho listened attentively and was excited. Now he just rolled tighter in the blankets that kept him from freezing. For the heater only worked when they were airborne. And it had to be 30 below zero outside, or more!

Tanaka didn't care about the cold. His mind had put the freezing weather and the snow storm behind him. It was the first day of the year and he had planned to be in Nova Scotia by nighttime tomorrow. He wasn't going to make it and he knew it. They still had to cross Hudson Bay to the North Belcher Island for, hopefully, the last meeting with their suppliers. He knew they had the gas to make it there but if they ran into strong headwinds, they'd end up landing in the middle of the Bay, providing a mystery for the people that found them dead in the spring, if there were such a thing as spring in this awful land. So they would sit out the storm and wait for their supplies. Looking down at the map, he knew they were over one thousand miles from their landing near Halifax. With this storm, they could be 10 miles away and not get there. He had allowed himself three days to sail from Halifax to New York. And in his gut he felt that if he and his two man sub were not in the East River by the 5th of January, Ford and the Pacific Clipper might be home and gone! Sighing, he folded the map, reached down for the thermos, took a little sip of water, pulled up his covers and stretched his legs. He closed his eyes and his last thought was of Captain Teshio's jaw hanging open as he summed up his idea for sinking the Clipper in New York. Tanaka grinned.

Chapter 14

Escape From The Congo

1530 Hours-1 January 1942-Stanley Pool-Leopoldville, Belgian Congo

The Pacific Clipper touched down on Stanley Pool and the muddy waters of the Congo River at exactly 1400 hours. While flying down the Ubangi River to the Congo, Lt. Kathleen Elmes, John Mack and John Steers had given the crew a thumbnail sketch of the history of the Belgian Congo, sans Ford, Poindexter and Jim Henriksen on the flight deck. The Third Officer had fully recovered from the pistol whipping the Japanese Sergeant had given him and although the stitches showed when he removed his cap, physically he was fine. He was a professional airman and when he told Ford he was ready to assume his duties, no fuss was made. He appreciated that. Below, the three took turns trying to pass on to the rest the little they knew about Leopoldville, the Belgian Congo and the Congo River itself.

"Actually, when Captain Ford kidded about our flying over the lands Stanley and Livingston explored, he was quite accurate," John Mack began. "Dr. Livingston was a Scottish missionary who was a very well known explorer, especially about Africa. He had discovered Victoria Falls. But for years after that nothing was heard from him. A number of expeditions were sent from England here to find him but all failed. Henry Stanley was also a noted explorer and journalist for a New York paper. His publisher sent him to find Livingston and the whole world followed the bulletins Stanley sent from darkest Africa. With no telegraphs and only runners to take his dispatches, sometimes weeks would go by before the world knew what was happening.

John Steers stepped in. "Whether Stanley said "Dr. Livingston, I presume," or not, it made for great copy and has become a grand cliche. In actuality, Livingston wasn't lost. He knew exactly where he was at all times and had no idea the world was seeking him. A modest man, he had brought the Bible to the natives and with their help was mapping this part of Africa. Later, he and Stanley mapped most of what is now called the Congo Basin. We'll be landing at Stanley Pool on the Congo and when we take off, we'll fly over Livingston Falls."

"Know anything about the falls, Mr. Steers?" Swede Rothe asked. "What I mean is that looking at the map, the Livingston Falls look like they are right on the edge of Stanley Pool."

"I talked to one of the RAF people at Khartoum last evening and told him we were headed for Leopoldville. He told me he'd only heard about the area but the river and the falls are supposed to be something special. And dangerous," Steers answered. Then the innkeeper from Surabaja stepped in.

"And Kathleen, why don't you tell us about that other country that shares the Congo as its border," Shamus Ginsberg asked, a mischievous grin on his face.

The Navy Lt. answered. "Shamus is talking about French Equatorial Africa. Their government supports the French government in Vichy and that means they are pro German. The Belgian Congo supports the Allies. The only thing that separates them is the Congo River. So far, as best I know, there hasn't been an incident serious enough for them to fight." Kathleen looked at Shamus and smiled. Then it hit her why he asked. "Good God. I hope it isn't us that starts it!"

"Don't worry Lt. Elmes. The rest of the trip will be a cakewalk. Landing at Stanley Pool should be easy for Captain Ford and from Leopoldville to New York, it is just a matter of flying," Swede Rothe said, smiling at her and the rest of the crew. And if the Engineering Officer said so, it must be true. He was wrong.

The landing at Stanley Pool was anything but routine. While the Congo River was broad, often the overhanging branches of the giant trees on both banks would narrow the river to almost a ribbon in width and there was no way Ford could bring the Clipper down through that. Since they had no maps of the local area, Ford was flying by the seat of his pants and could only hope that when it came time to land at Stanley Pool, the trees would be gone and the landing area open. It wasn't. The river seemed to get narrower and the trees taller and fuller. Then ahead, he saw it. Stanley Pool and it was just a pond!

They were at 2000 feet and he began to bring the Clipper down. Inside, the plane was silent, with only John Mack's voice reading off the altitudes as the Clipper descended to almost tree level. Ford eased back on the throttles, slowing the great plane from 150 knots to 120 then to 100. He held it there, just in case the landing area was too short and he had to do a fly around. Then he saw a small clearing in the trees and ahead the waters of Stanley Pool. He dropped the flaps and cut the power to 50 knots. As the Clipper skimmed the edge of the trees at the beginning of the Pool, Ford committed her, bringing the four Wrights to idle, flipping the flaps up and dropping the Clipper onto Stanley Pool. When she hit the water, she bounced like a basketball and by the time the Clipper finished its next two bounces there was at least a quarter of a mile of the Pool ahead of them before it funnelled back into the Congo. All on the bridge held their breath as Ford reversed the engines, moving the flaps down to help break the huge plane and prayed as the Clipper sped towards the shore of the Pool. Finally, she stopped, about fifty yards from the shore, her nose in a weed bed. Ford reversed the engines, moved the flaps to level and backed her out of the weeds. When the Clipper was clear, he pushed the throttles forwards and began to taxi towards the mouth of the Pool and onto the Congo itself. They could see the small native huts on the banks of the river and ahead, the small framed wooden houses that marked the beginning of the city of Leopoldville, the capitol of the Belgian Congo. To their right, Brazzaville of French Equatorial Africa.

In the middle of widest part of the river, Barney, Swede and John Parish secured the Clipper's anchorage. They could feel the current pull at the ropes so they doubled up the lines. As the crew readied for their departure, a contingent of Belgian officials arrived in a motor boat, large enough to take the whole crew to shore. Ford is not surprised when they tell him his arrival was a total surprise. John Wild had promised to alert Leopoldville of their coming but with what had happened earlier at Khartoum, he knew the Squadron Officer didn't have time. It didn't make any difference. No one shot at them and they didn't land in a mine field. They climbed in the bosun's boat that met them at the port sponson and with the officials, headed for the dock. They could see crowds of curious people lining the river bank and in front, standing on a wide and very long wooden dock, some hands and a distinguished looking man, tall, dressed in khaki shorts, knee sox, boots, a hunters' jacket, and on his head, a dark brown bush hat, the crown of it wrapped with part of the skin of a leopard. Even at a distance, Ford could see he looked like another movie character only this time, there was something about him that instinctively told Ford, there was nothing make believe here. As they approached, the man took off his hat and began waving it and laughing. He had a great smile and they could see him pointing to the boat and shaking his head.

The boat was about fifty yards away from the dock when Shamus Ginsberg explained who was awaiting them on the dock. "It's TG. He's an old friend. In fact, he was my mentor. He taught me everything I know. I joined him and his cut-throats in the mid-Twenties, running guns to the Ethiopians. His name is Thomas George Michael Patrick Joseph Maloney but he's called TG. And we are in for one hell of a good time tonight," Shamus Ginsberg stated as the boat touched the dock.

Before they could tie up, the big man reached down and pulled Shamus from the boat and wrapped him in a bear hug. Putting Shamus on his feet, Maloney looks at him with great fondness. "Jesus, Mary and Joseph. Shamus Ginsberg. Death must be near by because only Himself would bless me with seeing you before He calls me for the accounting. What in the name of Saint Patrick are you doing scaring the hell out of all of us flying in the belly of that beast and landing at my doorstep!" Then TG grabbed Ginsberg and hugged him some more.

Finally, Shamus gets free and begins to introduce the crew, standing on the dock and thoroughly enjoying seeing the two old friends being reunited. "TG, meet the crew of the Pacific Clipper, Pan American Airways luxury liner flying from Auckland, New Zealand to New York, with unscheduled stops along the way. This is Captain Robert Ford... "and Shamus stops with the introduction as TG moves over to where Kathleen is standing. Taking her hand he looks down at Kathleen. "Now I know I'm as good as dead because only angels look like this. Shamus, who is this vision that you've conned Himself into letting me see before they come for me?"

TG takes Kathleen's hand and kisses it as she blushes. If he were twenty years younger, Ford wouldn't have had a chance and she glances at the Captain who is thoroughly enjoying the whole scene, especially her blushing. "TG, meet Lt. Kathleen Elmes, of the United States Navy and a member of their Special Intelligence Group. Lt. Elmes, meet TG... Thomas George Michael Patrick Joseph Maloney, owner and operator of the finest hotel in Central Africa... the only hostelry in this part of Africa with running water, indoor plumbing and a bar that rivals the Black Swan's," Shamus pipes in with the introductions. In a few seconds, while Maloney holds tightly to Kathleen, the rest of the crew is introduced and two lorries arrive to take them to his hotel, the Magnolia Arms.

It is mid-afternoon. Leopoldville is located a few degrees below the Equator so the heat is intense. Even the few minutes riding from the dock to the hotel through crowded streets, the searing sun and humidity wilt the Occidentals. Leopoldville is a very modern city by any standards. The streets are clean and there are no beggars. Everyone notices the difference between Leopoldville and Karachi, Bahrain and Khartoum. The Magnolia Arms is only three blocks from the dock and situated overlooking the Congo, about a quarter of a mile below where the Clipper is docked. Driving through the iron gate towards the stairway that leads into TG's hotel, they see the grounds are surrounded with trimmed hedges, manicured lawns and beautiful gardens. Entering the lobby, they all smile and sigh for the temperature inside is about 20 degrees cooler. Looking around, some are reminded of the inns of the British Isles or in the States where those that could afford it escape to quiet elegance and privacy. Ford wondered as he walked in and looked around that if he left his shoes outside his door tonight, would they be shined and sitting there in the morning? Looking at TG, he knew they would.

After going to their rooms and freshening up, the crew and Bob Ford returned to the lobby. Shamus and his old friend are telling lies and roaring with laughter and getting acquainted again. Ford wants to study the takeoff area and walks over to the two old reprobates. After some innocuous banter, Ford tells TG what he wants to do. Their host nods and with Shamus, the three walk over to the rest of the crew. Ford tells Mack and Swede Rothe to join him. As the five walk towards the door, they are joined by Kathleen. She has changed into a light weight cotton dress that she bought in Khartoum. The color is an off white with aqua blue and teal green spots across the skirt part while the top is sleeveless, green buttons up the center, open at the throat with a small round collar. She looked like she stepped out of Vogue but Ford notices she has only sandals on her feet. He is about to say something but TG swoops in and takes her to the lorry. He'll drive and Shamus and Kathleen will sit in front with him, Ford, Mack and Swede in the back.

Maneuvering through the town along the dirt road that parallels the Congo,, TG brings them to the river at a spot about two miles away from where the Clipper is docked. They can no longer see her but that isn't what concerns Ford. All along the drive, he has seen boulders jutting from the river, some of them at least twenty feet high. TG stops and they get out to look. Walking over to the river bank, Ford and the others, except for TG, are shocked at what they see. For in front of them is a rock that looks like Gibraltar. The river rushes past it on either side and looking up stream and then down, Ford can see five, maybe more similar obstacles. He walks to the edge and peers down and from the movement of the water, he can see that the current will help him get up to speed. Looking at the boulders, he figures that they are spaced far enough apart that he might be able to maneuver the Clipper through them. But while he is doing that, he can't get the Clippers up to takeoff speed! No one is saying anything, just watching him. He looks at TF and nods towards the waterfall. They climb back in and now they begin to hear it. The roar, dull at first soon makes any attempt at conversation foolish. Finally Maloney brings the lorry to a stop. They follow TG to a spot that overlooks Livingston Falls. What they see stuns them!

The Livingston Falls are not one massive cataract like Niagara but a series of falls, about a quarter of a mile across, spaced downstream about a half mile apart, ripping away the granite so the walls of the canyon rise as the Congo drops almost 300 feet from where they are standing before the river levels out about twenty miles away and races to the Atlantic Ocean, at least another fifty additional miles. The chasm that forms the walls of Livingston Falls is awesome. Looking out, Ford can see that once they clear the lip of the falls here, he can climb and take the Clipper directly west to Brazil. But can he clear the lip and climb? For if he can't, then they'll just become part of the debris the Congo takes to her mouth, some forty miles away. There is no alternate route. The Clipper has to race down the Congo to the Livingston Falls and take off. And they have to have enough gas to fly to Natal, over 3,500 miles away!

Ford wants another look at the Congo where the boulders seem to be concentrated. TG takes them back in the lorry and when they get there, the six walk back to the edge and look out. Ford knows he can't taxi past these boulders and stop before attacking the falls. The current is too strong it would carry the Clipper to a sure death. He starts to walk away from the others, up the river along the bank. Now he can see that there is a narrow passageway near the opposite bank, where he might have some maneuvering room and still be able to maintain takeoff speed. But it will be tight.

Lost in thought, he doesn't hear Kathleen approach and when she puts her hand in his, he jumps. They both laugh and together begin to walk further along the bank, now about seven feet above the river. Ahead there are some wild flowers, beautiful yellows and whites, looking like small lilies. Kathleen walks ahead to pick some as Ford follows, a few yards behind, still mulling over his problems of getting up power to climb up and over the Livingston Falls while not crashing into any of the boulders along the river path.

Suddenly, he hears Kathleen scream and as he looks, she isn't there! He races to where he can see some of the ground has fallen into the river and there is his love splashing in the river, trying to swim back to shore. Without thought, Ford jumps in the river right next to her, briefly going under the dirty water. He surfaces and finds Kathleen still trying to reach shore. In two quick strokes, he is at her side and grabbing her waist, he begins to push her up the bank. As she grabs some small branches to help her climb out of the river, she turns to look at Ford and looking over his shoulder, her mouth drops open and as she tries to scream, nothing comes out! Ford turns and there not ten feet away is a crocodile headed right for them! Ford pushes Kathleen up the bank and turns just as the giant reptile arrives. As its jaws open, Ford looks into the Gates of Hell. As he tries to slide away to the side to dodge the jaws of the monster, the crocodile rolls over, blood spurting from its face and side. Then the report of two shots reach Ford's ears and in the back of his mind he identifies them as 30-30's. Turning back to Kathleen, the others have arrived and have pulled her up to the bank. Swede slides down to the edge of the water and grabs Ford's arm and pulls him up and out of the river. Standing on the bank, he looks up at a small bluff, maybe 400 yards away and sees a man carrying a rifle. The sun is behind him and Ford can't make him out. He looks at Kathleen, being held in TG's arms and shaking. Looking back to thank their rescuer, the shape is gone! The splashing in the river tells him the crock's buddies are feeding on it.

Ford moves over to where TG is holding Kathleen. He sits down next to them, his white uniform wet and muddy. She raises her head and looks at him. She's crying and looking at Ford, she suddenly sits up and hollers at him!

"You idiot! You were going to fight that crocodile, weren't you! You could have been killed!" And with that she pushes off TG and flings herself onto Ford, hitting him, hugging him, crying and laughing as they roll in the grass. The rest just stand there, grinning and shaking their heads. In a few seconds, Kathleen stops and begins to shake and cry and Ford just holds her. TG had gone to the lorry and returned with a blanket, and wrapping Kathleen in it, he stands aside as Ford carries her back to the car, the rest in tow.

That evening, after the crew had been filled in by Swede Rothe and John Mack about the incident, they sat in the lounge awaiting Kathleen. She had long become to each man, depending on age, either their sister or daughter and now they waited to see how she was feeling. Ford had come down earlier after changing into his last set of whites and was sitting with Shamus and their host, TG. He kept looking at the stairway for a glimpse of Kathleen. After he had carried her to her room, a doctor staying at the hotel came in to check on Kathleen and shooed him out. Later the doctor reported that she was fine and that one of TG's maids was tending to her now. He also promised to look in on her before going to bed later that night.

Kathleen was almost ready. An hour ago, she could barely breathe. She had lay on her bed after Ford had brought her to her room and the doctor had checked her over. He told here she was fine and he'd check back before going to bed. After he left, it took forever for her to get out of her muddy dress and into the bath. She sat in that tub for almost a half hour before dragging herself out, drying off and began looking for something to wear that evening. Then she looked at the dress she'd bought in Khartoum lying on the floor, mud stained and awful and she began to cry and shake again. All she could think about was that dirty river and that crocodile and Ford almost being killed because she wanted to pick some flowers! Throwing herself on the bed she sobbed. Then there was a knock on her door, a very soft tap that she heard but didn't want to answer. It came again and finally she turned, sat up and told whomever was out there to come in. It was Turfu, TG's housekeeper. She took one look at Kathleen sitting on the edge of the bed and shook her head. In less than an hour, Turfu, born in a mud hut near the Congo River, the daughter of a chief, who considered TG a friend, took the graduate of the University of Virginia, a woman who could speak several languages and decipher codes, an officer in the United States Navy and quietly but efficiently kicked her in the ass and got Kathleen Elmes to forget about the river, crocodiles and look ahead. So when the officer from Naval Intelligence swept down the stairs to join her shipmates, it would have taken a Coco Chanel or Edith Head to tell that just an hour earlier this beauty couldn't control her shaking and was crying so hard her eyes became so puffed she looked like a frog! Turfu wouldn't allow Kathleen to feel sorry for herself. To her, this woman of such beauty had everything. She'd heard about the crocodile but to someone raised on the Congo, it was no big deal. The woman's man was safe and so was she.

Ford watched as she came through the dining room towards their table and his heart swelled with pride and deep affection. Kathleen had been though so much and never whimpered. And it was obvious from the smiles and gentle kidding from the rest of the crew how high they esteemed her. He knew he was indeed a lucky man. As he and the other two rose to greet her and seat her, Kathleen bowed in thanks and sat. Taking a deep breath, she looked at the three, and asked, "So gentlemen, anything exciting happen today?"

1800 hours-2 January 1942-on the Congo River at Leopoldville

The heat, even at 1800 hours, was unbelievable. The crew had spent the morning double checking all operating parts and filling the engines' tanks with 100 octane fuel. Ford had overloaded the Pacific Clipper's capacity by 200 pounds of gas, carrying 5100 pounds, or over 33,000 gallons. They had to load up because once they left the Congo, they would be flying over 3500 miles without any place to land until they reached Natal, Brazil. He was worried about the extra weight and the unbearable heat. There was no breeze, no lift he could count on to help them take off. But he was going home and if there were no winds to help him get the Clipper off the Congo, so be it. But as a concession to the heat, he delayed the takeoff till evening and had the crew rest that afternoon in the coolness of TG's Magnolia Arms.

Everything was ready. Ford and John Mack had gone through the checklist and there was no reason to wait. Below, all were strapped in and very nervous. By now, they all had walked along the river and seen the boulders strewn in their way and knew what they faced just getting to the first of the Livingston Falls. Both sides of the river bank were crowded with spectators. And the people seemed to understand that this was no ordinary take off. Ever since the Clipper had landed at Stanley Pool and taxied to the center of the river, thousands from Leopoldville and Brazzaville had come to the banks of the Congo to view the giant plane. In Surabaja, Ford had Barney paint the American flag back on the fuselage and the crowds had heard the story of the Americans trying to get home. Almost all wished them well.

Now Ford pressed the starter for Engine Number 4. In a few seconds the engine coughed and the gas ignited sending a small puff of smoke out the rear of the huge engine. Then it was Number 1's turn, then 3 and finally Number 2. Gradually Ford added power to the engines and the tail of Clipper began to twitch as she tugged against the anchor ropes. At a signal from Ford to John Steers, the anchors were brought in and now the Clipper was free to begin its run. The engineers that built the 314A's at Boeing said that the pilots could only rev the Wrights at full throttle for 30 seconds before they had to release them from idle and begin their run. Ford held them wide open for one minute. Then for another minute. And when they still didn't begin their run, Swede Rothe rolled his eyes towards heaven in silent prayer that his engines would hold together. The Clipper was fighting Ford, trying to break free of his hold and begin her run down the river. But he keeps her on idle as he races its engines until he feels the Clipper is ready. Out of the blue, the face of Sister Francis, who taught him The Lord's Prayer in first grade at St. Ignatius, pops into his mind and he remembers her favorite saying when she was upset with the class, "Saints preserve us!" Ford smiles and softly repeats it as he reaches for the idle.

Three minutes have passed. Ford pushes the throttles forward from idle and the great plane almost leaps from the river as she races ahead. Ford can't open the throttles all the way because he has to dodge the boulders! Past the first one, then moving to starboard to avoid a small Gibraltar on the left, adding power but still not at takeoff speed. Past a third and dead ahead, maybe 500 yards is the lip of Livingston Falls. Now Ford aims for the narrow lane he saw earlier, points the Clipper's nose at it as they rush towards the edge of the falls, Ford goes to full power as the Clipper flashes ahead, the boulders forgotten as they hurtle through the waters of the Congo. 100 yards and Ford pulls up on the yoke to bring the nose of the Clipper free of the water. She rises slightly just as they tear over the edge of the falls! Ford drops the flaps for lift and pulls back even more on the stick. But the Clipper doesn't respond! Instead, she slowly drops towards the rocks and the rushing water that fills the gorge. The walls of the canyon rise about them as the Clipper heads for certain death. Ford quickly puts flaps level and the Clipper stabilizes, level off about ten feet above the white water and rocks and flashes past the lip of the second falls! Again, the downdraft of the air from the chasm pulls the huge plane down towards the fierce rapids. The walls seem to rise into the heavens but all Ford focuses on is that spot in the distance, the mouth of the Congo. Maybe twenty feet above the cataracts, the Clipper shoots over the brink of the last of the falls and still she drops. But ahead, Ford can see the walls of their prison begin to recede and past that, the dirty brown waters of the Congo River rushing into the blue of the South Atlantic. He seems to will the plane to stay level just above the reaching rocks and churning waters of the Congo. In what has seemed like forever, the Pacific Clipper shoots out into the open spaces of the ocean and slowly Ford banks the great airship to starboard and begins the slow climb to altitude and Brazil. John Mack looks out his window at the receding Congo River and Livingston Falls. To him, they seem to be smiling at the Clipper, almost in tribute. Mack smiles, shakes his head and salutes them.

When the Clipper began her run down the Congo towards the falls, the crowds ran ahead as far as they could to watch. From their vantage point they could see her drop down into the first chasm, then they could see no more until a few minutes later, they spotted the Clipper rising out over the mouth of the Congo. A great roar went up as friends and strangers congratulated each other on the survival of the Americans. One man turned, walked back to his bike and rode towards town to report the American's progress. When he entered a small office, a man behind a desk listened to his report then dismissed the bike rider. Picking up the phone, he told his listener of the American's successful departure from the Congo River. "And now they are headed for Natal. Alert the consulate there. Tell them the raider will be off shore in two days," The man was calling from an office in Brazzaville.

2230 hours-2 Jan '42-Somewhere above Quebec Province, Canada.

The Commodore was flying and Oho was using the small flashlight to read the map. The blizzard that had snowed them in yesterday finally passed and the Indians arrived with their supplies. They had taken off immediately to try and make up the lost hours and flown directly across Hudson Bay to their final meeting with the Canadian Indians. At the Belcher Islands, they refueled and took on some drinking water and food. And Tanaka decided to fly at night to try to get to Halifax the next day. He was gambling that no Royal Canadian Air Force planes would be flying at night or on routes that would take them this far north. He felt secure with the risk. They had locked on to Polaris, the North Star and picking up an occasional broadcast from Canadian radios on land, they felt they would have no trouble vectoring into Nova Scotia. Just to be on the safe side, they decided to fly high above Quebec to Labrador, then drop down and cross the Gulf of St. Lawrence into Kejimkujik National Park, about fifty miles from Halifax. They would land on the ice there, be met by car and taken to the docks in Halifax to their waiting cargo ship. The passage from Halifax to New York would take three days. Getting to Halifax early on the third of January was crucial to Tanaka's plans.

Tanaka had not heard anything about Ford's progress since the message at Dease Lake. But he had to assume the Americans were still headed for New York. They could listen to the broadcasts over Radio Canada and reveled in the news of the continuing success in the Pacific of their comrades. Occasionally they would pick up a broadcast from America and the news brought more smiles. The Canadians were more laid back while the American broadcasters would scream the news. And all of it was bad... for them! And since the flight of the Pacific Clipper was only of interest to him... and of course, Ford, there were no reports over the air about them. He would have more information about the Clipper when he boarded the ship in Halifax. The pilot of the sub was already on board, acting as an able body seaman and Oho would stay aboard the ship when it docked in New York and replace the sub pilot as part of the crew, in case anyone was watching the ship and counting heads, which Tanaka knew was impossible.

He went over the plan again and it was simplicity itself. The cargo ship was scheduled to unload at a dock in Brooklyn. Before that, she would wait in that part of New York's harbor called the Lower Bay. Since the ship would not be boarded by the American pilot to guide her to her dock until the dawn of the day after they arrived, he and the sub pilot would climb in the miniature sub in the special berth built for her and they would be basically slide out of the false bottom into the Bay. The Pan Am terminal was on the East River at the Marine Air Terminal, just south and east of the commercial airport, North Beach Station. They would go up the East River, turn at what the American's called Hell Gate, move down towards the Pan Am docking area and wait across the river for Ford to arrive. Tanaka smiled and in the dark, Oho could see the flashing of his teeth and knew the Commodore was again enjoying his mental view of the destruction of the American's plane. The fighter pilot had seen his emotions shift from exhilaration at the prospect of sinking the Clipper in her home harbor to intense dislike of the Commodore and his plan. But now as they were on the last leg of the flight, Oho felt the excitement returning. This was indeed an epic, a story that would be sung by school children for ages. And he was part of it!

2100 hours-2 Jan. '42-at altitude above the South Atlantic

The crew and the three passengers had finally begun to unwind from their terrifying departure from Leopoldviile. When they escaped the chasm, the cataracts and the rapids and shot out into the open of the ocean air, their collective sighs could have been used by Ford to help lift the Clipper when she was in the grip of the Congo and the Livingston Falls. No one moved from their seats for at least ten minutes as the Clipper climbed and headed for Natal, their next stop on the way home to New York. Finally, Barney's head came around from his seat up front by the galley and he stood and smiled broadly at the rest on the passenger level. His smile showed them he had been just as frightened as they were. Then he moved into the galley, and in seconds, the rest could hear the popping of corks and shortly, Barney and his partner, Verne Edwards came down the aisle with glasses filled with Dom Perignon. He passed them out to the group and as they sipped, Barney raised his glass and looking towards the bridge, raised it in toast to their pilot. The rest followed. Verne Edwards refilled the goblets as Barney made his way up to Ford and the flight crew with their glasses of the bubbly. In a few minutes, the engineers, Swede Rothe, John Parish and the Boeing Tech Rep, Giles Brown moved up to the bridge to check on their engines. The Wrights were running smoothly and the Swede looked at Ford in awe. The pilot just smiled, rolled his eyes upwards and then winked at his chief engineer.

Now, three hours later and flying in the late twilight of a January evening night, Barney and Verne prepared a buffet for those that felt like eating. Somehow they put together a delicious offering of a tossed green salad, choice of dressings, deviled eggs, scallions and sandwich meats; Virginia ham, roast beef and sliced turkey, with Swiss and American cheeses and white and rye bread. Deserts were seven layer cake and strawberry short cake with whipped cream, coffee and B&B's. Kathleen was reminded of the dinner that they had enjoyed aboard the Revenge with Captain Loud and her admiration for the larder that Barney and Verne kept continued to grow. Sitting around the two tables in the lounge with the Clipper purring along at 180 knots, 8,000 feet above the Atlantic, no one would even know looking at them, unless they had been aboard, how close the thirteen came to crashing on the rocks of the Livingston Falls. Three of the four men on the bridge thought they knew. But only Bob Ford really understood. What he had done with the Clipper was unbelievable even to him and his admiration for the Boeing plane knew no bounds. He had broken every rule the engineers had written and the Clipper had responded perfectly to each of his demands. He had been in the pilot's seat for better than three hours and felt great. He didn't want to stop flying! Everyone on the flight deck had taken their turn and gone below for dinner except him. Finally, he gave into the silent urging of his co-pilots and turned the Pacific Clipper over to John Mack and the others. No one said anything as he opened his seat belt, rose and checked the instruments again. He turned and tapped John Mack on the shoulder and left the bridge. Below, smiles greeted him and as they rose to express their thanks, he put his right hand up, shook his head and slid into a chair across the aisle from Kathleen and Shamus. Sighing, he put his head back against the partition, and closed his eyes. A few seconds passed and he opened them as Barney placed a cup of coffee in front of him. Verne Edwards was fixing the Captain's supper.

"You know, with all that has been going on, did anyone ever find out who it was who shot that crocodile?" he asked, looking at Shamus. "What I mean is, thanks to him, I'm here."

"You mean we're here, thanks to him... and you!" Shamus corrected and as the rest nodded their agreement, Ford smiled. Then he looked at Kathleen and she was grinning.

"What's so funny?" Ford asked.

"You," Kathleen answered.

"Me? Why?" the pilot asked.

"Captain Ford, unless you have forgotten, in the last 36 hours, you have hauled our asses to safety from German fighter planes, saved me from being dinner for some prehistoric monster and somehow got the Clipper out of the chasm of hell and all you can think about is some unknown rifleman," she answered, reaching over to take his hand and squeezed it. "But unless Shamus can shed some light on this, I haven't a clue. Has anyone?" she asked, looking at the rest of them. They all shook their heads.

Ford looked at Shamus. The innkeeper responded.

"I asked TG if he had any idea who it was. He didn't. Like you. Bob, he thought the rifle used was a .30-.30. I never saw anyone, just watching you push Kathleen to safety and the crock roll over dead. Although I heard the reports of the shots, when I looked back, all I saw was an empty hill. Whomever it was, thank God he was there," Shamus stated.

"Weird," commented Ford.

As Verne Edwards brought him his dinner, the rest moved to their seats, only Kathleen and Shamus staying to keep him company. As he nibbled at his dinner, the three of them discussed the rest of the trip. After a few minutes, Norm Brown, carrying a rolled up tube of paper in his right hand, and John Steers came down and Ford signaled them to join the group. John Mack and John Poindexter were still on the bridge with Jim Henriksen and there was really very little for them to do, especially at night.

As Barney served coffee to Mr. Brown and John Steers, Kathleen asked Ford how they could navigate at night, especially with radio silence and no radio signals coming from anywhere because of the war. She knew that the British Navy had secured the South Atlantic when about a year ago, Hitler ordered the scuttling of the Graf Spee in Montevideo rather than letting her be captured. She knew they couldn't radio the British for help or anyone. And without maps and charts, how did he plan to find Natal?

Sipping his coffee, he looked at her and Shamus and replied. "Actually, we have a sky full of stars by which we can navigate but to help us be more accurate, Norm here will make us a Mercator projection map to help guide us," Ford began.

"What is a Mercator projection?" Kathleen asked. She had heard the term before when talking with some other naval officers but never understood what it meant. Ford looked at Brown to do the honors.

The Second Officer smiled and began. "Simply put, what one does is take a piece of paper, lay it flat and draw lines on it. The meridian lines, those going from the two poles, North to South, top to bottom, are drawn parallel to each other with the spacing the same distance from each line. Then you draw one major line across the center of the page. That is the Equator. Above and below the Equator you make lines across the page, spacing each line ten degrees further than the last one. Now you have a grid. Then tonight, we'll drop flares and with our drift sight viewer, check the drift and ground speed against the Mercator projection and adjust our course to conform to what the projection shows. Combining this with reading the stars, we should be able to come within a quarter of a mile of our actual landing spot. In the daylight, we'll drop smoke bombs, read them the same way and follow the map to Natal."

Both Kathleen and Shamus looked at him as if he were explaining the mystery of Stonehenge. The look on their faces brought a laugh from Ford and John Steers while Mr. Brown looked disappointed that they didn't understand what a Mercator projection was. Then the Second Officer pulled the rolled up map he'd brought down from the flight deck and spread it on the lounge table. There was an outline of the world, traced in pencil from a double spread in one of Mullahey's atlases, and from top to bottom, the horizontal parallel lines, spaced in increasing degrees apart from the previous line. From left to right, the vertical meridian lines were perfectly spaced from 0 to 40 degrees to 80'to 120' to 160'. Shamus looked at Kathleen and the two looked at Brown with new respect. They could now see and understand what he was talking about and both suddenly felt more comfortable with their chances of reaching South America!

As Barney came back with more coffee, Ford suddenly felt very tired and looking about at the rest of his people, he could see they were also ready for some sleep. It had been a long day. They were only four hours into the flight and still had another twenty to go. He wanted to land in daylight at Natal, refuel and leave for Trinidad, hoping to get there early in the morning of 4 January, 1942. Nodding to Barney, he signaled he was finished eating and as the First Steward cleared away the dishes and coffee cups, Ford rose and bade everyone good night. Brown and Steers followed him to the bridge where he spelled out the flying schedule for the four pilots. Poindexter and Oscar Hendrickson worked out their schedule for operating the radio. Kathleen went to the Master Suite and the rest either stretched out on the seats or made up Pullman berths for the night. Soon, except for the drone of the engines and the occasional pop of a flare, the Pacific Clipper quietly continued the long 3500 miles crossing of South Atlantic. Next landing, Natal, Brazil.

CHAPTER 15

The Boys in Brazil

0415 hours-3 Jan.'42-Lake Rossingol-Kejimkujik National Park-Nova Scotia

Oho landed the fighter on the frozen ice of the huge park and rolled towards the spot where he had seen the one second flash of lights. He assumed they were from the headlights of the cars that were to meet them. They had arrived at their last landing and Oho was ecstatic. He never thought they would make it!

Tanaka never doubted they'd get to Halifax. His concerns dealt with Ford's location. Landing here if the Americans were either in the States or dead in some desert in Africa meant nothing. He had to know if Ford was still on his way. Without saying goodby to his companion, Lt. Oho, Tanaka entered the car waiting for him. Oho and those members of the crew of the Valesques helping hide the Mitsubishi would follow him in their car back to their ship, docked in Halifax. Sitting in the back of the sedan, Tanaka looked across at his companion as the driver moved the car from the ice onto a narrow road that led back to the docks of Halifax.

As they moved ahead, the Captain of the Valesquez, an Argentine-an, Alfonso Garcia, opened a thermos and poured a hot cup of coffee for the Commodore. The tall man took it and nodded his thanks. Then he got down to business.

"Where is the Pacific Clipper?" the tall man asked as he held the copper cup of hot coffee wrapped in both hands for its warmth even though the heater in the car was at full power. He assumed that Ford hadn't crashed or been detained and, hopefully, hadn't landed in New York.

"We have intercepted a message telling that the Americans left the Belgian Congo and are on their way to Natal, a port in Brazil. But the confusing thing is that message also said to alert the consulate that the raider would arrive in two days."

"Where did the message come from?" Tanaka asked.

"Brazzaville, French Equatorial Africa," the Captain answered.

"Germans! The goddamn Germans! They are trying to get the Clipper! French Africa is pro German so if the message came from Brazzaville and went to Natal, that means the Germans are after the Clipper. Of course! Brazil is a hot bed of Nazi sympathizers and if the raider is what I think it is, a German boat that looks like a cargo ship and lures Allied ships to sink them, then they plan to hold the Clipper in Natal for a German cargo ship!" Tanaka exploded. "What else?"

"That is all I know as of now, Commodore Tanaka. When we reach the ship, maybe more will be known," the Captain responded as he sat back in the sedan and in a few seconds, so did the Commodore. They were driving without headlights because of the blackout. The moonlight that reflected off the white snow and ice was enough for the driver as he drove along the deserted road to the port of Halifax.

1700 hours-3 January, 1942-Natal, Brazil.

The weather had been perfect from the time the sun rose over the South Atlantic at 0545 hours the morning of 3 January, 1942 until they landed at Natal, Brazil. The big bird flew so smoothly that one almost forgot what Ford had put her through getting the Clipper off the Congo River and away from the cataracts of the Livingston Falls. The flight had been flawless and with nothing to look at but the blue waters of the Atlantic, Ford broke a rule about non- qualified personnel on the bridge while the craft was airborne. He brought the rest of the crew, at intervals, up to the bridge and let them sit in his seat and fly the Clipper! Even Shamus and Kathleen enjoyed the privilege of handling the controls. The pilots, Ford, Mack, Brown, Henricksen and Steers took great pride in explaining everything about the flight instruments to the others. Swede Rothe and John Parish opened the doors from the bridge to the wings and the engines to show the others the Wrights doing their thing. And John Poindexter and Oscar Hendrickson explained the operations of the radio. They had to make believe they were sending messages and talking to other stations since they couldn't break radio silence. But they could pick up transmissions coming from the ships at sea and an occasional radio station broadcasting from South America. That was interesting especially when they heard a transmission between a British warship and a cargo ship, requesting the merchant ship to identify herself. When the merchant didn't reply after numerous requests from the British, the transmissions ended and those on the bridge looked at each other and shrugged.

After they landed at Natal and while the Clipper was being refueled, Ford planned to stop at the small American Naval weather station there to say hello and get any news about the war. When the ship was ready, they'd leave for Trinidad in the evening and fly to Port of Spain where Pan Am had a small relay station for flights crossing the Atlantic, spend the day there resting and head for New York on the afternoon of the 5th. He wanted to be flying up the East Coast at night and far out to sea to avoid any mistakes like the one in Surabaja. He was sure the Army and Navy were ready for any aerial attack from the enemy and if they even heard the engines of the Clipper as she flew by they would scramble fighter planes to shoot them down!

As Ford brought the Clipper down slowly to the water and softly landed at the mouth of the harbor, he spotted the harbor launch about 200 yards ahead and followed her towards their berth. He'd never landed at Natal and neither had any others. The city was home to about 90,000 people and its harbor was one of the finest in all of the South Atlantic. The harbor launch was directly in front of him now and the pilot of the boat was indicating that he should cut his engines. Ford did and as the Clipper drifted towards the dock, Barney and Verne Edwards tossed the docking ropes to the hands waiting and the Clipper was secured. When the starboard passenger door opened, Shamus was the first to deplane, and headed out the gate and towards town, probably looking for an old friend and setting up a nice evening for the crew before they left for the Caribbean. He'd given instructions for John Steers and John Parish to supervise the refueling. There wasn't anything for the crew to do since they had many hours on the long journey to take care of their few duties. Barney and Verne had policed the plane and everything was ship shape. After Shamus, the rest of the crew, Kathleen included, deplaned.

Ford paused as he walked through the starboard door and looked about. Steers and Parish had already climbed atop the wing and were opening the gas tanks for the refueling. Two huge gas trucks were parked along side the front of the Clipper and their hoses were already being pulled by their men out of their housing to be passed to others of the work crew on the wing with his men. Looking at the trucks a second time, Ford began to laugh. Emblazoned on their sides were huge sea shells, painted in bright yellow and above them, the name of the company, Shell Oil!

As usual, whenever a Pan Am Clipper ship arrived, the areas outside the docks were crowded with the curious. And this afternoon was no different. Most of the onlookers were natives but there were a number of foreigners and businessmen also watching. Ford didn't blame them. He too when he had the chance would go to watch one of his fellow pilots bring his Clipper in for their spectacular splashing landing on the waters of the harbor. Now as he moved off the sponton onto the dock, he was surprised and pleased as to see his men were standing there waiting for him and had not moved towards the cars to take them into the city. Kathleen was just in front of them, wearing mufti and just as he was about to join them, a Brazilian officer stepped forward and saluted.

"Captain Ford. Welcome to Natal. I am Colonel Pedro Segura of His Excellency's Rio Grande do Norte's Provincial Grand Army. The Governor has requested that you and Lt. Elmes join him at his palace. And where is Lt. Elmes?" the Brazilian asked.

As the Colonel was speaking, Ford could feel the hair on the back of his neck begin to rise. Something was wrong. Ignoring the Colonel, he looked around and for the first time saw that there were armed soldiers just behind the crew and at the exit gates. Looking back at the crew, Ford gave a very slight shake of his head, warning them not to do anything. Then he gave the Brazilian Colonel his full attention.

"Colonel Segura. It is very kind of you to come here to welcome us. What may I do for you? We plan only to go into town to have supper at one of your fine restaurants while our plane is being refueled. Then we shall be on our way," Ford said smiling and putting out his hand to the officer.

Somewhat taken back by Ford's smile and extended hand, the Colonel paused, then reached out and shook Ford's hand. He nodded and explained.

"The Governor, His Excellency Ramon Jorge de Pernambuco requests the honor of greeting you personally at his palace, along with Lt. Elmes. He extends the hospitality of Natal and Rio Grande do Norte to your crew and wishes you both to accompany me to his palace," the Colonel explained and bowing, asked again for Lt. Elmes. When Kathleen stepped forward, the Colonel blinked. Then he looked at Ford but before he could say anything, Kathleen spoke to Ford.

"Captain, since we are to be in the presence of his Excellency, might I have time to change into my uniform?" she asked, very serious and then winked at the pilot. She was having fun and he didn't think there was anything funny about being greeted by armed soldiers and being ordered, nicely but none the less ordered to appear before the Governor. Then it dawned on him what Kathleen was saying. In mufti, she was just another woman. In uniform, she represented the United States Navy and that might carry some weight here. So nodding his approval, he turned to the Colonel as Kathleen returned aboard the Clipper to change. The Colonel looked stunned that Lt. Elmes was a woman but that didn't stop him from ogling her as she walked to the plane. Ford had to suppress a smile and when Kathleen disappeared into the Clipper, the Colonel became all business again.

"Captain. The Hotel San Georgio is the finest in Natal and the Governor wishes that your men be his guests there while you and he visit. These two cars here will take them there while you and I will ride in mine. That is, as soon as Lt. Elmes is ready," Colonel Segura stated.

"That is very kind of the Governor and I look forward to thanking him on their behalf," Ford began and he was about to protest that they were too busy to take any time off but something told him to back off. The Colonel looked like a man who would enjoy ordering Americans about and there was now no doubt in Ford's mind that there was something much more serious going on than just entertaining itinerant crewmen from a passing American plane. So he kept quiet and when the Colonel turned to his men standing by the cars, Ford nodded his approval and the crew split up and entered the vehicles. Off they went up the ramp and through the gates and as he watched, he realized that not only was Shamus Ginsberg missing, so was the Boeing Tech Rep, G. Brown. He'd seen Shamus leave but not G. Brown. Now the Colonel came to attention. Walking towards the two of them was Lt. Kathleen Elmes, properly attired in the uniform of the United States Navy. She stepped up to Colonel Segura and smartly saluted. The Colonel returned hers and took her by the elbow towards his car. He had a grin on his face that was far from proper military bearing. Ford followed.

The Colonel's car moved quickly through the streets of Natal with the driver leaning on the horn and making the natives jump out of the way to avoid being hit. The Colonel and the driver seemed to enjoy this and Ford thought they were doing it to impress the Americans. Then the car turned off to a street that ran parallel to the harbor and the street rose up towards a small park atop the hill. When they reached the crown, below, maybe 500 feet below and a mile away, the Pacific Clipper sat serenely at her dock. Ford and Kathleen could see the refueling process continuing and as the car moved around the little park, there in the center, stood a howitzer, a five inch canon, raised above the ground on a stand and polished to a brilliant copper sheen.

About twenty yards away was a small hut and standing at attention were five soldiers that saluted when the Colonel's can went past. Kathleen leaned forward to speak to the Colonel.

"Colonel Segura. That canon is beautiful. And what a view of the harbor it commands. Do your men get much opportunity to use it?" she asked.

Flattered, Colonel Segura answered.

"Every morning, Señorita... my apologies, Lt. Elmes. Ahead you can see the Governor's palace and each morning when he is in residence, he stands at the window and the cannoneers fire one round in his honor. It also helps wake the villagers from their sleep," the Colonel explained with a laugh.

"And Colonel, is the Grande Army of Rio Grande do Norte a malitia group or are you part of the Armed Forces of Brazil?" Kathleen asked, slyly pumping the Colonel for information. She knew from intelligence reports that Brazil was a vast country, larger than the United States and dominated by the Governors of the different provinces. Stability was not one of the central government's strengths and the Colonel and his governor might have decided to form their own nation. It had happened before in South and Latin America, quite often in fact.

"Ah, Lt. Elmes. How very clever of you! Actually, each province has its own malitia to support the government in Rio. Because Brazil is so big and still much of it undeveloped, it is cheaper and more effective to have the local governors police their own province. But we are still part of Brazil and the Federalies, or the Army, are our direct authority when it comes to national security matters," the Colonel answered, explaining a great deal to Kathleen and Ford.

Just as the Colonel turned back from Kathleen and Ford, the car entered the grounds of the Governor's palace and in seconds, the driver stopped at the steps leading up and into His Excellency's residence. Getting out and joining the Colonel on the steps, they walked with him into the Governor's palace. It was more of a manor rather than a palace. The actual government operated out of offices in the center of Natal while the Governor oversaw it all from his personal office at his home. Walking down a long corridor from the entryway towards closed wooden doors, the three approached and Colonel Segura knocked. In a few seconds, the doors were opened by a servant and they walked in. The room was large but almost devoid of furniture, except for four leather chairs spaced around a coffee table that sat in front of tall windows that opened out and gave a spectacular view of the harbor. Ford had expected to see someone dressed in a uniform, with boots, a sword, epaulets and medals on his chest proclaiming him important. That wasn't what greeted them. The Governor sat behind a long narrow desk, devoid of papers with just a telephone on the side, a tray with pen, inkwell and paper and to his right, some books. As the three moved forward, the man behind the desk looked up from what he was reading and when he saw Kathleen, he stood, took off his horn-rimmed glasses, laid them on the desk, walked around the desk to the center of it and stopped. Clicking his heels and bowing, he walked forward, put out his hand to Kathleen, took hers and kissed it and turning to Ford, shook his hand. He'd had not spoken and as Ford looked at him, he saw a very serious man, almost bookish, slender, of average height and dressed in a perfectly tailored light grey suit. His dark brown hair had traces of grey along the temples. Nodding dismissal to the Colonel, the Governor pointed to the chairs by the window and escorted the two American there. As they sat, a butler came from one side of the room carrying a tray with silver service and cups. Putting the tray down, he served coffee for all three and bowing, left.

"Captain Ford. My compliments. Lt Elmes, my admiration," the Governor began. The two Americans nodded their thanks but said nothing. The Governor nodded to the cream and sugar and when they nodded no, he sat back and smiled. They sat easily in the comfortable chairs and enjoyed one of the best thing about Brazil, its coffee. Sipping, they waited for their host to speak.

"My complements Captain Ford are for all you have achieved bringing your plane almost around the world. If the people that call themselves leaders had not begun this idiocy of a war, your exploits would be headline news everywhere. My admiration to you Lt. Elmes is for your intelligence, strength, grace and beauty, a rare combination," the Governor began. For some reason, his compliments to Kathleen didn't move her and she felt that there was something much more to this meeting than sipping coffee, not as good as Barney's and being flattered. Ford on the other hand knew there was much more here. He waited for the Governor to spring his surprise. It took all of ten seconds!

"Captain Ford. On behalf of the government of Rio Grande do Norte I commandeer the Pacific Clipper as a prize of war!" the Governor stated without histrionics. "You and your crew will not be detained any longer than a few days. Arrangements will be made for you to be transported to Port of Spain, Trinidad. No harm will come to you or any member of the crew as long as you honor your parole in Natal."

Ford closed his eyes and sighed. "Holy Christ. Is this man nuts? The government of Rio Grande do Norte! What in hell is that? What would this Lilliputian province do with the Clipper? And isn't Brazil an ally of ours? Ok, keep cool. Find out what is going on."

"Sir, I'm afraid I don't understand. What are you talking about, commandeering the Clipper as a prize of war. I mean, isn't Brazil an ally of ours?" Ford began, trying to make sense out of the latest crazy thing happening to them. He didn't look directly at Kathleen but could see out of the corner of his eyes she had her mouth agape and her face was flushed.

"Captain Ford. I no longer recognize the government in Rio de Janeiro. I have decided that they were wrong in supporting the Allies rather than Germany. Most Brazilians, at least those that I know, support Chancellor Hitler and the aims of the Third Reich. When word reached me that your wonderful plane would be coming to Natal, I decided that I would help the German cause by capturing your plane and giving it to them. With the technology that you Americans have built into the Boeing plane, German engineers can convert it to the Luftwaffe's use, throw a curtain over Europe and destroy the communist monster in Russia. With the Boeing to copy from, the Germans can build their own long range bomber force and bring England to its knees. With England gone, the United States will sue for peace with Germany and focus on Japan. I don't care what happens to them," the Governor explained.

Ford and Kathleen couldn't believe what the man was saying. As Ford began to argue his case, he thought about what the Governor had said and decided against cajoling to indignation. "This man isn't doing this on his own," Ford thought. "The risks are too great. When word gets out what he's done, and it will, Rio will have troops here in a minute. And I'll bet if the Clipper is taken to Germany, Ramon Jorge de Pernambuco will be with her. So this isn't for the good of Hitler. That was bullshit. It has to be money. Big money to risk his life and future by helping capture an American asset. There are others involved. There has to be," And Ford's mind immediately shifted to Khartoum and the German's attack there and he realized this dapper man sitting having coffee with them was part of the conspiracy to capture his plane. "But where did it start? With that goofy Jap, Tanaka? Is he still trying for us. His commandos are in a British jail somewhere in Southeast Asia so he doesn't have any troops out here to help him. Or has he?

But this guy is talking about Germany. Can I believe him? I have to take him seriously and find out what he has planned for us." Ford decided to attack.

"Governor. What you told us about the reason you are taking my plane is total bullshit. You are nothing but a traitor, conspiring with others to take the Clipper not for the good of Fascism but pure greed. I could have some respect for a patriot who believed in a cause but your nothing but the front man for a group of mercenaries who will sell the Clipper to Hitler for money, not giving a damn that putting her in that madman's hands will eventually mean the death of thousands of innocent people. Who's Daddy Warbucks? Who's paying you to betray your country?" Ford quietly hissed at the Governor.

The man's face was flushed and sweat was beginning to form on his mustache. He was incensed that Ford had so easily seen through his charade about supporting Hitler. But he had the soldiers and held the plane and there was nothing the Americans could do about it. So he took a deep breath and stood, ending the conversation.

"Colonel Segura will escort you back to the hotel. I warn you that I will have you thrown in jail if you cause any trouble. My soldiers are guarding your plane, excuse me, my plane and that canon you saw on the hill as you came here will blow the Clipper apart if you try to escape. There is no escape from Natal, Captain Ford. If you attempt one, I will not hesitate to have you and all your crew shot. You are right, Captain Ford. When the Pacific Clipper leaves Natal and goes to Germany, I will be enjoying some champagne from your larder, with more than enough money in a Swiss account to never have to worry about my finances," the Governor sneered at Ford and Kathleen.

As Kathleen moved to rise from her chair, Ford put his hand on her arm and stopped her. He had the Governor bragging now and wanted to keep him talking. He'd hit a nerve with that traitor talk and he'd keep at it as long as he could. So he went at the traitor again.

"Governor. How much? I mean Judas went for thirty pieces of silver so what was your price? You getting it in Deutsche marks? Pounds? Or are you smart enough to know that the only money worth anything after this war will be American dollars. They paying you in greenbacks? When we were in Java, the head of Royal Dutch Shell wouldn't accept payment in pounds, kronas, gilders, or deutsche marks for our gasoline. He wanted dollars. Who has enough dollars to pay you to sell your soul? Or is your soul not worth much. Governor, someone is behind this, certainly not you so since we can't escape, indulge us. Who is paying you and your fellow turncoats?" Ford began, trying to get the Brazilian to react.

Smiling, the Governor turned and walked back to his chair. He sat and poured himself some coffee. Sitting back, he smiled and nodded. Taking a sip form his cup, he put it down and leaning forward, he laughed.

"Good try Captain. You want to bait me to tell you who is behind this. Well you happen to be right, somewhat. I do believe in the Fascist cause and want to see Hitler and Germany win. However, I know they can't beat the United States. But with the Clipper's technology and their engineers, maybe they can get a standoff after destroying Russia. But the plan to capture your ship was developed only a few days ago, when you landed in Trincomalee. Yes, the evening you and your friends visited A.B.E. Winjaym the jewel merchant. One of his biggest clients is the Shah of Iran. When you left his house, he contacted his man in Tehran and began telling him of an idea he had for the Shah, knowing the admiration the young Pahlavi has for Adolph Hitler. And very much aware that the Shah would reward him generously. There are so few real patriots in this world so don't be too harsh in your judgement of Wijjy. He never expected you to return to Trincomalee but it was very fortuitous, giving him time to solidify the plans of capturing the Pacific Clipper with the Shaw's men in the Peacock Palace. When you arrived in Bahrein and visited Sheik Abu el Shar, there was someone already there from the Shah who was a friend of the Sheik's. He waited until you and the other guests left before joining the Sheik, and your friend, Shamus Ginsberg," the Governor began.

When he mentioned the innkeeper, Kathleen caught her breath. She couldn't believe Shamus was involved in this! As she was about to leap to his defense, Ford's hand touched her elbow and she sat back, glaring at the Brazilian. Ford was also thunderstruck but he wanted to hear everything the Governor had to say before he commented. The Governor was so pleased with himself that he didn't notice the byplay between the two Americans.

"Captain Ford. Lt. Elmes. Adolph Hitler has many admirers in the Arab world, especially among the ruling families. They appreciate his methods of keeping his people, shall we say, docile, while at the same time getting rid of "elements" in his society that are distasteful. These families and certain rulers want to see the Axis win, or at least force the Allies to call their armies home to protect the homeland. Once the British and French are gone, the lands of the Middle East will return to the control of the Sheiks, Sultans and the Shah. And believe me Captain Ford, those Arabs have more than enough money to buy whatever they want. As of the moment, they want the Pacific Clipper in the hands of the Germans. And they will make me and my friends financially secure for life," the Governor taunted.

"The Shah. Who is that? I don't remember hearing of a shah?" Ford asked, hoping for more information from the Brazilian. Kathleen hadn't said anything but she cut in to answer Ford. She deliberately misnamed the Shah's country, hoping Ramon Jorge would correct her. He did.

"No, Lt. Elmes. Shah Reza Pahlavi is the ruler of Iran, not Iraq. It is he that is the leader of the Arabs that support Hitler, but he does it very quietly while paying lip service to the Allies cause. It was his man that was visiting Sheik Abu. You landed in Karachi before going on to Bahrein. Tehran is not that far from Karachi and when news of your landing in the Indian city reached the Shah, knowing from Mr. Ginsberg you would be next landing in Bahrein, he sent his man to Sheik el Abu's to find out more about your plane and your route back to the States. That night, after your man Ginsberg went to bed in the Sheik palace, the two refined the scheme. The Sheik couldn't and wouldn't try this in Bahrein. The British would arrest him and his family," the Governor began, thoroughly enjoying himself. "The Shah's man returned to Tehran early the next morning so he was explaining the finer details of the plan to the Shah just as you were leaving the Persian Gulf! The Shah approved and the money went into separate Swiss accounts, in our individual names. The plan was so simple. We knew your probable landing sites from talking to Ginsberg. And since the last site where we could capture you would be here in Natal, I was contacted to see if I would be interested in participating. Needless to say, the Shah's offer was one I couldn't pass up," the Governor explained.

"But Governor. The Germans tried to shoot us down in Khartoum. What would have happened to your money if they had succeeded," Ford asked, keeping the man talking, even bragging about his part in the plot.

The Governor waved his right hand as if brushing away a gnat. "As I said, the Shah is a generous man. His people contacted those of us they knew felt the same about Hitler and that would be in position to help capture your plane. When I agreed, a deposit was made in a coded account in Zurich. If the plan failed, we still would keep the money. And if and when we did capture you, everything would be doubled. As to what you thought was a failure really wasn't. The

German planes were not trying to shoot you down, just to get you in the air and then force you to fly to Tobruk. When you outsmarted them and reached Leopoldville, the next stage went into effect. If you had crashed in Leopoldville, too bad. But if you made it out of that canyon, our people in Brazzavillewere to notify me. They did. By the way, Captain Ford, your feat in bringing the Clipper off the Congo and through the cataracts of Livingston Falls has already taken on the stuff of legend. Our German attache here says the Luftwaffe pilots can't wait to fly her," the Governor bragged. Reaching for his cup, he sipped the coffee as he looked across the rim to the two Americans. Lt. Elmes looked pale and very angry. Ford's face showed nothing. And the Governor wondered why. Ford should have been reacting someway, showing anger or threatening him with the power of the American government. Instead, he just looked at the Governor. Swallowing, Ramon Jorge continued.

"Now my phase of the operation takes effect. First step was your getting here and our taking the plane. Next step... well, let us say that is of no interest to you now," the Governor summed up and was ready to dismiss them Americans.

"If you don't mind, Governor, another question. How do you plan to get the Clipper to Germany?" Ford asked.

De Pernambuco looked at Ford and again he smiled and Ford was getting sick of the Cheesier Cat grin. "I know you are a great pilot Captain Ford but even you must know that there are others, while maybe not as good as you, that can fly a plane, even one as demanding as the Boeing. And there are other ways to get the plane to Germany. Suffice to say, we have a number of plans to make sure the Clipper will be in German waters. Believe me, we will make sure that not one scratch will mar the body of the plane and the engines will be in perfect condition when she arrives. But that is no concern of your's now, is it, Captain Ford!

Ford needed to know the answer to one more question. So did Kathleen.

"Mr. Ginsberg. How was he involved?" Ford asked softly.

The Governor laughed. "I'm tempted to tell you that he helped us plan this. Mr. Ginsberg is Jewish and that is justification enough. But I'm in such a good mood now that I have your plane, I'll tell the truth. He did indeed help but he didn't know it. He told the jeweler in Trincomalee your planned route who in turn informed the Shah's man, Hasmir Benehana, who visited with the Sheik and your friend after you had left for your hotel. As I said, the Sheik is an admirer of Hitler as is the Shah. He also hates the British and all infidels that occupy Arab lands. When your friend was telling them of your exploits and how marvelous the plane was, the two let him talk. After Ginsberg went to bed, the two came up with names of contacts supporting Germany that along the way could help capture you. Obviously, if Germany wins the war or even gets a standoff with America, they will owe a great deal to the Shah and the Arabs. Benehana called the Shah, explained the plan and the Shah approved it on the spot. The next morning when Benehana went over the details with the Shah, I was contacted. I agreed to take part in the plan but only when I was assured the money was in the bank. When Zurich called, I was in. You had just left Bahrein. Captain Ford, you must understand that everything depended on either the Germans forcing you to Tobruk or your making it this far. So here you are and in a few days, after the Clipper leaves Natal, you'll be released and taken to Port O' Spain. Oh, by the way. A detachment of your Marines arrived here yesterday. They came uninvited and encroached on our sovereignty. So I ordered our men to remove their arms. They were going to resist but their commanding officer realized what a shooting would mean in terms of diplomatic relations so he cooperated. The Marines are billeted at one of the hotels in the town, free to move about but always watched by my men. I'll make sure you can visit with them. Both groups can commiserate with each other!" and the Governor began to laugh at his small joke.

It was over and Ford knew it. Now the Governor stood and Ford did as well. Kathleen looked at Ford, pleading with him to do something but he was totally stymied. The Governor held all the cards so all they could do was walk back through the doors and down the hallway to Colonel Segura and his driver. Retracing the route, the Colonel dropped them off at the hotel. He bowed to Kathleen and shook Ford's hand and then reached over and put his hand on Ford's shoulder.

"Captain, I know what you are thinking. But I beg you, please do not do anything stupid. The Governor would turn the troops on you and your people in a second if he thought you were trying to escape. You have no weapons and in a few days, your people will be contacted and they will come to get you and the Marines. I'm sorry it has come to this but the Governor is doing what he thinks best for Rio Grande do Norte," the officer finished and saluted Ford. The pilot of the Pacific Clipper just turned and escorted Kathleen into the lobby of the Hotel San Georgio.

0615 Hours-3 January 1942-aboard the Valasquez.

When the car carrying Captain Garcia and the Commodore arrived at the docks of Halifax, it moved slowly along the darken area watching for Canadian shore patrols guarding the area. There was no activity on the docks and with the lights out, the black sedan pulled up to a warehouse, directly across the dock from the Valasquez. As the driver got out, a small door opened on the side of the ware house and Tanaka and the Captain slipped inside. The driver stayed outside for a few minutes, watching to alert them if any patrols were coming. Then he climbed back in the sedan and drove off. In the few minutes inside, Tanaka quickly changed from his pilots clothes into those of a regular seaman, including an extra large black peacoat. Wearing that and a black sailor's cap, he slid out the side door as the Captain left the warehouse by the front. The Captain strode across the dock to the gangplank that led to the first deck of his ship. As he walked up it, the officer of the deck came to attention and saluted. He did not notice a tall form move from the moonlit shadows on the side of the warehouse. The form slid under the gangplank and entered the ship through a small door that quickly opened and closed. Inside, a crewman waited to escort the sailor to the Captain's quarters. Once inside, Tanaka took off the peacoat and cap and accepted the coffee the Captain had ready for him. He looked around and noticed that at least here he had some headroom, unlike the Arista. Walking over and sitting on the edge of the bed, he tested its firmness and kicking off his shoes, Commodore Tanaka stretched out on the Captain's bed. It was too short for him but he didn't mind. It had been a week since he had slept on a mattress and the last thing he remembered was the Captain of the Valasquez turning off the lights as he left. A few hours later Tanaka awakened and for a second was disoriented. The room was dark and then he felt the slow roll of a ship at sea and he grinned. They were off to New York. He was tempted to get up, anxious to confer with the Captain about their course and any news of Ford. But he knew he needed the rest with what was, hopefully, to come. Putting his head back on the pillow and curling up, he was soon fast asleep.

He was awakened when his subconscious told him that four bells were ringing. A soft tapping at the cabin door brought him totally awake and when he told the tapper to come in, a white coated cabin boy entered, carrying the Commodore's breakfast. As the boy put the tray on the Captain's desk, Tanaka walked over in his stocking feet and pulling back the curtains covering the porthole, he looked out on the rolling waters of the Atlantic Ocean. It was a grey, overcast morning and the Atlantic was throwing some large whitecaps at them. The pitching of the ship was quite pronounced but Tanaka felt exhilarated. He was at sea again and after his prey. Stretching, he walked away from the porthole to his breakfast. Looking across the room, Tanaka could see that a change of clothes had been laid out for him sometime while he'd been asleep. Stretching to his full height and pushing his arms towards the ceiling, Tanaka grinned. He felt his karma was good.

An hour later he was on the bridge with the Captain, who told him the good news that Ford had landed in Brazil. Quickly Tanaka figured Ford would leave Brazil today for the Caribbean, get there tomorrow and then fly to New York. He'd land on the night of the 5th or the morning of the 6th. Tanaka prayed for a delay, of any kind!

1845 Hours-3 January, 1942-Ford's Suite at the San Georgio Hotel

Ford's room was large but when the crew, Shamus and Kathleen entered, it became obvious that it wasn't big enough. But it would have to do. Fortunately, the windows opened and there was enough of an evening breeze so nobody was too uncomfortable. Ford had ordered some drinks and food sent up and it was waiting for them when they entered. Those that wanted a drink helped themselves but no one paid much attention to eating. Finally Ford quieted them down and tried to explain what was happening, as best he could.

"Ok, let's begin. Simply put, the Governor of this province is in cahoots with Arab leaders that want to give the Clipper to Germany. He has claimed the Clipper as a prize of war, advising us that Rio Grande do Norte is at war with the United States and has defected from the nation of Brazil! How does that strike you?" Ford started. The hoots from his crew only made him snort. For he had no answers, none what so ever. In the time since he and Kathleen left the Governor's house, he had run through so many possible scenarios of "what if and how about" that he'd finally come to the conclusion that they were indeed captured and there was nothing he could do about it. And as for trying to overpower the Colonel's troops and taking the Clipper, as soon as that idea popped into his head, he dismissed it. Three of his crew did well against the Aussies at the Kings Gateway but here they faced guns of men who wouldn't hesitate to use them against his crew.

"Ok. Here is what we face. The local soldiers have control of the Clipper in the harbor. They have taken away the guns of the Marines sent here. The Marines are tough, no one can fight with bare hands against guns and bayonets. Plus there is a howitzer on a bluff aimed right at the Clipper and so even if we could get to the plane, overpower the soldiers and take off down the harbor, that canon would eventually blow us out of the water before we got airborne," Ford summed up.

"The Marines. Can't we get to them and between all of us, overpower the guards and..," and Swede Rothe's voice tailed off as he realized how inane his suggestion sounded. Others looked at the engineer and shrugged. Then Shamus spoke.

"Look, how far are we from getting to an American base? I mean, a place where we could telephone or send a telegram and alert them to come and help us? We just can't sit here!" the innkeeper offered. And then even he who had an answer for everything nodded that it was a silly idea and sat back to think. The rest looked at each other and then at Ford who shook his head and spoke.

"I have no answers. I'd go for the idea Swede broached of getting the Marines and trying to overpower their soldiers. But they probably outnumber us five or ten to one. Ok, we're Americans and suppose to overcome great odds. But that damn canon on the hill is the killer. There is no way they won't be alerted if we attack their men," Ford answered.

Again, the group murmured their anger and sat back, not one solid idea among the group. Fixing himself a Scotch, Shamus looked at Kathleen and then at Ford. They had earlier told him the story the Governor had told them and of Shamus' unintended contribution to their plan. And of course he felt terrible. But there was nothing he could have done, Ford assured him since they had to file a flight plan in Bahrein and any boob with an atlas could chart the Clipper's course to Khartoum, then to Leopoldville and on to Natal. As for the jewel merchant, Wijjy, Shamus swore he'd cut his heart out if they ever met again...selling his friend and the Clipper for money! As for his Arabian friend, the Sheik, Shamus was too much an Irishman not to understand why his Sheik would want freedom for his people from the British. So he could empathize with Abu but he couldn't forgive him for putting them in harms way! Then he asked what everyone hadn't but each had thought. "The Boeing man. Where in hell is G. Brown?"

They all looked at each other and then at Ford. He also hoped that one of them might have some information about the missing tech rep. None did. Then there was a knock at the door, not hard but loud enough that all could hear. Ford looked at the rest and shrugged his shoulders. The rap was repeated and Jim Henricksen looking back at Ford, got his nod and opened the door. Entering and closing the door behind him was their missing tech rep from Boeing, Giles Brown!

No one said anything. Brown was still dressed in his civilian clothes and looked somewhat excited and somehow different. Kathleen, Shamus and the others also noticed the change in the Boeing man's persona. Standing with his back to the door, he looked taller than they remembered and more assertive, or commanding, not the diffident person they had gotten use to on the flight.

"Captain Ford, my apologies for leaving the Clipper without notifying you. But when you hear my explanation, I'm sure you and the rest will understand. My name is indeed Giles Brown. However, I am not a representative of Boeing Aircraft. In actuality I'm a member of the United States Navy's Counterintelligence forces," Brown began and the room buzzed as they looked at him with new eyes, especially Kathleen, still dressed in her Navy uniform. The stir quickly ended as Ford put up his hand and nodded to Brown to continue.

"I won't bore you with all the details but when Lt. Elmes was assigned to bring the Purple machine to Pearl Harbor... " and Brown paused as the crew looked at Kathleen and some asked what in the world was a Purple machine. As Kathleen was about to answer, she looked at Brown and when he shook his head slightly, she looked at the rest and shrugged. Then all looked back at Brown and he continued.

" Simply put, when you landed in Hawaii, the Boeing Tech rep didn't take ill, I just replaced him. I was to guard Lt. Elmes and make sure she returned safely to the States. When Pearl happened, I had to stay with you to watch over her," Looking at Ford, Brown continued. The whole crew, especially Kathleen hung on every word and then suddenly her mouth dropped open. She quickly closed it and shot a glance at Ford. "How close was he to us those few evenings!" she asked herself. Then Brown continued and she, like the rest became totally caught in his narrative.

"As we approached the dock I saw the soldiers guarding the gates and knew that there was probably going to be some trouble. Knowing that I could be of more use to all of us if I was free, I decided to hide in the hold until you deplaned. After the Colonel took you and Lt. Elmes and the crew went into town, I just walked pass the guards and into town. Dressed as a civilian I could move freely about the city and contact our Naval Weather station here to find out what was happening. By now you're aware that a detachment of Marines came here the other day and the Governor had them stripped of their weapons. When I got to the weather station, the officer in charge took me to where the Marines were. I met their commanding officer, Lt. William Clifford. He and his men have been able to move freely around the town but always under the eyes of Colonel Segura's troops. The Marines haven't made any attempt to recover their weapons. To do so might lead to bloodshed and Lt. Clifford wisely has decided to wait. He knows where their weapons are stored. The Weather Station in code has advised the Navy at Port O' Spain what has happened. Clifford has no idea of what they will do, probably nothing. Navy will have to inform the State Department and he's sure the diplomats will advise against any action. So Clifford wanted to know if he and his men can hitch a ride back to Port O' Spain when you leave tonight. He figures the Governor will have no objection to their leaving," Brown concluded.

Looking at the group, he waited to field their questions. Then Ford told Brown about the commandeering of the Clipper and the former Tech Rep didn't seem too surprised. "Well, we'll just have to get her back won't we," Brown casually stated.

"It was you, wasn't it!" Ford stated. "On top of the hill... at Leopoldville...you shot the crocodile... a 30-30 wasn't it? It had to be you... watching over Kathleen. That was some shooting. Thank you," and Ford moved over to Brown and shook his hand as the rest of the crew smiled at him with a few tossing in "well done," Brown was thoroughly embarrassed but didn't bother trying to deny his heroics. The counterintelligence man snuck a glance at Kathleen and laughed when he saw her questioning glance as she looked at Ford then back to him. He just smiled walked over to the open bar and fixed himself a Scotch. Then the serious business of escaping from Natal began.

Looking at Ford for his permission to plan things, the Navy's Brown took a small map of Natal from his back pocket and spread it out on the coffee table. He pulled the table into the center of the room as the others moved their chairs around it so all could see. Ford stood behind the lounge, in back of Kathleen and Shamus with John Mack beside him. The Clippers' people looked at the layout of the town, with the harbor and the Atlantic Ocean on the right hand side of the map and the rest of the town laid out in back of that. They looked at the Navy man and he began.

"First, what are our liabilities? One, they have armed troops, a lot of them. Second, the Clipper is under guard in a fenced-in area that looks difficult to scale. Third, the canon overlooks the harbor, it's trained on the Clipper and they man it 24 hours a day. Fourth, the Marines have no weapons," Brown indexed their weaknesses and they all nodded in agreement.

"What are our assets? First, the Marines. Second, these soldiers are not fighting men. They probably are not drilled or trained for combat, just use to picking on the civilians. Third, we know what we want to do. The Governor knows what he wants to do but he has to wait for the Germans. So that means he is not ready but we are. Tonight is the best time to strike. They won't expect us to try so soon. And fourth, we won't be alone. Lt. Clifford and his Marines will be with us, armed!" Brown stated. "By the way, it is my guess that the Germans won't try to fly the Clipper from Natal but take it out by ship," Brown stated.

"By ship?" John Mack asked. "With the British in control of the seas, German ships would be immediately attacked," he stated. Others chimed in until Ford put up his hand for silence. "Why not fly her out?" John Steers asked and the others nodded.

"If they had the pilots here, they would have left right after refueling the Clipper and flown at night. But Mr. Steers, if you were flying a strange plane, one that has to land on water and the seas are controlled by the Allies, where would you land once you left Natal?" Brown asked. The rest looked at the navigator as he thought about it. "We'll, they could try for Morocco. There is a port at Rabat. But if I were a German flying an American plane, I'd head for Lisbon. That's an open city," Steers replied. Then the others chimed in with their ideas of where the Germans would go but when each had his say, it seemed that there was no place for them to land but Lisbon. But the Portuguese capital was too far from Natal. And Rabat was in Allied hands. The Pacific Clipper landing there and asking for fuel without clearing things with the port authorities would cause an investigation and obvious capture of the Germans.

"Why a ship, Giles?" Bob Ford asked. "And if they planned to use a ship to take the Clipper to Germany, why refuel us?

"Simple. Why alert you to what will happen by refusing to refuel you? You would ask questions and cause a big flap and they can't have that in public. Only the Colonel and the Governor really know what is happening. How would it look to the locals if suddenly, you and the crew jumped back on the Clipper and locked the doors. No, they had to treat everything as if all was normal until they got you in town and sealed off the area after the people left," the Navy officer explained. "As for why a ship, simple. It is the easiest and the safest. I know that the Clipper seems too big to fit on a cargo ship but remember, the Germans don't care about the body or the wings of the Clipper. They could disassemble the Clipper here in Natal, load her aboard a fast ship, like a raider, and then the ship could use the South Atlantic as a great big schoolyard to play hide and seek with the British. There is no aerial

American presence in the South Atlantic yet so all the raider would have to do is avoid the British warships. And a raider is a formidable foe. She is as fast if not faster than any cruiser, and in the hands of a good captain, they could run from here and safely dock at Cadiz in Spain, or any of the Portuguese ports. If they wanted to, they could go through the Straits of Gibraltar and into the Mediterranean. All of that is under German control and their sympathizers who would welcome and protect the ship. Flying the Clipper limits their opportunities for a secure safe harbor," the counterintelligence officer explained.

"Mr. Brown is right. The Eastern Mediterranean area is dominated by the Germans and their friends. So their risks are much smaller putting the Clipper on a ship and sailing to Europe. And if they took her apart, how would any British ship know she was carrying our plane!" Kathleen interjected. "By the way, Mr. Brown. Your rank?"

He laughed and reaching inside his shirt, pulled out the scapular chain with a small cross, taking it over his neck, then breaking open the cross, he handed it to Kathleen. She took out a small piece of paper and opening it, read it out loud. "Lt. Commander, Giles Brown, United States Navy. The picture doesn't do you justice, Giles," She folded the paper but couldn't get it back inside the cross. Finally, she just passed the chain, the cross and the paper back to the Commander, who just stuck in his pants pocket.

Ford looked at his watch and saw that it was almost 1945 hours. He was worried about the time going by so fast and the Brazilians getting suspicious if they didn't see the crew. He looked at Brown and the Navy man nodded and Ford spoke.

"Some of you go on down and have dinner on the Governor. I want the soldiers guarding us to know we are still in the hotel. Kathleen and Shamus, you as well. Commander, whom among the crew do you need to plan this 'recapture' of our plane. And if the Marines are going to join us, how are they going to get their arms back?" Ford ordered and then asked.

"I know where the Marines' guns are and I confident we can get them. As for your men, I'll need Swede, Barney, Mr. Mack and yourself. But the Brazilians will want to see you, Captain Ford as well so I suggest you escort Lt. Elmes to dinner and after a few minutes, return. The four of us will have some ideas for you when you get back. Ok?" the Commander suggested. Kathleen smiled at Brown as she rose and, grinning, he winked at her. It was a nice wink.

When the Americans entered the dinning room of the San Georgio Hotel, they were greeted by the Maitre d'. Bowing to Kathleen, he escorted the group to a large table in the center of the room. The room was crowded and everyone stared at the Americans. As the members of the crew looked around, those staring quickly lowered their eyes and a discrete silence pervade the dining area. When the menus were passed, no one was particularly interested in ordering food but to keep up appearances, they did. Ford reminded them that this was on the Governor so they ordered the most expensive entrees.. The service was quick and Ford waited until he had taken a few bites before excusing himself. His departure was noted by all in the room and the soldiers sitting on the veranda outside.

When he entered his room, the Commander had a surprise waiting for Ford. Standing near the window was a tall, broad shouldered United States Marine and Ford knew it was Lt. Clifford. The officer was at least 6'3", crew cut brown hair, his uniform khaki pants, shirt, with an olive green tie, knotted at the neck and stuck inside the second shirt button from his throat. The bar on his left shirt collar was silver, the small brass Marine Corps symbol on the right collar. In a quick stride across the floor Ford shook the Marine's hand and grinned at him. Clifford's smile was just as wide. Ford turned and looked at Brown and his eyes asked the question.

"The Lt. is free to move about Natal. When he and I met, I told him I'd be meeting with you and asked him to join us once I made sure the coast was clear. When you left for dinner, he was standing in an exit way down the hall and came in after I signaled him. Bill has had a day to case the town and I thought we'd begin planning this caper with him telling us what the situation is. Bill," Brown stated as the planning of the Pacific Clipper's escape from Natal began.

Clifford knelt down by the coffee table and pointed to the hill where the canon was. "Here is the key. We have to take the canon out before you can start the engines. But to do that, we have to get our arms back. Giles knows where they are stored," the Lt. began as Brown pointed to a place not too far from the dock where the Clipper rested. "Ok, here is my plan and I want any of you to step in whenever you want. Part one. My men are watched constantly but we're not going to need all 24 so what I plan is this. I'll spread them around the center of town, in groups of five or six, and have them wander around and casually move towards the square across from the hotel, here. The Brazilian soldiers will be watching them but I figure they won't be counting heads so a group of five will walk by a side street and five will become four and then six will become five. Those that peel off will meet us here at the warehouse where the guns are. It will be late at night, probably around 2230 and there should only be a token group on guard there."

Clifford looked around at the four Pan Amers and Brown. They nodded and he continued. "Now, Part Two. This will be the tricky part. We have to do three things at the same time. One, Commander Brown, I'll assign four Marines to you to take out the guards. Second, as soon as the Commander signals, Captain Ford, you and just a few of your men board the Clipper and get her ready for takeoff. I don't want all of the Pan Am people congregating at the dock. That means that the majority will have to stay around the hotel until we are ready with Part Three. While the Commander is securing the dock, the rest of my men will help me break into the warehouse and get our arms," Lt. Clifford outlined. "In the meantime, those Marines on the dock with the Commander, after they take out the guards will join me and the others and carry the arms to pass out to the other men. We'll arm them and break up into two groups," the Marine Lt. explained. "One group, with me, will move up the hill and take out the guards at the cannon. The second group will form a perimeter security defense ring at the base of the hill to hold off any attempt by the Brazilians to get to the gun. And Captain Ford, you can't start the plane's engines until you get my signal," Clifford stated.

"Have a problem," Ford began. "The Clipper's nose is pointed inland and I'll have to turn her to head out to sea. The harbor is too narrow. I'll have to use the engines to maneuver so I can turn her towards the mouth of the harbor. If I started the engines to do that, by the time I got her turned, the whole city would be awake."

"Have an idea, Captain," Swede spoke in a controlled voice. "When we were docking, I saw a couple of rowboats stacked on the end of the dock. What say after we take care of the guards, Barney, John, myself and Verne, take two of the boats, tie a couple of ropes to the nose of the Clipper and row her out into the center of the harbor, turning her towards the mouth. That way, when you start the engines, we can begin rolling immediately and not worry about following the checklist. After all, what you've done so far with her, we can throw away the manuals!"

Ford looked at his First Engineer and laughed. "Excellent, Swede. Good idea. We'll pull the dock ropes when you're ready and a couple of us will push the nose away and get you started. You should be able to turn her, then cut the ropes, row back and climb aboard. Just make sure that boat isn't bobbing loose out there near the Clipper," Ford kidded. "But Bill, what about those of my crew that aren't on the dock when we take back the Clipper. How are we going to get them?"

The Marine looked at the Navy and both looked at the Captain, who looked back at both of them. Ford wanted to escape Natal but with all his people. The six just sat there. The Marine got up and walked over to Ford's bar and put some ice in a glass and poured some water into it. Taking a sip, he looked back at the rest and shook his head. He had no answer and he knew that Ford had punctured a huge hole in his plan. How would they get the rest of the crew onto the Clipper without bringing the Governor's whole army down on their heads? Walking back to the map, he joined the others looking at it.

"Ok. Here is the hotel, here is the dock and here is the hill with the canon," Giles Brown began. "Bill, lets assume, without being missed, your few men and I can overpower the guards at the dock. At the same time, you and some of your men will break into the warehouse and get your guns. Now we have the guns and the guards are gone from the Clipper. Now what?"

Clifford looked at the Navy man and then at Ford. "We need a diversion, don't we?" Brown nodded his assent and the two military men looked at the four civilians to see if they had any ideas.

"A barroom brawl?" Barney suggested.

As the two military types looked at the First Steward, Ford grinned and nodded his approval. "With whom, Barney? The locals or among ourselves?"

"No sense bruising any of our people, Capt'n. The locals will do," Barney responded, smiling.

"Like Australia?" Swede asked. "And where?"

"The docks. The Clipper is down there and it would seem rather natural for some of us to wander down from the hotel to do a little pub crawling. We'd want to pick a bar where foreign sailors are. I have an idea the locals don't hang out in those joints," Barney responded.

"Wait a second. Let's think this through," Ford began. "First, there are many risks here. Follow along. Let us say that Barney, Verne and Swede go into a bar on the docks. How many soldiers will follow them? We don't know but it will be more than a few. Where are the rest of us? You know that Colonel Segura is going to be where I am and with him will be some of his men. I like your idea Barney but there are others to be involved in this escape and there is no guarantee that in a bar room brawl, no matter how tough you guys are, that you'll get the same results as in Australia."

Clifford looked at Barney and saw a man he'd want on his side in any fight and his look led Barney to laugh. "Lt. a few of us had an altercation with some Aussies at a bar in Darwin and had a good time. We walked away but the Captain is right. It was just the three of us and the rest of the crew was at the dock. So a barroom brawl isn't the answer, right Captain Ford."

Ford nodded. But he had an idea. Something Clifford had said about the canon on the hill and the fire ring around the hill.

"I have no definite plan in mind but just some thoughts so follow along and let us see what we come up with. First, we have to get the guns and at the same time, take out the guards at the gate by the Clipper. Then Lt. Clifford and his men will climb the hill, secure the canon and signal we can leave," Ford began. "We all agree we need a diversion. But even though Barney is willing to risk his jaw for the good of Pan Am and the American military, it wouldn't accomplish what we need," Ford began. "They have soldiers watching us. So we need something to get them away from our crew. But how? Here is a thought."

Ford walked over to the bar and fixed a glass of ice water. He was planning to fly tonight so no booze. Turning he looked at the two military types and his men and then walked back to the map. Pointing his right forefinger at the hill, he started.

"Bill, let's hold the part of your plan where we get aboard the Clipper. But instead you and Giles get the guns and arm the men with you, the six or seven. And Giles, let us assume that instead of taking out the guards at the gate, we wait for the diversion to bring them away from the Clipper," Ford began. And almost as one, the two military types jumped aboard.

"The canon!" they both said as one. "Great idea," Brown began and Clifford cut in. "We take back our arms. But I only have five or six men with me. So we need a way of getting the rest of the men their weapons. Any ideas?"

Swede, John Mack and Barney were looking at the two as if they were speaking in a foreign language. Giles caught their look and explained.

"The Captain is suggesting that rather than try to get everyone on board the Clipper then capture the canon, do that first, use the canon itself to create the diversion and when you are all on board, you take off and the Lt., myself and his men will hold the hill. Once we have the canon, we'll probably have no trouble with the locals," Giles Brown explained.

"But Bill, how will I get you and your men aboard? It isn't like you can take the canon and walk down to some point on the water and we'll pick you up," Ford stated.

"We're not going with you, Captain. Once the Clipper is gone, the Governor will disappear, and probably the Colonel. Before we begin all this, Giles will go over to the Weather Station and have them send a coded message to our embassy in Rio about the situation. The Brazilians will have troops up here to help us in half a day. I don't think the local constabulary will put up much resistance to armed United States Marines, especially with a five pounder looking down at them," the Marine Lt. stated. Then he continued. "And Commander Brown, I suggest you accompany them back to the States. You still have to deliver Lt. Elmes safely home."

Brown was about to protest and then he realized Clifford was right. So he instead began to summarize all that had to be done by the different groups to escape from Natal. "First, Bill and I with a few of his men will break into the warehouse and get their arms. Bob, you and the crew stay at the hotel but spread around so you occupy more of the Colonel's troops. Now, how will I let you know Bill has the guns and his men are moving to the hill?" the Naval Counterintelligence officer asked. Then he answered his own question. "I'm a civilian and some of the Colonel's troops have seen me. When we have the guns, I'll walk back to the square and stop across from the hotel. I suggest you and a few others be sitting on the veranda having a smoke or drink and I'll signal Bill's on his way. When the canon goes off, you and the rest head for the dock. It shouldn't take you more than two minutes and the gate will be cleared. I'll meet you there. You'll have enough time to turn the Clipper around and we'll be off to Trinidad."

The four from the Clipper looked at their two countrymen and grinned. Then Ford, Clifford and Brown checked their watches. It was already 2200 hours! He'd been gone from the crew the better part of an hour. Quickly, Barney and Swede left, to fill in the others downstairs. John Mack left a minute later to make sure all the men were in a place where they could get to the dock when the shooting started. Ford waited.

"What time do you think you'll begin the fireworks?" Ford asked

"Don't know. Just be ready. It'll take me at least a half hour to get my men and take the warehouse. Another to get up the hill, take out the guards so sometime around 2300 hours. By the way, this is summer down here so the sun stays up late and the moon gives off a big light. They may roll up the streets for the natives, tourists stay up as late as they want. The San Georgio has a good bar and it's open until the last gringo goes to bed!" the Lt. kidded and with that, walked to the door, looked back, and winked. Ford just put out his hand and Clifford shook it. Ford couldn't say anything so he didn't. Then Clifford stopped and looked at the two. "Be very careful of Colonel Segura. He's the only one in this town that is smart enough to figure this out. So if he is near you and doesn't respond to the diversion, someone take him out," the Lt. stated and looking at Commander Brown, he brought his right hand across his throat. Giles nodded.

The Marine was out and gone in a second. Brown waited about half a minute, picked up the map and shaking hands with Ford, said "See you across the square," and the two began to laugh at the inanity of such a statement. And then Brown was gone. The Captain of the Pacific Clipper walked over to the bar, scooped the last few ruminants of ice and put them into a glass. Grabbing the Scotch, he laughed as he poured a goodly amount from the pinch bottle. In a few minutes he might be shot so knocking it down, he shook his head in wonder at what had befallen he and his crew since they left New Zealand. "Flying is so easy. But this other crap. I'll have to tell Trippe he is the envy of the aviation world. Everyone wants the Pacific Clipper," With that, he placed his glass back on the bar and exited to what he knew not.

When Ford entered the lobby of the hotel, he saw Swede, Barney and John Mack each talking with a few of the men and he was pleased that they were spread around the big room so they didn't look to the soldiers outside watching that there was a conspiracy going on. He looked for Kathleen and saw her blond hair bobbing as she was talking to someone on the veranda. He walked out and saw it was Colonel Segura she was in such animated conversation with as Shamus sat next to her listening. He stood in the doorway and looked across the park. Giles Brown would be there soon, he hoped. He fought the impulse to look at his watch as Colonel Segura caught sight of him.

"Ah, Captain Ford. Please join us. I am having a most enjoyable evening and may I say that Lt. Elmes is thoroughly delightful. She is explaining to me how useless the Axis cause is and why the Governor and I should rethink our plans. Would you care to join in this geopolitical discussion?" the Colonel smiled.

"Thank you Colonel but I'm just a poor pilot trying to get home. I haven't had time to think about the global situation, or as those in the know say, the big picture. But maybe you can tell us how long we'll be your prisoners?" Ford asked.

"Please Captain Ford. You and your men as well as the Marines are free to come and go as you please. You can't call that being prisoners. As to how long you'll be here, it will only be a brief period. We want you to enjoy our beautiful city while you are here. And please, don't think badly of us. For poor politicians and soldiers like the Governor and myself, an opportunity to become rich only happens once in a lifetime. Your plane is our ticket to financial security. Please don't begrudge us this one chance. You Americans have so much and what is the loss of one plane to you. You have so many!" the Colonel answered, so smugly that it took all of Ford's self control to not walk over and flatten the bastard. But he needed the Colonel close to them to keep an eye on him. Heeding Clifford's warning about Segura, Ford decided to get involved.

"Colonel, we Americans are all for capitalism, for seeing people succeed and make a buck. But please tell us why the break from Rio? You know we don't buy the Governor's profession of admiration for the Nazis. Was it just for the money" Ford asked innocently.

Before the Colonel could answer, one of his men, a Sergeant that had been watching the Marines came over and whispered to him. The Colonel nodded and laughed, and whispered in Spanish to the Sergeant. They both laughed and Kathleen blushed. Ford noticed and was about to ask her what they said when he remembered he didn't want the Colonel to know Kathleen understood Spanish. That might come in handy later. Looking past the Colonel, he spotted a few of Clifford's Marines coming into the park across the street. He hoped the mates of those Marines were doing what Clifford and Brown had planned.

They were. Clifford and four of his Marines met at a small street a few blocks from the San Georgio. They were only a short walk to the street where the warehouse with their guns stood. In seconds, Giles Brown joined them with three other Marines. He had a .45 on his hip. While Ford had been downstairs at dinner, the original plan had Clifford and his men taking the warehouse while Brown and his waited to make sure they had succeeded. Then all nine would haul the weapons out. After that, Brown and his would take out the guards at the Clipper. But the tough thing was the moonlight lit the Clipper's docking area like it was daylight. So Brown decided that when they took out the Brazilians, they'd tie the men up, hide them in back of the rowboats and don their uniforms so if any NCO was making a visual inspection from the street, he'd see his men still on guard. Now it was time to execute the plan.

Clifford led the way towards the warehouse, keeping to the shadows. There was one guard at the door but they could hear others inside talking. Waiting, they heard three different voices near the door where the outside guard stood. Then a few seconds later, a fourth, a distance away like he was further inside the building. Brown passed the .45 over to Clifford who signaled one of the Marines to go over to a window on the side of the warehouse and let him know where the others were inside the building. In a few seconds, the young Marine was across the darkened street and softly walking along the side of the building, he came to the window. Sliding underneath the base of the window, he slowly rose and with his head laying against the siding, peeked in with his left eye. He could see three of the guards near the door but not the fourth. As he was about to move to look deeper into the building, a form passed right by his nose, headed for the others. The fourth guard. He watched and when all four were standing together, he dropped below the window ledge and raced back to Lt. Clifford. Reporting that all four were near the door, Clifford signaled his men to be ready as he crept along the dark street towards the single guard, standing in the light, talking into the room. The guard laughed and moved away from the door towards Clifford, crouching in the dark. As the guard passed him, Clifford rose quickly, and smashed the barrel of the .45 over the guard's head. As the man fell, Clifford quickly grabbed his inert body and the man's rifle before it hit the ground. Out of the dark came one of his men, taking the Brazilian's rifle from Clifford. Then the two moved towards the open door. They were just five yards from the door when another guard came out! The two stopped but the other guard turned away from them and never heard or saw what hit him. It was his amigo's rifle butt. As he slumped to the ground, the other three marines converged on the door with one grabbing the fallen guard's rifle. Clifford and the first marine were inside the door and as the startled guards looked, before they could utter a sound, Clifford's .45 silenced one while the marines took the other two with blows to the stomach and hatchet chops to their exposed necks.

Quickly, they tore the shirt off the unconscious Brazilians and ripping them into shreds, gagged and tied up the South Americans. The two bloodied guards outside were dragged in, still unconscious, and also stripped, gagged and tied. Brown had told Clifford where he'd seen the Marines' arms stacked and he found them in seconds. Each man took five rifles and the sidearms. Each rifle was loaded with a six round clip. The sidearms, .45's had seven rounds. "Not much to stand off an

Army," Lt. Clifford thought. And then he signaled for them to get the hell out of there.

Brown and his three Marines had already left the moment they saw Clifford's group had secured their weapons. Brown had given his .45 to Clifford and had no weapon but he didn't mind. He'd get one from the Brazilians. As they came down a side street towards the dock, they could see the definitive tail of the Pacific Clipper and as they turned the corner towards the dock, the three guards watching the American plane were nowhere to be seen! The gate was open and then Brown understood what was happening. Directly ahead, the starboard passenger door was open and the lights were on inside the Clipper. Brown and the men quickly raced pass the gate and stopped just to the aft of the open door. Looking inside through one of the port holes, he could see one of the guards with a bottle of champagne and some things he couldn't make out. Just then another guard came down from the flight deck and he had Ford's binoculars around his neck and Steers' sextant in one hand. Both began laughing, looking down the passage way towards the rear of the plane. Brown leaned back and looked through another port hole as the third guard laughingly came past carrying woman's clothes! Brown shook his head and looked at the three Marines and mouthed, "The bastards are robbing the Clipper!" As he finished saying that, one of the Marines pointed past the entryway and there standing against the bulkhead were the guns of the guards. Brown pointed inside and signaled that they would take the guards when they came out of the plane. Crouching outside the light shining from the Clipper onto the dock, the four waited. As the three burglars came out carrying their loot and their guns, they were smothered by the Marines and knocked out. Stripped, gagged and tied up, the Marines dragged the inert bodies out of sight in back of the row boats, but first taking their caps and jackets so from a distance, it would look like they were still on duty. Brown quickly gathered the stolen goods and deposited them on one of the lounge tables. Then the three Marines, shouldering the Brazilian guns, went outside the gate while Brown went ahead to check on the condition of Clifford and his men. When he got back to the warehouse, he found the Marines gone, on their way up the hill to take the canon.

Back at the hotel, Ford had gotten involved in the conversation with Kathleen and the Colonel. He hadn't had time to tell her or Shamus what was going to happen. So he'd stay close to them so when the canon went off, he'd lead them to the Clipper. But if Segura didn't react... well, he didn't know what he'd do but he'd do something!

Shamus had taken up the cause for liberty and freedom as Ford looked at the park, seeing it for the first time. It was a big park, taking up a full square block and around the streets bordering it were the shops and hotels that serviced the tourists. It was too dark to tell what the flowers were or their colors but he remembered they struck him as very beautiful. The park was criss crossed by diagonal paths from corner to corner and trees that he recognized as eucalyptus bordered the whole area. It seemed very peaceful and then he spotted Brown!

The Navy counterintelligence man was standing just inside a darkened area on the edge of the path that led across the street to the hotel. And as Ford's eyes followed a line from Giles to them, he looked right into the big brown eyes of Colonel Segura. And about twenty five yards down the street was the Colonel's car, not the one that took them to the Governor's house but another, open, with a machine gun sitting atop a bar that crossed from fender to fender in the back. Sitting in the driver's seat was one of his non-coms. Ford hadn't paid any attention to the armored vehicle before and now it took all his poker playing abilities not to blanch as he stared at the Colonel.

"A centavo for your thoughts, Captain Ford. You seemed to have left us. Is there something on your mind that I might be helpful with?" the Colonel asked and then looked around the park. He saw nothing and then looked back at Ford. "Remember Captain Ford. I warned you not to do anything foolish. The Governor might order me to shoot you. Now that would be a most unpleasant way to end a very profitable transaction. We don't want any bloodshed. So I hope that my feelings of suspicion are unwarranted. Are they Captain Ford?"

Conversation had stopped, everywhere. The silence was deafening and even those who had not heard specifically what Colonel Segura said could see the tenseness between the two men. Then Kathleen smiled.

"Colonel Segura, it is getting chilly. My wrap is on the Clipper. Would you mind escorting me there to pick it up? I'm sure the guards will let me go on board with you there to vouch for me," And Ford almost died!

"Very good, Lt. Elmes," Segura commented. "That was excellent. You're quite a distraction. It would be so easy to accompany you to the plane as you and Captain Ford wish but I don't think it is that cold. But I do think it is time for you and the crew to call it a night and go to bed. You have had a long day flying and I'm sure a good night's sleep will make what will happen tomorrow more palatable."

As Ford reacted to that, Segura laughed. "Yes, Captain Ford, the ship that will carry the Governor, myself and your plane to Germany will be here tomorrow. When we are at sea, your conciliate will be notified you are here and they will come and get you. Now, before I have to resort to more persuasive methods, let us not have any problems in front of the townspeople and our other visitors," And standing straight, Colonel Segura unhooked the flap of his holster. All could see the narrow butt of a Luger. Ford didn't move and didn't dare move his eyes away from the Colonel to look for Brown. Then it happened.

The sky out over the harbor became stunningly bright and in seconds, the report of the exploding shell reached all in the square by the San Georgio hotel. Then another as people screamed and ran for cover. Ford waited and watched Segura. The Colonel turned and waved for the car and he jumped in as it slammed to a stop. Standing, with his right hand holding onto the windshield, he looked at Ford and yelled, "You're a dead man, Captain Ford!" As the armored car moved forward, the Colonel didn't. A body had crashed into him and knocked him over the driver and into the street at the feet of the Americans. On top of the Colonel was Brown. Looking at Ford he yelled to get moving. Grabbing Kathleen, Ford and she with Shamus and the rest of the crew following broke for the docking area. Looking back, he saw Brown throw the driver out of the car as another shell exploded in the sky. Then Brown pulled up next to him and yelled to get in. He jumped into the front seat as Kathleen and Shamus jumped in back with the machine gun and Brown raced for the Clipper and the dock. Looking back, he saw John Mack wave them ahead as he and the others raced along the street. Brown's hectic ride took only seconds and when he pulled up to the gate, the three Marines threw off their Brazilian uniforms and came to the armored vehicle. Ford jumped out and ran into the plane as the others followed.

Brown told the Marines to take the car up to Lt. Clifford. "Tell Bill the machine gun may come in handy. Also, tell him Colonel Segura is dead, the Weather Station has sent the coded message to Rio and take those other guns with you. Good luck. And God's speed," The marines jumped into the car, one driving as the other one pulled the safety off the machine gun and the third readied the ammunition belt to feed it. Waving goodby, they raced up the hill to reinforce their comrades. No more canon shots were seen or heard as the rest of the crew came puffing up to the gate. Pausing to catch their breath, John Mack counted heads and all were there. Swede and Barney raced to pull the lines as the others piled aboard. In seconds, Ford had the engines going and instead of waiting for a tow out into the harbor, Brown joined Swede and Barney as they pushed the nose of the great plane away from the dock. Jumping aboard, Barney slammed the passenger door shut and the three strapped themselves into the nearest seats. Jockeying the Clipper, pouring more power to one engine cutting that and adding more to the next, Ford had the Clipper turning into the takeoff path in half a minute. As soon as he felt he had her turned enough, he just poured the power to all four of the Wrights and the Clipper hurtled down its watery runway, bouncing and fishtailing as he brought the plane into the center of the harbor and headed her towards its mouth and the Atlantic ocean. John Mack didn't bother reading off the ground speed. Ford would take her off the water when he felt it was time. Then far to the right, another shell exploded, lighting up the water and the sky. It was Bill Clifford's way of saying bon voyage. Into the blinding brightness of the exploded shell, Bob Ford lifted the Pacific Clipper off the waters of the harbor at Natal and climbing towards the light, he rolled the Clipper right then left in salute to the Marines below. As the light from Clifford's volley faded, Ford brought the giant plane back down on the deck. He'd stay low until he felt they were out of range of the howitzer. He hoped that Bill Clifford and his marines were holding the hill but he couldn't take a chance of turning either left or right, just in case. Finally, after five minutes and no further canon shots exploding, Ford gradually brought the Clipper off the water and began climbing to altitude. The night was clear and the moon reflected off of the Clipper and looking below at the dark waters of the Atlantic, it acted like a giant beacon leading the Americans towards Trinidad.

Ford sighed and thought to himself that it was only in the air that things righted themselves. "Christ, when we're on land all hell breaks loose. But up here, we're safe, and Bill Clifford and his men. What's happening to them? Can they hold off Segura's men long enough for Rio to respond. Maybe I can find out when we get land, And Shamus, poor bastard. He thinks what happened back there is his fault, And what about Giles Brown, saved my ass in the Congo and then taking out Segura. Have to thank him properly. Pretending to be a Boeing Tech Rep and pulling it off! Well, the rest of the trip should be a cake walk, didn't I say that before, But what in the world can happen now. Trinidad then into New York, a cake walk," Then he spoke to the crew on the bridge. "Should be a straight shot to Port O' Spain. Everyone Ok?" he asked. They nodded and smiled as each quickly remembered what had just happened to them. John Mack began to laugh and then shook his head. Ford looked at him and understood perfectly.

CHAPTER 16

Ford Meets Tanaka on the East River

0930 Hours-4 January, 1942-aboard the Valasquez-Atlantic Ocean

The grey skies over the Atlantic held the threat of heavy rains to come. Already the winds were whipping up enough that the First Mate had ordered safety rigging along the outside passageways for the crew to hold on to. The freighter was pitching and rolling and the Captain, much to Tanaka's displeasure, had cut back on the speed the Valasquez was maintaining. The Captain was well aware of the Commodore's mission but the safety of his ship took precedence. And as he had explained to the august Tanaka, if the Valasquez capsized or ran aground on the rough shoals of the low fishing waters off Brown Bank, they wouldn't make New York anyway. So Tanaka decided it was time for his crash course in handling the midget submarine that he would ride into the East River to sink the Pacific Clipper. He'd only met his driver, a Lt. Buka, for a few minutes last evening. The man seemed competent and now Tanaka left the bridge to climb down four decks to the hold where the sub was held in its special, secret compartment.

As Tanaka entered the hold, he saw the sub sitting there, held upright by two long metal clamps that encircled its body, one by the bow, the other by the stern. The sub was about 20 feet in length and eight feet wide at the center of the body. From its base, it rose just nine feet to the top of its tower. Lt. Buka was waiting for him along with four members of the Valasquez' crew, those responsible for tending to the sub while she was aboard the ship and launching her into the harbor waters at New York. Tanaka walked around her and the bright overhead lights in the hold gave the black metal skin a silvery sheen.

The sub reminded Tanaka of an Orca, those killer whales that plied the frigid waters of the Arctic. They had rows of serrated teeth to capture and devour their prey. Tanaka's sub had just two. But they could sink a carrier. He walked over to the small step ladder that led up to the miniature conning tower. One step took him to the top and with the hatch open, he bent over and looked down into a maze of tubes, wires, gages and other mechanical apparatus that drove the small sub. And he realized his biggest problem wasn't handling the sub. It was getting into it! He lifted his right leg over the lip of the hatch and put his foot on the only step that led down into the sub. When he brought the left leg up, over and into the small hole, it took all the self discipline of those watching not to break out laughing. The Commodore looked almost bigger than the sub. Putting his hands on top of the hatch, he took his feet off the single rung and slid down the small banisters. He almost made it. But his shoulders got stuck in the mouth of the hatch. With only his bald head showing above the lip of the hatch, his ridiculous position broke up the men and they quietly began to laugh. Tanaka was impervious to their laughter as he tried to negotiate the hatch. Turning left, then right, he felt his body begin to slide through. Repeating this, but this time dropping the left shoulder first, he finally was able to get one shoulder under the lip. A second later, the other shoulder came under and Tanaka landed both feet on the floor of the sub. Now that he was inside, he had to be able move about and that might be even more difficult than getting in!

The lights were on inside and as he looked around, he realized the sub was almost too small for one man, let alone two. And if one was six foot plus, well, he was going to be very uncomfortable. Tanaka didn't care about his comfort. All he wanted to be sure of was having the room to fire the torpedoes that would sink the American plane. And it would be he that fired the explosive fish into the side of the Clipper. He knew enough about the interior makeup of the miniature subs to immediately find where the periscope and the firing mechanisms were. With difficulty, he moved to where he'd be when he fired at the Clipper. He lay down on the floor, moving his feet cautiously towards the rear so he wouldn't hit any wires. But he was too tall. He could feel his feet touching the metal of the hull, and craning his neck to look back, he could see they could go no further. And his shoulders were ahead of the periscope. Raised, it wouldn't be too bad but he knew they couldn't motor around the East River with a periscope sticking out of the water! Moving his body backwards and bending his knees, he was able to get his shoulders slightly behind the periscope. But there was no way he could stay in this position to sight from the periscope in the bobbing waters of the East River and at the same time fire the torpedo. And Buka couldn't do it because he'd be handling the controls, trying to keep the sub level.

Tanaka brought his knees forward and, grabbing the back of the pilot's chair, pulled himself up and stood, his shoulders hunched and head tucked in his neck. He turned, looked around and shrugged. "So I'll be uncomfortable for a few hours. I'll talk with Buka and get his suggestions but right now, let me get out of this straight jacket!" Getting out was almost as difficult as entering but he figured it out and avoided any more comic routines. He stood back and watched as Buka secured the hatch, then one of the crew walked over to the wall and pushed a button. The grinding of gears told him he was about to witness how the miniature sub was hidden. The twin metal grips surrounding the sub began to slide slowly back towards the side of the hull and lifted the sub slightly off the deck. Then the floor of the freighter slid backwards towards the center of the hold. When it stopped, Tanaka walked over and looked down as sea water rushed into the hole. As the water filled the hole to a prescribed height, the sub was slowly lowered into the hole. When the metal bands holding her placed her upright in the water, they stayed there holding the sub steady. Now the water closed over the sub and soon it was totally submerged in the hole. Seconds later the floor of the hold slid back over and as far as any one could see, the hold was empty except for a few nets and boxes. Tanaka was impressed. And his nod to the crew expressed that to them. Saluting, he turned and climbed the steps back to the Captain's quarters. He felt good about the sub, even though he knew he was far too big for it. But he'd handle that. His comfort meant little now. He'd come around the world across the most desolate lands anyone could imagine so a little discomfort wasn't going to interfere with his triumph. Now all Ford had to do was cooperate and make it to New York. It was still early in the day but he felt tired. He was Navy but the bouncing of the merchant ship in the rough waters of the Atlantic in mid-winter had shown him he still didn't have his sea legs. A little nap would help. Climbing the ladders to the top deck to the Captain's quarters, he lay down on the Captain's bed. He closed his eyes and in his mind, he could see his thumb pressing down on the firing button and the torpedo flashing white through the waters of the East River towards the bow of the Pacific Clipper. He fell asleep before the torpedo struck the plane.

0415 Hours-4 Jan.'42 Aboard the Clipper-off the coast of Brazil

John Mack was at the controls. They were four hours into the flight to Trinidad and had at least another nine hours to go. Thus far, it had been as Captain Ford had thought, an easy flight. Out of habit Mack checked the altitude and ground speed and it was as it had been for three hours, 175 knots at 8,000 feet. Only the dimmed lights from the pilot's instrument panel gave any illumination to the bridge. Norm Brown was in the co-pilot's chair and Oscar Hendrickson had replaced Poindexter at the radio console. Jim Henrickson, now fully recovered from the pistol whipping at Surabaja was navigating by the stars. The rest of the group was sleeping. Ford had ruled against dropping any flares to help in the navigation. They were all very aware of potential danger from fighters attacking any unidentified aircraft and a series of exploding flares in the night would certainly bring a quick response if there were any based in Brazil. Giles Brown didn't think that American aircraft were even down here yet but Ford didn't care to find out the hard way. Especially since they were still flying silently. Mack didn't bother to ask Ford when they would break radio silence. He knew the answer. "When we dock at North Beach!"

Mack stretched and tapped Brown on the shoulder. He was going down for a smoke and some coffee and Brown assumed control of the ship. Down below, the only light that illuminated the passenger level came from Barney's galley. Like the one on the bridge, it was muted. Mack looked around and with the exception of someone softly snoring, everything was quiet. Pouring himself a cup, he put his back against the stove and lit a cigarette and almost had a heart attack when someone touched his arm. It was Swede Rothe and even in the dim light, Mack could see from his smile he got a charge out of frightening Mack. The First Officer was about to say something but thought about waking others so he nodded his head upwards inviting Swede to join him on the bridge. The First Engineering Officer's head bobbed in the affirmative as he reached over and poured himself some coffee. Following Mack up the stairs, the two stood in back of the bridge, enjoying Barney's brew. Then Mack asked the question that all wanted to know ever since Giles Brown revealed who he was back in Natal. Had he and John Parish known earlier who Brown was?

"Now Mr. Mack. Do you really think I'd be fooled by an amateur?" the Swede answered Mack's question with a question. Then he smiled and sipped his coffee. Mack was about to ask again when Norm Brown called to him.

"John, look up ahead," the Second Officer requested.

Mack moved back to his chair and Swede moved behind him. Both looked out the cockpit and ahead they could see black clouds. Now Henricksen and Oscar Hendrickson joined the Swede behind the two pilots. All five were quiet as they looked ahead at what seemed to be a wall of blackness stretching like a giant stage curtain from the water below to high above them. One look told them they couldn't climb above what was in front of them. As they moved closer, they could see the jagged bolts of lightening racing through the clouds.

"How far ahead would you guess, Norm?" Mack asked.

"50, no, probably 75 miles. At this speed, we'll be on it in a half hour," Brown calmly commented.

No one said anything. There was nothing to say. They knew they couldn't climb over it, and the massive front stretched as far as they could see on either side of them.

"Just a squall?" Mack asked, hopefully.

"Don't think so, John. And it's no hurricane, too wide and high, plus there is too much lighting" Jim Henricksen stated matter of factly. "Haven't the damndest idea of what that is. Hope it isn't as thick as it looks from here.

Mack had taken the controls and was debating on whether to bring the Clipper down closer to the deck or just stay at this altitude. He decided to stay up. At least that would give them some cushion in case they hit one of those down drafts that could drop the Clipper 500 to 1,000 feet in seconds. Now the five on the bridge could see that is wasn't a solid wall but almost a maze of clouds, a labyrinth of rapidly shifting, huge gatherings of clouds, some rising while others seemed to drop. None of them had ever seen anything like it.

"It's a cyclone," Bob Ford said from behind them. None had noticed the Captain's return to the bridge from his room in back. "Like a typhoon. They form this time of the year in the Southern Hemisphere when very hot air and high humidity meet. And since we are again crossing the Equator, that's what that is. By the way, is this the fifth or sixth time we've crossed the Equator?" Ford asked to no one in particular.

"Sixth, Captain," Norm Brown offered.

"Well, we'll have a hell of a King Neptune party in Trinidad to celebrate crossing the Equator six times. Now let's prepare for what's coming. Norm, you and Swede get below and wake up everyone, including Lt. Elmes. They are all to strap themselves tightly into their seats. I don't want anyone plastered on the ceiling when we hit one of those downdrafts. Have Barney and Verne secure the galley and the rest of you, secure all your equipment on the bridge. No charts, atlases, earphones, sextants... nothing loose. Then join the others and find a nice comfortable seat. This could be very rough," Ford instructed. Then he took his pilot's chair as John Mack shifted back to his.

"John, what do you think? There are a couple of ways we can play this. Obviously we can't climb over it and we can't go under it. So we can pour the power to her and try to muscle our way through or dodge around the biggest clouds, weave our way through her," Ford asked rhetorically. Mack knew the Captain would do what ever he had already decided on no matter what he offered but he appreciated being asked.

"I've never flown through something like this, Captain. Either way, it's going to be hairy," the First Officer responded. Ford just nodded as they began to feel the turbulence of nature's handiwork. The Clipper dipped and then came back on course and they were still miles away from the blackness. Ford flipped on the landing lights to give them some illumination as they sped towards the wall.

"We might be lucky, John. From here it doesn't look like it has reached its full power. The clouds are still forming. Check our heading and when we come out of this, we'll turn back to that. With all the turbulence, we'll be lucky to emerge within 100 miles of our course. Ok, here we go. We're going to play "dodge 'em!" And the Pacific Clipper sped into the storm.

For the first minute, there was just the usual bumpiness of any normal air disturbance. And John Mack looking up saw nothing but black and grey clouds above them while straight ahead there seemed to be a kind of path through the clouds, like a lane in a forest that winds around the big trees. Ford moved the Clipper easily through the first group and suddenly, there was a giant black one right in front and he couldn't dodge it. When they hit it, they couldn't see a thing and Ford flipped off the landing lights. The reflection off the clouds hurt his eyes, like having your bright headlights on when driving in fog. And the first downdraft hit! The Clipper shuddered and dropped like a stone. Ford held her steady as she fell... 500 feet... 1000 feet... 1500! Mack's eyes were fixed on the altimeter and he was reading off their decent quite calmly. He just didn't know he was talking! Then Ford suddenly pushed on the pedals and raised the left ailerons and the Clipper veered to port. In a second they were out of the blackness and into a lighter grey area and Ford leveled off at 6500 feet. They had dropped 1500 feet in three seconds! Now, without anything Ford did, the Clipper rose as an updraft threw her back up into the clouds. They were bouncing like a beachball, totally at the whims of the winds!

And then they heard singing, not the voice of an angel but someone below! The two looked at each other and laughed as Shamus Ginsberg's voice reached them... "daring young man on the flying trapeze, he floats through the air with the greatest of ease," And then the others below joined in and although it wasn't pretty, it was reassuring. The next downdraft ended the singing and they could hear a couple of "wee's" from some of the crew. This time the Clipper only dropped 1,000 feet in ten seconds. There was nothing Ford could do but keep flying, hoping they would soon be through the clouds. Banking to starboard, he skirted the biggest cloud they'd seen and suddenly, came the lightening... huge thunderbolts all around them and the thunder buffeted them, shaking the Clipper to her rivets. And seconds later, rain... not falling down but coming at them almost horizontally. The noise the rain made against the fuselage sounded like machine gun fire and the wipers were useless. Ford couldn't see so he checked his instruments but the compass was spinning like a top, the horizontal horizon had them climbing but he knew it was another updraft causing that. All the engines were performing beautifully so Ford just hung onto the wheel and let Mother Nature have her say. There was nothing he could do. Unlike a hurricane, there was no eye for them to enter to find a few moments of calmness. They just had to ride it out. Mack had stopped reading off the altimeter. He just sat there in awe of the fireworks outside the cockpit.

Suddenly, they heard a scream below! The Pacific Clipper was on fire! The whole plane was covered in flames and when Kathleen saw it, she screamed. Then gales of laughter followed. This was Kathleen's first experience with one of nature's great phenomena, St. Elmo's fire! Now, except for the droning of the engines, the Clipper was silent as all aboard just stared out their windows at one of the most stunning shows in nature's repertoire. In a few minutes, St. Elmo left them, leaving just a few flickering flames lingering on the tips of the wings to remind them how little they knew about nature and how really weak they were when she wanted to flex her muscles.

When St. Elmo left, he took with him the heart of the storm. Now the rain, while heavy, was falling normally and the clouds, still towering above them seemed less awesome. And while the Clipper was still being bounced around the sky, the roller coaster ride seemed less fearsome. Ford could see more grey clouds and to port, a break in them. Banking the Clipper towards that area, in minutes the plane broke free of the cyclone and sped into the brilliant star filled night sky above the South Atlantic. He didn't bother to check their heading but sat back, heaved a sigh of relief and lit a cigarette. Mack looked over and noticed Ford's hands as he cupped them around his match. They were perfectly steady. He didn't have to look at his. He just hoped the color would quickly return to his white knuckles.

Ford reached over and flipped on the intercom. "Hope you enjoyed the show and the ride. Pan Am aims to please. Barney, how about rustling up some grub for the good folks and your beloved pilots up here. Sorry about interrupting your sleep. But we'll get plenty in Trinidad. Swede, you and John and our former Boeing Tech Rep check out the engines before you eat. Ok?" Then looking at Mack, Ford smiled and checking the compass, moved the Clipper back on course towards Trinidad. They still had another 1500 miles of flying before they landed at the Pan Am facilities in Port O' Spain. There they'd get 100 octane, have the Clipper serviced and sleep under fresh sheets. At least he thought they would, if the war hadn't struck the Caribbean.

1230 hours-aboard the Valasquez-off the coast of Maine

The rain had begun and the grey skies seemed to wrap the merchant ship in its arms as if to hide her from prying eyes when Tanaka rose from the Captain's bed. He was hungry and was about to ring for the steward when there was a soft tapping on the door. Telling whomever it was to come in, the steward entered, carrying a tray. Placing it down on the Captain's desk, the young man in the white jacket bowed and departed. Before the door closed, the Captain entered.

"Ah, Commodore. I assumed you'd be waking soon so we had some food prepared. And I have good news about Ford and the plane. He has left Natal. I have no details but our ship, the Guienna intercepted a transmission from Natal warning the German raider not to dock. The Guienna is headed for the Caribbean, now just off the Brazilian coast, spying on American movements down there and in South America. She picked up the transmission and as instructed, forwarded it to us. She has no idea where the Americans are but we must assume they are headed for Trinidad. There is a Pan Am relay station there. Their planes that make the Atlantic run from New York to Lisbon land there on their way to the Azores. Ford will go there," the Captain stated.

"Do you think he will stay at Trinidad or refuel and keep on coming to New York?" Tanaka asked as he poured himself some tea.

Picking up a piece of lemon he squeezed it into the tea and sipped as he looked at the Captain of the Valasquez.

"I have no idea, Commodore Tanaka. But my guess is that he'll spend the night there. We don't know what happened in Natal but he left there last night and we know they flew at least 24 hours non stop to get there. So they haven't had any rest since leaving Leopoldville. They have to rest sometime and Ford probably feels he is almost home when he lands in Trinidad.

"How far are we from New York?" Tanaka asked. He knew that in this rough weather the Valasquez wasn't making the time he wanted but there was nothing he could do about that. If Ford did stay in Trinidad overnight, and Tanaka felt the Captain was accurate, then he might just get to New York before Ford. But it was going to be close. Tanaka's phlegmatic attitude surprised even him. Ever since he had been given a new life in Tokyo, he had become almost fatalistic. The old Tanaka would have been screaming at the Captain, at the weather, at everyone for the delay in getting to New York. He wasn't sure he liked the new Tanaka but he knew his stomach did.

"About another day and a half. We should be entering the Upper Bay about 2200 hours tomorrow night, the 5th," the Captain explained. Then he continued with a briefing of the schedule for the two man sub. "Assuming that Ford hasn't landed, we'll drop you into the waters of the Upper Bay about 0400 hours on the next morning, the 6th. That gives you almost two hours before daybreak to reach the Pan Am terminal area. Since New York will be in a total blackout, Ford won't try to land until daylight."

Captain Garcia continued with their plans. "Depending on traffic, the harbor pilot probably will not come on board until mid-morning. We are docking near the Brooklyn Naval Yard. We'll be there most of the day. After you have destroyed the American plane, your best escape will be to retrace your route back to us. You'll have to go back through Hell Gate but by that time, the tides should be easier for you so you'll have little to worry about. Lt. Buka has gone over the charts with our navigator a number of times. Once you leave the East River and return to the Upper Bay, he knows what dock we have been assigned and will bring you there. The procedures for reentry to the Valeaquez are the reverse of leaving. Do not worry if you have to stay in the water for a few hours after you make contact with us. We have to make sure there are no dock hands on board and no ships moving close to us in the harbor. Once we have you safely aboard, and have unloaded our cargo, we'll continue on our regular route to Baltimore, load there then out to sea and onto the Caribbean. It is too dangerous to try and transfer you to a submarine in these waters. However, off one of the Caribbean islands, St Lucia, we'll rendezvous with one of your own subs. It is now in the South Atlantic on a joint mission with the Germans and will be waiting for us when we get there. They will take you home." Tanaka was very pleased.

The Imperial Navy would make sure he returned home and not desert him in this part of the world. But going home was secondary to the mission; completing the mission meant getting to New York before Ford. "Well, I'll be there Captain. Will you?" he asked, to himself.

1730 hours-4 Jan. 1942-Pan Am Relay Station-Port O' Spain, Trinidad

There hadn't been a Pan Am plane or any plane for that matter, landing in Trinidad for over a month. The relay station sat quiet and empty in the small harbor a few miles south of Port O' Spain, near the mouth of the Caroni River. The Pan Am station was set about a quarter mile in from the rolling waves of the Gulf of Paria on the Caribbean Sea. The hotel was directly south of the dock on a slight hill, with a beautiful view of the bay and some of the small islands just off the tip of Chaguaramas. One could walk up the hill in back of the hotel and look across the small isthmus and see the Atlantic Ocean not a mile away. Trinidad was blessed with marvelous beaches and great swimming, on the Caribbean or leeward side of the island. The waters of the Atlantic, while blue and pretty were very treacherous, with tides and eddies that were dangerous for the amateur swimmer. But that was of little matter to Walt Poff these days. He was caretaker of a ghost village, with an empty hotel, a deserted dock and unused maintenance facilities for the Pan Am Clippers and their passengers. With the advent of Juan Trippe's four engine Boeings that could fly non-stop from New York to the Azores and on to Lisbon, the Clipper ships no longer landed in Trinidad to see him. Not too long ago, when it was the Martin's carrying Pan Am's passengers to Europe, they had to stop at Port O' Spain to refuel. And the stationed hummed with activity and the nights at the hotel swung as the guests enjoyed the best cuisine in the Caribbean. Now that was almost a memory to Walt although one of the Martins, the Azores Clipper had landed two months ago. Then he'd been able to entertain the passengers and his men took care of the maintenance of the Martin while the guests partied. But with Pearl Harbor, nothing flew into Trinidad anymore. Rumor had it that the Army was planning an air base somewhere in the Caribbean but he hadn't seen any surveyors coming around to see if Trinidad could handle the big bombers being built to go to England and Africa. His last communication from Pan Am Headquarters in New York was for him to "mind the store" until further word. So Walt Poff and his three assistants kept the store and waited for orders from New York. But it was boring.

He'd been with Pan Am for almost eight years, working his way up from mechanic to Second Engineer and then Pan Am offered him the opportunity to attend their management school, to learn how to supervise the operations of their relay stations. After graduation, in 1939, he was assigned to Trinidad and he found the life idyllic. And while Walt wouldn't admit it, he'd "gone native," He enjoyed the beautiful days and starlit evenings and the slow pace. He was still a top technician and devoured all the latest literature on the new Boeings while making sure he stayed current with the latest information on resort management. His maintenance men felt they were more than adequate to handle any challenge these new Boeing super ships might throw at them. Unfortunately, they flew over Trinidad, not to it. And the hotel was now more for the tourists than the passengers. The restaurant was a first class attraction on the island and the hotel was filled most of the time. But with the war, there were no tourists and the natives couldn't afford to eat as Chez Pan Am. However, some of the Englishmen and Americans that lived in Trinidad year round made the restaurant their special habitat so Walt's friend, Charlie Coe had dinner guests most evenings.

He had made his rounds of the grounds and checked with the cook in the hotel to see what the specials were this evening. "Filet of Dover Sole, Almandine, Tournedos Rossini and Pompano en Papillote," Gus the chef answered. He was another displaced American from Boston, who got off a tramp steamer in Trinidad ten years ago and never left. Walt had forgotten Gus' last name. It was Polish and very long with some witz's in it so everyone just called him Gus the Chef. It was way too early for dinner and he had no lady friend set up for cocktails so he walked back down to the shed to talk to the men. As he passed by the dock and began down the sandy path towards the quonset hut that held all their equipment, he heard something that made him stop. Shaking his head, he tried to place the noise, his mind quickly shifting through his files and when airplane engine came up, he dismissed it. A few more steps and he heard it again. Now the men in the shed came out. They looked at him and then stepped onto to the dock and began walking down it towards the end where it jutted out into the bay. Walt joined them and now it wasn't a figment of his hearing. They all heard it. A plane... a big plane. And suddenly the four were racing down the dock, waving and jumping as they could see a silver form banking to port and heading right towards them, not five hundred feet off the deck. No one had to tell them what it was!

As Ford brought the Clipper into its landing and she splashed into the harbor waters, he cut the engines to idle and let the ship glide towards the dock. He could see the men running at them, smiling and waving. It was obvious that they were not ready to dock the ship so he just feathered the props and let the big plane drift, the wake from their landing pushing them slowly to where Barney and Steers could throw the lines to the men when they arrived. Finally secured, Ford waited until the rest deplaned. He was beat and so was the rest of the crew. They all needed sleep. He rose from his chair and stretched. As he walked out the passenger door, he could see Swede Rothe chatting with the members of the ground crew. The rest of his gang were walking slowly towards the hotel and he stepped on the dock, looked around and smiled. He was looking forward to relaxing on the beach tomorrow, maybe getting in a swim before they headed for New York. As he was walking past Swede and the other men, he nodded and smiled at them and continued on towards the hotel and some serious sack time. Ford was about twenty yards past them when Poff spoke softly to Rothe.

"Heard about him," Walt spoke, looking at Ford walking away from them. "Good as they say?"

"Better. The best I've ever flown with. He's done things with that plane I wouldn't believe unless I'd been aboard. In fact, I'm not sure I believe it now!" the Chief Engineer of the Pacific Clipper spoke as he and his friend walked down the dock towards the hotel. The other three stayed to finish securing the Clipper. Rothe had been one of Poff's instructors at Pan Am's engineering school in New York a few years ago.

"And the plane? Everything I've read about?" Poff asked, one professional to another.

"Like Captain Ford, better than they say. Even when we had 87 gas in her, she ran like a dream. Wait till we get a drink and I tell you about Leopoldville. Wow! You won't believe what the Captain did to her and how she reacted. No wonder the Japs tried to steal her!" the Swede stated. Poff stopped and looked at his friend.

"Japs? What in the world are you talking about?" he asked incredulously. "Japs trying to steal the Clipper?" Rothe just laughed.

"And the Germans!" he added and promised Poff to tell him all about it over a couple of cold drinks.

"Well, Swede, get yourself settled and I'll send a message to New York that you've landed here," Poff offered.

"No radio transmissions. Orders. We can't break radio silence and you can't radio New York to tell them where we are. Don't ask me why. It seems wherever we landed, they knew we were coming!" Swede Rothe told to his friend. "So we haven't been able to radio for any help since we left Auckland. We could only listen to transmissions and where we were flying no one was sending out information about winds, currents, tides and weather. So, thanks for the offer Walt but no radio transmissions. Ok? And tell your men the same," Swede instructed.

Two hours later, they were sitting at the bar in the hotel kidding with each other. John Parish and the rest of Poff's crew had joined them while others of the Clipper were either having dinner, walking along the beach or sleeping. One of the ground crew, Rod Finn, hadn't said much. And it wasn't because he was shy. He just couldn't keep his eyes off Kathleen Elmes. Neither could anyone else in the hotel's dining room or at the bar. She had changed from her uniform into a light cotton dress, basic white with a green belt, an orange, green and gold scarf around her neck, white sandals and gold earrings. There were other attractive women in the hotel that evening as word circulated through Port O' Spain that an American Clipper ship had landed. So Charlie Co had a full house with guests waiting up to an hour to get a table. The guests were filled with questions about their flight but were too polite to ask the crew directly about where they had come from and where they were going so they went to Charlie Coe for the answers. By the time he had told ten or eleven different stories, the guests gave up and just enjoyed being in the vicinity of the Clipper's crew and their enchanting passenger.

"Where did you get her?" Finn asked. And the rest sitting with him at the bar broke up laughing. "I mean... well you know... " he tried, blushing somewhat, to explain what he meant but they all understood.

"It's really quite simple," Swede stated. "She came on board at Pearl Harbor to brief the brass at Wake and Guam and got trapped with us when the Japs struck. When we decided to try for the States, she came along rather than staying in New Zealand. She is bright, articulate and a terrific companion. Like a daughter to me and the older men, a sister to the rest."

Finn was about to ask about Kathleen and Captain Ford then thought better of it. She was sitting at a table with the Captain, the

First Officer and the older man he had heard them refer to as Shamus. Looking at them, he realized that if someone that looked like her looked at him like she was looking at the Captain, he'd faint from sheer fright! He forced his gaze away and his eyes caught Mr. Rothe looking at him, smiling, a smile that told him not to ask!

The foursome that Finn and the rest of the room had been sneaking looks at paid no attention to the others watching them. They were enjoying a delightful dinner and relaxing, beginning to unwind from the tremendous pressure they'd been under since they left Auckland. The conversation ranged from laughing about Kathleen's scream when she saw St. Elmo's fire to head shaking when they talked about Natal. John Mack was fascinated about the wealth of two of Shamus' friends, the Sheik in Bahrein and the jeweler in Trincomalee. He asked the innkeeper for his opinion as to who was the wealthier and the Irish Jew smiled.

"No contest. The Sheik... because of the oil. Wiggy has lots of jewels and ivory and such but he is basically a middleman. Very rich, that is true but if the government didn't let him operate, he'd be in a bad way. But I wouldn't worry about him. He's got lots of money, American dollars, in a bank in Switzerland. And from what Captain Ford said, he has some of the Shah's money there as well, the bastard. As for Abu, he's secure. If the British tried to take over his oil fields, they'd have a riot on their hands and they don't need that now. The Arabs could be the balance of power in the Middle East. If collectively they were to join the Shah of Iran and supported the Germans, it could spell big trouble for the Allies. But the Arabs will never work together. Their blood feuds go back too far... for centuries in most cases. And the British play these animosities like a violin. They can't afford a united Arab world and while they give lip service to independence, the last thing John Bull wants to see is an Arab nation, free of British control," Shamus began. He'd been quiet since leaving Natal and Ford knew he felt great remorse for being a pigeon for Wijjy, the Sheik and the Shah's man. Ford had told Shamus it wasn't his fault and to forget it but he knew the innkeeper was very hurt. John Mack getting him involved again was great and Ford 's smile at his First Officer let him know how much he appreciated it.

Suddenly, Ford wanted nothing more to do with any conversation about rich Ceylonese, power hungry Arabs or traitorous Brazilians. The dinner had been terrific but he wanted to get away. He looked at Kathleen and she caught his glance and nodded. Making their excuses, the two rose and walked out the door and headed towards the beach.

As soon as they reached the sand, Kathleen stopped Ford and leaning against him, took off her sandals. Then she ran down to the water's edge and wadded in. Laughing and raising her skirt, she wadded up to her knees. Ford just stood on the edge, grinning. Then the two of them walked along the shore away from the hotel, Kathleen just in the water, Ford on the hard sand. Neither said anything. Then Kathleen spoke.

"The water is so nice. And clear. Reminds me when I was young and we'd go to Gwynn, a small town on the lower Chesapeake Bay. There were miles of beach and we'd wander up and down, looking for clams or muscles or boys. And some nights when my folks would let us out to 10, we'd go skinny dipping off one of the points!" she confessed to Ford.

"Tisk, tisk," Ford commented, shaking his head.

"Don't tell me you're an old fuddy-duddy!" Kathleen chided.

Ford laughed. "When we we're kids living in Chicago near Loyola University, there was a spot on the campus where steel pilings had been put into Lake Michigan to stop the erosion of the bluffs. At night we'd sneak down there, strip and dive in. The water was deep and the waves would crash into the pilings and rebound. So we'd swim to where they'd meet the waves coming in and it was great fun."

"Why Captain Ford, don't tell me your youth was so risque!" Kathleen kidded and walking out of the water, she put her hand in his and they walked along the beach. A few minutes later, they came upon a piece of land that jutted out into the water. Climbing up on top of it, they walked about thirty yards to the end where some grass and sand offered them a place to sit. They did and looked out across the bay at a small island. The evening sun was setting behind them and its rays reflected off the blue waters. Looking back towards the hotel, they could see a few others on the beach and just ahead of them, the Pacific Clipper riding majestically at rest by the dock. The setting sun reflected off her and gave her a golden sheen. In the sky, the stars were just beginning their nightly show of dazzling the earthlings. Within an hour, the sky would be black and the stars would look like jewels scattered on a velvet cloth that stretched forever.

Ford leaned over and kissed Kathleen. She snuggled up to him, putting her head on his shoulder and the two sat quietly with their thoughts. Finally, Kathleen spoke.

"We'll be home soon, won't we?" she asked. Ford just grunted. He was enjoying the quiet, the stars and the few moments to think about nothing. But Kathleen wanted to talk.

"What about us?" she asked.

"Let's get married," Ford responded.

"I'm serious," she responded.

"So am I. I'm the Captain of a ship and I can marry anyone. So let's get married. We'll do it tonight. Go back to the hotel, have the crew act as ushers, the guests in the hotel will be our guests, Shamus can give you away and John Mack will be my best man. How about it?"

Kathleen just looked at him and even though it had gotten dark, she could see his face and he was smiling, not an "I'm kidding smile" but... and suddenly Kathleen's stomach flipped! He was serious. Robert Ford, Captain of the Pacific Clipper was proposing to her! She put her head down and didn't know whether to cry, laugh or jump up and shout her happiness at the stars. So she stood and walked a couple of steps, turned and looked at him sitting on the grass.

"No," she said and could have bitten off her tongue as she saw the disappointment spread across his face. "No... I don't mean no... I mean yes but... " and she stopped as Ford stood, walked over to her and gathered her in his arms. They just stood there and finally, Ford lifted Kathleen's chin and looked at her.

"I understand. But I meant it," he told her and they kissed. Then they sat down again on the grass and Kathleen tried to get control of her feelings, to explain to Ford how much she loved him but with the war, now was not the time to get married. She stood again and moved a few feet ahead. Looking out across the water she tried.

"I love you. You know that. But I want it all when we get married. Ten bridesmaids for me and you'll have ten ushers, the crew. A church filled with guests, Admiral King and everyone from Intel there, and I'm wearing a wedding dress made of silk on satin with a train that stretches to Richmond... my Dad walking me down the aisle, your folks and family there, my niece walking ahead of us with a huge basket of flowers spilling onto the aisle... you standing there waiting for us, pale with fear, John Mack whispering in your ear that you can still back out! And the reception will last for three days! Do you understand?" she explained, turning to see his reaction. He was lying on the grass, his head on his right arm, sound asleep.

0645- 5 Jan 1942-aboard the Valasquez off Long Beach, N.Y.

The weather had finally broken and the skies cleared. The Captain of the Valesquez had brought his ship to this spot by driving her at night without lights through the churning waters of the Atlantic, all the time fearful of submarines, not American but their allies, the Germans.

He knew the U-boats were out there, waiting to sink any ships leaving American ports. If the Germans spotted them, they wouldn't check their silhouette charts to see if it was an ally; they'd shoot and ask questions later. Even as close as they were to New York's Lower Bay, he was still fearful and the clear weather didn't improve his mood. He hadn't brought the Valasquez to New York in over three months and with the war on now, American security at the docks would be very tight. They couldn't make one mistake. With the Commodore aboard and the two man sub in the hold, he was doubly fearful. But he had his job to do and that was simply to proceed to Brooklyn, drop off their cargo of machine parts from Halifax, pick up the new cargo of dairy and meat products for the Caribbean Island of Antigua. Of course, their real mission of spying would continue as they plied their course down the Atlantic. Thus far, he wasn't sure what they were reporting to their contacts was that important to winning the war. They hadn't seen any movement of American naval vessels, any aircraft or troops shipping out or even merchant shipping. It was as if the United States had closed itself in and had no intention of fighting. He didn't believe that but he didn't give a damn about who won the war. He was a mercenary and as long as the Japs and Germans kept their part of the bargain, he'd sail up and down the Atlantic until it was all over. He already had enough money stashed away in Switzerland to let him live like an alcalde back in his home town of Mar del Plain. Another year of this and he'd own the town!

Although the sun was out, Garcia could see from the barometer that there were still storms in the area and the thermometer showed that the temperature was well below freezing this early in the morning. He didn't think ice would be a problem, not with the Gulf Stream flowing twenty or thirty miles off shore. Unless something unexpected happened, they would be in New York's Lower Bay by early evening and anchored in the Upper Bay near Brooklyn shortly thereafter. "Then early tomorrow we can dump the Commodore and his toy in the water. I don't give a damn if he sinks the American plane as long as I can get my ass out of there and be at sea by early evening," Captain Garcia thought to himself. "I'll wait for him until we lift anchor. Not one second more. Quite frankly, his scheme is full of horse dung so I doubt I'll ever see him again."

Garcia looked at his First Officer whom he had ordered to secure all the Japanese electronic surveillance equipment. The last thing he needed was to steam up the East River with an antenna hanging out the portholes! As his man nodded he had completed his mission. he caught sight of the tall Japanese headed up the stairwell towards the bridge. There wasn't anything for Tanaka to worry about now. He'd be putting up the East River in his little sub in less than a day and what would happen would happen. As the Commodore entered, Garcia put on a huge smile and welcomed him.

"Good morning, Captain Garcia. We have good weather for a change. I was wondering if the sun ever rose in this part of the world. How far are we from New York?" Tanaka asked as he took off his gloves and rubbed his hands together for warmth. Even though the sun was out, it was still very cold at sea.

"We should be sighting land in a few hours. We are off the coast of Long Island, probably somewhere around what the Americans call the Hamptons. I expect we'll be in the Lower Bay by mid-afternoon and move into the Upper Bay in the late evening. They probably won't let ships move about the harbor area after dark. All running lights on every vessel will be out because of the blackout. They wouldn't want us ramming into each other in the dark, would they!" Garcia laughed and walked over to a hot plate where the coffee pot sat. Nodding, he offered the Commodore a cup who accepted. After pouring two and giving one to Tanaka, they moved over to the navigator's desk and looked at the charts of New York harbor. Tanaka's trained eye showed them that it would be at least mid afternoon before entering the great harbor. Assuming a few hours wait before moving through Narrows that separated Staten Island from Brooklyn, they would be anchored off the docks of Brooklyn, awaiting only early morning before he and Buka climbed in and headed for Hell Gate, then to North Beach, and the Marine Air Terminal, where Ford would bring the Pacific Clipper.

"Any word on the Americans?" Tanaka asked.

"None," Captain Garcia answered.

Tanaka sipped his coffee and looked again at the map. When the Valasquez dumped them in the water, Tanaka knew they would have the high early tides to help them up the mouth of the Upper Bay and into the East River. There were no charts of the currents at Hell Gate but he didn't kid himself. It wasn't named that for no good reason. Once they turned there, it was a straight shot down to the Marine Terminal. Looking at the chart, he again envisioned Ford's landing pattern. He would probably come up the Atlantic to a point where he'd turn across Long Island, then out over Flushing Bay, and begin his decent past the Whitestone Bridge and College Point, landing just past the North Beach airport. Then Ford would turn towards the Marine

Terminal and have about a quarter of a mile before getting to the dock. And it was in that stretch of water that he'd sink her!

Garcia stood to the side from the charts, watching Tanaka's expressions in the soft early morning light. He was looking at the charts and he was no longer an inscrutable Oriental. His face showed the fierce desire to destroy the Americans and Garcia was glad he wasn't the Commodore's enemy. The man was totally obsessed and Garcia realized that this mission had noting to do with Japan defeating the United States. Tanaka had a blood lust for the American captain and Garcia knew that if the sub failed to sink the plane, Tanaka would somehow destroy it himself, even if he had to do it with his bare hands!

Tanaka, aware that he was being studied, straightened and forced himself to relax. He smiled at the Valasquez's Captain and nodded at the charts as if to say he knew them by heart. Then stretching and walking over to the hot plate and pouring himself more coffee, he looked at the sea. To no one in particular, he spoke out loud. "How are you sleeping this morning in lovely Trinidad, Captain Robert Ford? Will you be leaving soon or later after a nice swim in the Caribbean. No matter, I'll be here when you arrive," Smiling again at Captain Garcia and taking a last sip of coffee, he placed the cup on the tray and departed. Garcia felt cold, and not from the draft of fresh air that came in when the Commodore left.

0345 hours-Pan Am Relay Station-Trinidad

Ford had beaten his man and the pass was spiraling into his hands. He caught it and turned up field, racing for the goal line and a waterfall appeared, towering above him. As the water cascades down, he can see some of the guys swimming in the pool and he runs, yelling that he was coming in. He dives off the cliff and suddenly he's spinning in a Navy Corsair as he rolls the plane through its test dives. He can feel the skin on his face pull back as the forces of gravity grabs at him and the blue plane. He loved stretching these fighters up to and past their limits. Another roll and smiling, Ford pulls back on the stick and it snaps off in his hand. He tries pushing the joy stick back into its socket but he can't because it's a baseball bat! As the Corsair spins towards the earth, Ford reaches over to jettison the canopy but it's stuck! He swings the bat as hard as he can and pops the ball up to the Purdue shortstop. Jogging down towards first, Ford looks out towards right field and over the fence he sees the clouds. A storm is coming, a big one and he yells to the other players and points at the clouds. They ignore him and continue to play. But the storm comes faster and a funnel begins to form. Ford runs towards the storm cellar and pulls on the doors. They won't open and he bangs on them, yelling for help and he can see Ambassador Leach inside laughing and shaking his head. Turning to run, the funnel is on him and blackness sweeps over him.

Ford had always wondered what the inside of a tornado looked like and he was surprised that it was bare. No houses, no boats, no debris, nothing. He feels like he's in a wind tunnel. Ford wants to get out but there were no doors. Looking up, he can see the top of the funnel collapsing in on him and he begins to run away from it. Suddenly the cloud becomes a face and it's that face, the one from Darwin... from Frisco. Ford looks for something to fight it and the stick from the Corsair lays in front of him on the ground. He reaches for it and as the face comes at him, with that hideous mouth and terrifying green and red eyes, Ford swings his Jimmy Foxx slugger and smashed the barrel into one of the face's eyes. The eye explodes and showers Ford with 100 octane gas as the face screams and a flame shoots from its mouth. Ford ducks and runs and he can hear the face screaming. Ahead is a river, filled with crocodiles and on the other side, Shamus stands laughing and pointing. Ford looks over his shoulder and the face and the cloud are gone. Stopping at the edge of the water, a tiny boat no bigger than his hand floats towards him. It's the Cutty Sark and Shamus is signaling for him to board. Laughing, Ford steps towards the boat and as his foot moves over the water, the boat disappears and the face comes crashing through the water, grinning, its eye gone but ready to swallow him. Ford can't stop his forward motion and just as he falls into the mouth, blood spurts from the face and it disappears. Falling into the water, Ford tried to swim and began flailing his arms. He's drowning and knows it. As he goes down for the first time, he wills himself up and pulling against the water, his head breaks the surface and gasping for air, he tries swimming to shore.

Ford wakes, his arms wrapped in the sheets, twitching, his body bathed in sweat. He doesn't move, waiting until he knows where he is. Slowly he rolls his legs over the side of the bed and switches on the table lamp. Lighting a cigarette he looks at his hands and they're steady. His hands may have been but his heart isn't. He's exhausted, feeling as if he'd played four quarters against Ohio State and gone nine innings batting against Bob Feller. He was beat and again it was the dream that had shaken his usual self aplomb. Standing, he walks over to the window and looks out at the night. It's pitch black but as his eyes adjust, he can see the silver caps of the waves rolling into shore. Putting on his Bermuda shorts, he walks out the side door onto to the patio. Standing on the edge of the wooden deck, he begins to laugh at his dream. Already the details are blurred in his memory except for that face. "Who are you?" Ford asks softly. "And what do you want? Once is a freak but for you to come to me again in a dream, I don't believe in voodoo or omens but something is happening. What?"

Ford reaches for another cigarette and lights it with the fading ember from the butt he had in his hand. As he did so, he shook his head. He had never lit cigarettes back to back until now. "Wow, am I shook up or what. I'm even talking to myself, out loud! Well, it has been some day, and night. I wonder how Bill Clifford and the Marines are doing. Giles is probably right. With Segura dead, the locals won't fight, I hope. The cyclone could have been a lot worse had we hit it an hour later. And what a jerk I am: proposing to Kathleen and then falling asleep!" he continued. "She got even, telling everyone about my falling asleep after I proposed, Man, did they get on my ass, and with good reason. But she did say yes and I'm going to keep her to that promise."

Looking up at the stars, Ford checked to see where Polaris was and he spots it just over the horizon. They were so close to the Equator that the North Star wouldn't be totally visible in the sky until tonight when they head north. Checking his watch, he saw it was just past 0400. He needs sleep as does the rest of the crew. Poff's men would begin in the morning checking the Clipper with Swede and Parish supervising. Most of the crew would sack in until late morning and probably get in a swim before getting ready for the last leg home. From Trinidad to New York should take 17-18 hours, depending on the winds. He didn't want to fly during the day knowing that trigger happy fighter pilots in the Army Air Corps were guarding the coast line from Florida to Maine. By keeping far out to sea, flying at night without lights, they should be able to get to New York without being detected. He hoped. Flipping his butt into the sand, he mentally apologized to his Dad for not field stripping it as he walked back into his room. He thought again about the face in the dream but only briefly. Sleep came in a few seconds and his last thoughts were of Kathleen, her wonderful laugh and how much he loved her!

Some twenty miles east of Tabago, Trinidad's little sister island, a merchant ship slowly moves through the mild swells of the Caribbean Sea, running lights off. She is of Uruguayan registry, headed for Puerto Rico. Just a skeleton crew tends to the minor chores as the rest sleep, except inside the radio room. There, two men sit. One is reading a four month old magazine while the other with the headset on plays solitaire. As he begins to move a red seven of diamonds to a black eight of clubs, he stops, his hand in midair. Dropping the card he begins decoding a message. The reader quickly comes over, reads the message, smiles and orders it sent on to their sister ship, the Valesquez. The message is brief. "PC at Tr.

1700 Hours-5 January, 1942-aboard the Pacific Clipper

"Where do you think we'll be sent after we land?" John Parish asked Swede Rothe. The two were sitting in the starboard lounge having coffee as others of the crew were milling about in different stages of finding something to do. They had taken off from the waters of Trinidad less than an hour ago and now Captain Ford was bringing the Clipper up to her cruising altitude of 8,000 feet. The evening sun was falling behind them as they headed home and everyone was finally relaxing. Most had gone swimminga few hours earlier and got in some serious sun bathing time. Now the question Parish posed to the Swede was the same as all the rest of the Clipper's crew had. What would happen to them when they landed at North Beach, especially since they were from the Pacific division of Pan Am. On the bridge, John Steers posed basically the same question to his colleagues. On both levels of the Clipper, the answer was the same. No one knew. An hour later, when they were having dinner, the bigger question arose. Norm Brown asked it and this time there were some answers.

"What will happen to the Clippers and what about us? I mean, the planes are far too valuable to ground just because there is a war and we have too much flying experience to just beach us," the Second Officer stated with some vehemence when it came to the "beaching" part. Both lounges were in use and the crew, except for Ford and Poindexter, joined by Shamus, Giles and Kathleen were enjoying a special repast fixed for them by Gus the Chef at the Trinidad relay station. They had a choice of entrees, Red Snapper with Oyster stuffing or Lamb Chops broiled Gingery. Barney, not to be outdone had fixed appetizers of mushrooms caps stuffed with bread crumbs or pork sausage and Hearts of Artichoke, baked on small rye bread pieces covered with a combination of mayonnaise and Parmesan cheese. A tossed salad with cherry tomatoes, croutons and choice of dressings complimented the entrees. Hot garlic and French breads sat in covered baskets on the tables. Since Norm Brown's query was directed at no one in particular but all in general, it was a while before anyone addressed his question. They were all busy eating but each of the Clipper's crew had some thoughts and finally, Swede answered John Parish's question and part of Brown's as well.

"I don't know whether Pan Am will send us back to the West Coast but I doubt it. Remember Bill Mullahey told us that only one of the Clippers got back to the States and there are plenty of engineers back there to take care of her. So I guess we'll be assigned to the Atlantic division. Doing what, I don't know," the Chief Engineer stated. "As for the planes, well I guess that is Mr. Trippe's decision. I doubt there will be any pleasure flights to exotic lands for a long time."

Everyone nodded in agreement and then Jim Henricksen did a very strange thing. His seat was next to the built-in lounge radio and he reached over and turned it on. In the whole flight thus far, no one had turned either of them on! There was no reason to because where they had flown, regular radio broadcasting was non existent. Now the lounge filled with static and he turned down the volume level and began dialing trying to pick up a broadcast from the States or one of the islands. Nothing. At the other table, John Steers did the same with the same results... static.

After a few minutes of searching across the radio frequencies, both gave up. It was just an off chance they might hear some kind of broadcast from one of the big networks like CBS or NBC or Mutual. But with the war on, maybe radio broadcasts had been banned. No one knew.

"Your questions, Mr. Brown are well taken and while I don't really have an answer, I have an educated guess," Giles Brown began. "As you know all too well, we weren't prepared to go to war with Japan or Germany or anyone. The horror stories you've heard about how poorly prepared we are for war are true. But we are flying on a plane that everyone wants and so will our military when we get home. The Clipper and her sister ships are sea planes and I'll bet that the Navy and your boss, Mr. Trippe have already made a deal to turn the fleet of Pan Am planes over for the Navy's use. Wouldn't you agree, Lt. Elmes?"

"I would indeed, Commander Brown," Kathleen smiled and nodded at the Counterintelligence agent. "Unless they have lost their minds, the Navy can make great use of these Clippers ships for transportation of key personnel and cargo great distances. Certainly there is nothing in the Navy now that has the range or carrying capacity of these Boeings so we'd be fools not to use them. And Norm, I think you guys, at least those of you that are past thirty and too old for active duty will be flying the planes and training others to fly amphibian cargo craft. As for the rest of you that want to join up, as I'm sure you all will, your experiences aboard these ships is invaluable. Unfortunately, you'll all probably end up at a training base, teaching fuzzy faced kids how to fly rather than going into combat. That is just a guess but I can see Admiral King wanting to see Admiral Nimitz in the Pacific and he'll fly there on a Clipper ship.

Everyone was relaxed. Barney and Verne Edwards served coffee and mints and asked for orders for after dinner drinks. Most selected a brandy while a few passed. John Steers looked at John Mack and winked.

"You know, there are some of us that are checked out in the latest Navy fighters so I'm sure we'll be wanting combat assignments, right John?" Steers asked, not looking at Kathleen.

"You bet, John. The first thing we'll do after we land is find a Navy recruiting station and enlist. With our background, we should be put into a combat squadron right away, right Commander Brown?" John Mack stated as he looked at Giles Brown and smiled. Brown caught on right away.

"Definitely, John. I can see you and Steers here going right to Norfolk for carrier assignment. Of course, Captain Ford with his test pilot experience will be shipped out immediately to the West Coast and probably join Admiral Halsey in the South Pacific. He could be seeing action in a week or two. The Navy can't have enough good fighter pilots like you two and the Captain. In fact, rather than waiting till we land, I'll swear you three in right now so you can go to war without waiting. What do you say?" Brown said in all seriousness.

"Over my dead body!" Kathleen Elmes informed one and all. "The man flying this plane is going to be grounded as soon as we hit North Beach. And Giles Brown, rank or no rank, you stay away from him?"

The man flying the Clipper had thoughts on the same thing Giles Brown was kidding Kathleen about. And it was a continuation of what he and his betrothed had discussed on the sandy beach of the Pan Am hotel and relay station. Kathleen had been given a bathing suit by Walt Poff out of the small but smart shop in the hotel. It was a one piece and Betty Grable couldn't have filled it any better. After all the wolf whistles from the crew abated, she and Ford had their swim and walk along the beach. Both wanted to settle things but neither knew what they wanted to settle! They were in love but there was a war on. She was Navy and he was going to be soon, in one form or another. She had to report to her headquarters in D.C. and he to Pan Am in New York. So they talked, both knowing that what they decided wouldn't mean a thing after they landed.

"When do you think we'll be home?" Kathleen asked.

"Probably land at North Station around 0600 tomorrow morning," Ford replied. And they continued along the shoreline, Ford kicking the water with his right foot as Kathleen looked at him in a very possessive manner. Ford caught her look and laughed as she did. Without another word, he took her hand and they continued. Behind them they could hear some of the men joking and having a ball in the idyllic waters of the Caribbean. To Ford, the sounds were good, his people having time to unwind. To Kathleen, the sound was of close friends enjoying themselves.

"So?" she asked.

Ford didn't answer. He understood immediately what she was asking. He'd thought about nothing else since waking after the "face" had destroyed his first sleep. And he had no answers. He loved Kathleen deeply but... the war!

"The war... this fuckin war!" Ford thought. "You bastard Tojo... and you, you sick son-of-a-bitch Adolph," And then he stopped thinking. He'd done nothing else since waking and he knew he was wasting his grey matter bitching about things he couldn't control. But he could with Kathleen and now was the time for the two of them to settle things.

"Last night I proposed. Last night you accepted. Last night I fell asleep and you teased me unmercifully!" Ford began and then smiled and laughed, admitting he'd earned all her teasing. "I'm holding you to that, right?" he asked and smiled as he saw her head nod as she smiled. Then he stopped, the water at his ankles and pulled her close to him and hugged her. She felt so warm and he wanted the world to stop now. But it wouldn't. So he pulled her down on the sand and asked, "So?"

Kathleen laughed and kissed him on the cheek and then stood and moved into the water. Turning, she looked at Ford and nodded, as if she had been privy to his thoughts as they walked along the edge of the water.

"You're right... the goddamn war... we'll have to wait," and as she said wait, her eyes filled with tears and she quickly turned away from Ford to hide her emotions. But Ford's laughter brought her angrily spinning around to see what he thought was so funny.

"Were you reading my thoughts?" he asked, chidingly. "If you were, then we really are made for each other and you can start your own psychic salon," Kathleen stood hands on her hips looking and smiling as he stood and walking to the water, he put his arm around her shoulder and they continued down the beach, not saying a word. They had agreed to get married when the war was over.

Now as he sat in his chair on the bridge of the Pacific Clipper and recalled the early part of the day, Ford felt relaxed and looked forward to the landing and finally being home. All that was ahead of them was the sky, still a brilliant blue while below the Caribbean stretched as far as he could see. First check point was Puerto Rico, about three hours away. He'd stay at least 75 miles east of the island just in case there were any coast watchers looking for enemy ships or aircraft. Once past the island, he'd keep the Clipper on a straight course towards New York, staying as far out to sea as practical. He and the other officers had plotted the course before taking off and the ETA was 0500, assuming they didn't run into any extreme weather. Once there, Ford planned to fly past Manhattan and come down above Long Island, and keeping the Clipper low, drop down over the Whitestone Bridge and onto Flushing Bay. That way they would be in New York before any planes could be scrambled to attack them, he hoped. So he sat back, flexed his shoulders and settled in for the long flight home. Home. Ford smiled broadly just thinking about finally landing in the States!

0330 hours-6 January 1942-aboard the Valasquez-Brooklyn Docks

Tanaka's time had arrived. The disappointment at Koto Bharu had been forgotten and the race across Canada was a dim memory. He didn't give the past a second thought as he looked at his instrument for the destruction of Ford and the Pacific Clipper. Captain Garcia had brought word from the ship watching Trinidad that the Clipper took off from Port O's Spain at 1350 hours yesterday, January 5th. Tanaka knew Ford would not try a night landing on waters he was unfamiliar with. Giving him 17 hours to reach New York and another half hour to land, he estimated Ford would bring the Clipper down on Flushing Bay around 0530-0600. Add another 15 to 20 minutes to taxi to the Marine Air Terminal and he would be firing the torpedoes at Ford just as the dawn broke over New York! Tanaka's face didn't show any emotion but anyone looking closely into his eyes would have seen the excitement and joy he felt knowing that at last he would complete his quest. His uncle would be proud of him. Garcia and Lt. Oho had joined the launching crew in the hold to see the Commodore and Lt. Buka off. The two had already agreed that the big man would climb in the sub first and get settled before Buka would enter. Now he turned and saluted Garcia then walked over to Lt. Oho and extended his hand. Oho almost fainted but held his composure long enough to clasp the

Commodore's right hand, then step back and salute. Tanaka did the same, turned and climbed up the small ladder. Everyone held their breath, watching the big man squeeze his body through the conning tower. This time he didn't get stuck and after a few minutes, Tanaka tapped on the side of the sub, signaling Buka to come ahead. The sub driver also saluted the officers and crew and climbed in, pulling the hatch shut as he entered. Immediately, the crew moved to flood the tanks and as the water rushed into the bay where the sub sat, the metal plate that hid her began to slowly move to cover the hole. When the hole was filled, another switch was thrown and the two stabilizers unclasped the craft and she floated free in the hole. Now the plate slid forward and the hole was closed. The chief that was supervising the launch looked at the gauge and when the needle moved from red through blue to green, he knew the hole was filled and the false bottom open. They would wait for the signal from the two man sub that they were in the Bay before closing the shell. Captain Garcia and Lt. Oho left, knowing there was nothing more for them to do and returned to the bridge.

Inside the sub, Buka waited for the water to grab the sub and pull her into the Bay's current. The two could feel the small craft begin to float and looking through the periscope, Buka could see the side of the Valeaquez as they rose slowly towards the surface. He started the motor and put out the rudders from the sides of the sub to stabilizer her. Now that he had her under control, he moved up to just below the surface and looking through his periscope, only the moonlight illuminated the Bay. There was not one light to be seen. New York harbor was pitch black. Rotating the viewer, he searched the harbor for any ships moving about. There were none. Periscope down, Buka looked at the Commodore and smiled. They were on their way to Hell Gate and then to the site of the ambush. Buka felt they had plenty of time so he proceeded slowly ahead. Both men could feel the strength of the Atlantic tide rolling up the Bay. Buka knew this would be the easiest part of the trip. So he moved the sub quickly towards the East River. An hour later they were in the grips of the tides in the river and the ride had become very rough. Buka wanted to slow down, fearing the sandbars he knew were everywhere. No sense in running aground on any of the shifting sands of this very treacherous river. But Tanaka didn't and ordered Buka to move faster. Now the little sub began to bounce around from the turbulence the tides created and Tanaka's body became bruised from flopping on the metal floor of the sub. But he wouldn't let Buka slow down, not until they had gotten past Hell Gate.

Captain Garcia had warned Buka about Hell Gate, calling it the most dangerous area they would have to cross to get to position opposite the Marine Air Terminal. And he understated it. The Captain's experiences were based on bringing a 40 tom cargo ship around Hell Point and out into Long Island Sound, all above the water where he and the pilot could see what they were doing and avoid the biggest swirling eddies that made Hell Point so accurately named. Buka had none of that going for him. His instruments only gave him the basic information of depth and speed and didn't warn him when they were entering rough water. So he had to rise almost to the surface, punch his small periscope up for a quick peek, look around and bring the scope back in. But all that showed him was the surface from the surface, no way to judge where the dangers were. Garcia had also warned him that most ships were damaged in Hell Gate by the rocks that jutted into the river from the shoreline, not the currents. The charts were almost useless because the currents were so strong that even in a few days, sand bars could shift. Weather could also play a major role, especially if there had been a powerful storm hitting the area. One had come through the harbor area just two days earlier and Garcia told Buka that his charts of the East River were over six months old. As far as the sub's pilot was concerned, only Buddha could get them to where Tanaka wanted to be.

Again, he brought his little sub up to periscope depth and this time Tanaka looked through the eye piece. Turning it to look left and right, he also saw only the surface of the river and it looked calm enough. Then the first of the currents hit them and the little boat almost tipped over. Underwater, they was suppose to be less turbulence but Hell Gate didn't know that. Righting itself, the sub pushed hard towards the main part of the bend, where the waters from the East River collided with her islands and sent back their rebounding waves to shake the hell out of Tanaka and Buka. Even underwater, the sub bounced like she was hit with the shock wave of a depth charge. Buka tried to level her off and dive down but the turmoil surrounding the sub made him forget that maneuver. He drove her straight ahead, adding speed and hoping to get close enough to the island itself to have it act as a buffer between his ship and the currents. He was going well past the turn towards their hiding place but he knew they'd never get there unless he could escape Hell Gate. Tanaka lay silent on the floor.

Buka came up to the surface again and put the periscope up as high as it would go. If there was an American crazy enough to be patrolling this area, so be it. But he had to know where they were. An island on the map, named Rivers Island was what he was aiming for and looking through the periscope, he could see it, about 1000 yards ahead. The little sub rode up and down with the swells like a cork adrift at sea but Buka kept the power as high as he could and the tiny boat struggled against the strongest currents. In what seemed like an hour, they finally reached it. The shaking and bobbing abated enough for him to bring the sub lower under the water while keeping the periscope up. Like a swimmer treading water, Buka cut the subs power to keep her moving just enough so as not to stop. Even with the island acting as a shield from the currents, Hell Gate still had enough power to pull the sub back into its clutches if he allowed her to drift. Spinning the scope around, he saw directly across the water what the maps showed him to be North Beach, the commercial airfield that serviced New York City. There were no lights but against the backdrop of the night, the shape of buildings and hangers could be discerned. That being North Beach, Buka decided that by crossing over to it and then heading west towards the land on the opposite side, they would reach their hiding place to await the Pacific Clipper. He was about to explain all of this to the Commodore but didn't bother. That was what he was going to do and if the big man had other ideas, let him pilot the damn thing. Looking down at Tanaka, Buka smiled. "We are close to North Beach. I will take us across the river to the hiding place. The Americans will turn just past where we are now to move towards their docking area. We will be about 300 yards across from her as she taxis past us. You will have a direct shot."

0430 hours-6 Jan. 1942-aboard the Pacific Clipper

They had been in the air better than half a day and the only things of interest had been the sunset last evening and the dinner that Gus the Cook had prepared for them. Most of the crew had slept through the night expect for the pilots. They alternated between commanding the Clipper and getting some shut eye. But now as the plane came closer to New York, like a silent alarm awaking each, the others began to rise and wander towards the lounge and Barney's coffee. Not much was said since most of last evening had already been taken up with everyone guessing what the future held. Now, in the semi darkness of the passenger cabin, they sat and chatted. Nothing heavy, just light banter. They guessed the Clipper was somewhere off the North Carolina coast but Shamus looking out the porthole couldn't see anything but blackness. It didn't make any difference. They were almost home and after what they had been through, knowing in an hour or so they'd be landing in the States, made them almost forget the last two weeks. Almost. Now it was simply flying and landing. A piece of cake.

Ford was standing on the bridge while John Mack piloted. He had a cup of coffee in his hand and was thinking about the landing at New York. He'd never landed a Clipper at North Beach but Pan Am's training was so complete that all pilots had to know each and every Pan Am landing site worldwide. So he felt reasonably secure about bringing the Clipper in there. It was dark outside now but by the time they reached New York, dawn should just be breaking through. It was a clear night and they were still far out to sea, maybe 150 miles off the coast. Checking his watch, he figured that it was about time to change the Clipper's heading, bring her down slowly and head for home!

"Home, John!" Ford spoke to Mack. "How does that sound?"

The First Officer turned and looked at the Captain. He wanted to say something special so the two of them would always remember this moment but all he could do was smile. John Poindexter, sitting at the radio console just nodded and thought how his wife would react when he finally was able to break radio silence. Then he laughed to himself, knowing he'd have to call her long distance! Ford wouldn't break radio silence until they docked. But he didn't care. He'd call collect and charge it to Pan Am! Now Norm Brown, Jim Henrichsen and John Steers all came up the steps from below, carrying their coffee cups and just standing on the bridge, looking out the windows. Ford understood. They just wanted to be here when he brought her in. So John Mack moved back to his co-pilots chair as Bob Ford took the controls of the Pacific Clipper. Checking all the instruments took about ten seconds and everything was standard. The Clipper had been the one constant throughout the long journey and she wasn't throwing any problems at him now. Pushing the yoke forward and down, the Clipper gradually turned to port and began her decent towards the air space of the United States of America. They'd made it...all the way around the world and the weather looked good for an easy last landing. Ford reached up and patted the instrument panel, just to let the Clipper know how much he appreciated all she had done for them. The rest nodded their approval.

Below, each of the others took a seat near a window trying to see land. The clear air they had enjoyed at 8,000 feet out over the Atlantic was now beginning to cloud up somewhat. The first rays of the rising sun were just adding enough light that they knew night was fleeing and soon they would see America. It was Shamus that spotted land and yelled to all. Smiling, each man looked out and there it was, just a darker mass ahead on the horizon but it was below them and solid.

Now as Ford moved the plane lower, they could begin to see New York in the distance, the tall buildings barely discernable in the early morning darkness that still surrounded the city. It was eerie. The world's busiest and largest city totally dark, not a light shining anywhere. Suddenly, John Parish shouted.

"There... ahead, about 10 o'clock... the Empire State Building... see it. I mean there's the top of it," And there it was, the tip of the silver cone jutting into the sky, clouds still below the giant tower, hiding the rest of the world famous landmark. Now as Ford banked to starboard, leveled off headed up the coast towards Long Island, the clouds broke and the beaches and small towns could be seen parallel to their course. Then Shamus yelled.

"What is that on the ground? That white stuff?" He asked, looking at something he'd never seen before, land all white, nothing brown or green.

"Snow," Oscar Hendrickson answered. And the rest of them broke into gales of laughter, not at Shamus' expense but realizing that it was indeed winter and they were delighted. The humidity and oppressive heat of the lands along the Equator that had been their home for the past two weeks were gone. The white snow seemed to lift all their spirits even higher, telling them they had made it home. As Ford turned the Clipper to port towards land and descended over the shore and across Long Island towards Flushing Bay, the crew quickly policed the area and then returned to their seats, strapping themselves in, ready for this final touchdown on their flight.

0530 hours-aboard the midget sub, East River, New York

They sat in the sub, waiting. Buka had brought the sub across the river to the edge of the North Beach Terminals then running parallel to the station, crossed the wide channel to a spot about a quarter of a mile above the Marine Air Terminal docks. His charts showed that there were many coves for them to lie in wait for the Americans and he chose one that gave them a broad view of the harbor. It was about 300 yards across from where the American were to taxi to their dock. Looking through the periscope, he noticed warehouses and oil tanks dotting the area, between the North Beach Terminals and the Marine Air base. Buka assumed correctly they serviced both operations. Although it was dark when he turned the sub to face her torpedo doors directly at the opposite shore, now with the first faint glow from the east telling him the day was here, the cove they were in was so totally hidden and if he had wanted, he could have surfaced and no one could spot them. If the

Commodore wanted, a surface shot at the Pacific Clipper was available to him.

Now, a few minutes later, as the two sat in ambush, it was Tanaka at the periscope. Buka kept the propeller turning slowly, just enough to compensate for the mild waves that bounced against the rocks behind them. They were about ten feet below the river's surface. When Tanaka fired the torpedoes, the force of their ejection would drive the little boat backwards and up. He could control that. Buka was confident of their success. No one knew they were here and the American plane would be so close, the Commodore couldn't miss. His single concern was that he had only fired his torpedoes in practice, never in a real combat situation. And those were dummy torpedoes. Couldn't waste real ones in practice. So now he sat in silence, waiting for the Commodore to tell him what was happening.

The big man was strangely reticent. He had gotten control of his nerves after all those minutes bouncing around the East River. He felt almost as if he had won, making it to their ambush site. He hadn't said more than a few sentences to Buka and now as he looked through the eyepiece, he could see that his pilot had selected an ideal place for the destruction of the Clipper. Ford had to come right down the river towards them and his bow would be at right angles to them when he fired. He would lead the plane by some seventy yards and the speed of the plane and his torpedoes would bring them together within ten seconds. He'd fire the right one first, count to three and then the second. He didn't expect to miss but by spacing the two, he gave himself a little protection. It would only take one to blow the Clipper out of the water. The second would finish what ever was left.

Checking his watch, he saw that it was almost 0530 hours. Ford should be landing in a few minutes. Giving the periscope one more turn to check the surface and finding it as it was a minute earlier, he looked at the buttons he'd press to send death on its way. In the few minutes he'd been looking through the periscope, he realized that this golden moment that was about to happen didn't bring the elation he thought it would. Never an introspective person, Tanaka began wondering why. "Was it Thu's failure to capture the Clipper... maybe. Had he succeeded and I'd flown back to Tokyo aboard her I'd have felt vindicated and basked in the glory of the capture of such a prize. Now I sit in the lapping waves of a dirty river waiting to blow a defenseless plane out of the water all for the glory of the Emperor... No, that isn't right. I'm not doing this for Hirohito, no matter what I told Teshito. It is my ego. That is why I'm here. Ford beat me in Surabaja. I couldn't walk away after they laughed at me in Kota Bharu and Tokyo. I have to beat him and now my turn is here. Sorry Bob Ford... and the rest of you. This is war... nothing major like capturing you and building bombers from your designs... but it's my war and I have to win even if Tojo and Yamamoto never hear of my victory. Before that wouldn't have been good enough. Now it is." Tanaka stopped his justifying why he was sitting in the freezing waters of the East River and looked out the periscope. Nothing. Ford hadn't arrived yet.

0545 hours-aboard the Pacific Clipper on Flushing Bay, New York

"Touched down on Flushing Bay, New York, New York, 6 January, 1942 at 0535. We are home," John Steers looked at his entry into the Pacific Clipper's log and laughed as he remembered the entry he erased just a month ago. Returning the Smith Corona to its place in his locker. he hoped he'd never have to use it again. Standing behind Captain Ford, he looked out the cockpit window at the grey waters of the Bay. To his left he saw the North Beach Terminal ahead and just past was the bend towards the Marine Air Terminal. Steers saw Ford's head begin to turn towards him and knew what orders were coming so he turned and walked down the steps to the door leading to the anchor room to get ready to secure the Clipper at her docking area.

Ford had brought the Clipper across Long Island and turned west over Long Island Sound, dropping the Clipper 500 feet per minutes and skimming over the Whitestone Bridge, put her on the water at 0535. He could hear the cheers going up below and looking at John Mack, he smiled. Reducing her speed he brought the plane under control and moved past North Beach towards the turn to the Pan Am depot. He put behind him all thoughts of what they had accomplished and concentrated on berthing the Clipper. He'd never been here before, knew nothing about the currents and tides and had no charts or information to help. But if the East River was all it was cracked up to be, he better be careful. Then he heard John Steers calling up from below but the words were garbled. Looking at John Mack, the Second Officer laughed and translated.

"John says it is so cold, the water has frozen the hawser. And there is ice on the sponsons!" Mack reported. Ford just shook his head. Two days ago it was 100 degrees plus as they flew through the chasms of Livingston Falls. Now water was freezing his plane! He was about to issue an order but since there was nothing he could say, he didn't. Now as he passed North Beach and entered the final water path leading to home, they could see about a quarter of a mile down the way, the silhouette of the Marine Air Terminal. Ford moved the throttles forward for a little more speed, anxious to reach his landing.

Tanaka had grown tired of looking through the eyepiece and sat back. He was about to look back at Buka when something moved him to look out again. There! There she was... the Pacific Clipper and it was moving towards them. Then it turned and against the grey sky behind her, Tanaka saw the plane begin its run into the Marine terminal. She was a good 1000 yards away but to Tanaka, she looked so close he could reach out and touch her silver body. Buka caught the Commodore's excitement and without waiting for orders, moved the small sub out further into the water. As he did, the boat pitched a little as it left the safety of the cove but not enough to upset Tanaka's shooting level. Buka opened the tubes and the water rushed in. He compensated and now the sub was level and ready. The Clipper was moving easily towards the docking area, about 900 yards away now. Tanaka would fire both torpedoes when she was about 75 yards to port of him, letting the plane "run into" the torpedoes. The Clipper was also about the same distance across the river from where they lay in wait. Closer she came... 150... 100... 75 yards! Tanaka's brain shouted fire and a second later, his thumb hit the button. A great shaking and threshing of the sub happened as the first torpedo rushed out. The tiny craft flipped over, Tanaka's head hitting the side of the periscope as his thumb automaticallyhit the firing button for the second torpedo. Again the sub shook and spinning like a top in the churning water, hit the bottom of the river. Buka couldn't control her as the sub smashed into the rocks that lined the river bed. Tanaka's head was bleeding badly but somehow, Buka got the boat upright and began to move away from the rocks. The periscope was bent and water began seeping into the sub. Tanaka panicked and fought to throw open the hatch. But the water pressure above was too strong so all he could do was sit as Buka fought to keep them stable. Then they heard it. The explosion! It shook them again as the concussion reverberated across the water and again Buka could do nothing as the tiny boat almost capsized again. Then the second explosion. The periscope was out and Tanaka couldn't see the Clipper sinking. All he wanted was that and he yelled at Buka to surface so he could witness his triumph!

As Ford moved the Clipper down the strip towards the dock, he was about 700 yards away when it happened. Crunch! Then a grinding of the prow as the Pacific Clipper came to a screeching halt! Ford sat there and closed his eyes. "First I land in a mine field and now I've hit a goddamn sandbar just when we've almost made it!" No one on the bridge said a word but Ford could hear someone below yell "What happened?" And John Steers, still in the anchor room knew and yelled to everyone, "We hit a sandbar!" Ford knew they could hear that in San Francisco. He reversed the propellers and giving them full throttle, began trying to shake the Clipper loose from the grip of the bar. Just then, Steers yelled something else and Ford and the whole plane heard it clearly.

"Holy shit. Moby Dick just went by us!"

"Boom!" A warehouse suddenly ceased to exist as it went up in flames and then one of the gasoline tanks near it blew. The semi-dark loading area was engulfed in flames and threw almost sun like illumination across the water as Ford and the rest looked in awe at the fire.

The Clipper came free and as Ford turned her away from the sandbar and towards the center of the river, it happened again.

"Boom!" Steers began yelling as another explosion rocked them. A few hundred yards behind them, another loading area blew up!

"John, can you see anything?" Ford yelled down to Steers. But before he could respond, John Mack, looking across the river saw what had caused the explosions.

"Bob, about 7 o'clock. A boat of some kind. Across the river," He commented, quite calmly.

Finally free of the sandbar, Ford kept the Clipper on reverse engines until he'd had her facing across the river. Now he could see it and the light coming from the explosions showed him a small boat that looked like a whale! Ford didn't waste a second. He switched the four engines to forward and as the giant propellers caught the air, the Clipper picked up speed, Ford aiming the Clipper right at the boat bobbing in the water. She leaped across the short space and as he bore down on her, he saw the hatch begin to open and an arm come out. Ford had her up to twenty knots and as the Clipper's steel nose hit the ship, she sliced through the sub like a surgeons knife. The grinding of metal on metal took just seconds and the Clipper was past the sub and Ford cut power to avoid the rocks looming ahead. Turning to starboard, he brought the Clipper around and taxied back to the spot where they had sunk the boat. Steers, still in the anchor hole looked around for survivors or debris but there was none. It was too dark even with the light from the fires across the river to see a body floating near the rocks.

"Any damage to the nose, John?" Ford asked Steers.

"None that I can see, Sir. But we'll have to check the bottom when we dock to make sure," Steers replied. Now the light from the fires across the river was beginning to be augmented by the arrival of daylight. Steers could hear sirens somewhere racing to the fire and on the bridge, Ford was slowly moving the Clipper to her docking area. They still had about 200 yards to go and everyone was speculating on what had happened. Kathleen and Giles Brown requested permission to come up and Ford gave it.

Kathleen walked over and stood behind him as Brown spoke to Ford.

"Any ideas of what it was, Captain?" the Naval counter intelligence officer asked.

"A sub of some kind, small, very small. But big enough to sink us," Ford answered. Brown had an idea as did Kathleen of what kind of sub it was but both looked at each other before Brown nodded to her.

"Probably a midget sub, Bob. The Japanese have them," she explained. Brown nodded. Ford remembered those dreams and the face that tried to kill him. Could the man that had masterminded the attempt to shanghai the Clipper have come all the way to New York to destroy him and his plane? Ford's head bobbed in the affirmative as he answered his own question.

"Tanaka! It had to be him," he stated and no one disagreed.

Now the Clipper was within 100 yards of the dock and the fires were still burning behind them. Yet not one light could be seen in the terminal building. They must have heard the explosions! Looking at his watch, Ford saw that it was 0605 hours. They were still a few minutes from docking so Ford thought he'd better wake up the control tower. The crew wanted to hear what he had to say. After twenty one days of total radio silence, Bob Ford was finally going to make a transmission!

Picking up the mike, switching on the transmitter, he spoke.

"Pacific Clipper, inbound from Auckland, New Zealand. Captain Ford reporting. Due to arrive Pan Am Marine Terminal North Beach, five minutes."

The Pacific Clipper was home.

EPILOGUE

Like all the Pan Am planes, the Pacific Clipper went to war and the men that flew them also became part of the world wide conflict America was facing. Becoming part of the United States Navy, both performed with superb professionalism. The British finally got their Clipper ships when Juan Trippe made three of the Boeings a gift to America's ally. But when the war was over, the Clipper ships were discarded by the Navy as obsolete. By 1947, all were either scuttled or broken up and sold for scrap. Not one Boeing 314 or 314A survived the purge so all that is left of these magnificent flying ships are yellowing pictures and wonderful memories.

A newspaper article in a suburban Charlottesville newspaper in the spring of 1946 mentioned a wedding that took place on a special Virginia Saturday. The cause for the article wasn't so much about the beautiful bride and handsome groom, or the many Naval luminaries in attendance as much as the reception which continued for three days. It seems that the owner of the manor had called the police. When they arrived he prefaced his statement by saying he wasn't upset with the Irishman wearing kilts and playing his bagpipe non-stop. Or even that he and the others had consumed the state's supply of Cutty Sark. He called when he heard them yelling and laughing and talking about the fight that was coming, fearing his place would be ruined. The owner sheepishly explained that it was all a mistake on his part. What he had overheard wasn't about a fight... but a flight!

PERSONS & PLACES

Historical:

Crew of the Pacific Clipper:

Ford, Robert, Captain
Mack, John Henry, 1st Officer
Brown, Roderick Norman, 2nd Officer
Henriksen, James. Third Officer
Steers, John, Forth Officer
Poindexter, John, 1st Radio Officer
Hendrickson, Oscar, 2nd Radio Officer
Rothe, Homans, 1st Engineering Off.
Parish, John, 2nd Engineering Officer
Swacki, Barney, Chief Steward
Edwards, Verne, 2nd Steward

Pan American Airlines:

Juan Trippe, CEO
Charles H. Lindbergh, Consultant
William Mullahey, Wake Island

Japanese:

Emperor Hirohito
Count Tanaka
Baron Giichi Tanaka
General Hideci Tojo
Admiral Isoroku Yamamoto

Pan American planes:

Sikorsky's 42
Martin M 130
Boeing 314 & 314A's
Tripps Fokker F 7

Other Nations' Planes:

Japan: Zeros, Mitsubishis
England: Sutherland

Germany: Messerschmitt, Folke Wolfe
Dutch: Brewsters

Pan Am Pacific bases:

Hawaii: Pearl Harbor
Midway Island
Wake Island
Guam
Philippines: Manila
China: Hong Kong, Shanghai
Malasia: Singapore
American Samoa: Pago Pago
New French Caldonia: Noumea
New Zealand: Auckland
Australia: Gladstone, Darwin

Geographic Locations--USA:

Alaska: Attu Island, Kayak Island
San Francisco
Los Angeles
Seattle
New York

Asia:

Japan: Tokyo, Okinawa
China: Manchuria, Hong Kong
Malasia
Singapore
Java: Surabaja, Batavia, Bali
Australia: Darwin
New Zealand: Auckland

Subcontinent:

Ceylon: Trincomalee
India: Karachi
Arabia: Bahrein
Saudi Arabia: Mecca
Iran: Tehran

Africa:

Egypt: Cairo, Tobruk
Anglo Egyptian Sudan: Khartoum
Belgian Congo: Leopoldville
French West Africa: Brazzaville

South America:

Brazil-Natal

Trinidad, Port O'Spain

Canada:

British Columbia: Dease Lake
Saskatchewan: Lake Athabaska
Hudson Bay
Nova Scotia: Halifax

Where the Pacific Clipper Landed:

Pacific Ocean
Indian Ocean
Atlantic Ocean
South China Sea
Timor Sea
Java Sea
Bay of Bengal
Arabian Sea
Persian Gulf
Red Sea
Nile River
Congo River
Flushing Bay
East River

Fictional:

Americans:

Kathleen Elmes, USN Intel. Off.
Giles Brown, USN Counterintel.
Walter R. Welch, Ambs. to NZ
William Clifford, USMC
Walter Poff, Pan Am in Trinidad

Japanese:

Commodore Isodecki Tanaka, IJN
Captain Nagoma, IJN
Captain Teshio, IJN
Major Seishu Thu, IJA
Lt. Oho, Pilot-IJA

Australian:

Jocko MacDonnald, Harbormaster
Archie, Bar-room fighter

Dutch(Java):

Capt. Rolph Vander Kellen, Dutch, pilot.
Colonel VanGelder, Commander, Surabaja Defense Forces
Henry Oberveldt, Manager, Royal Dutch Shell Petroleum Co.

British:

Sir Reginald Leach, Ambassador to Indonesia
Capt. Brewster M. Loud, Commander HMS Revenge
Governor Chauncy McCloud of Bahrein
Governor Edward Heath of Anglo Egyptian Sudan(Khartoum)
Capt. Jonathan Wild, RAF

Irish:

Shamus Ginsberg, Owner, Black Swan Inn, Surabaja, Java.
Thomas Maloney, Owner, The Magnolia Arms, Leopoldville, Belgian Congo

Arabians:

Sheik Abu el Shar, Emir of Bahrein
Ali el Shar-his Heir
Ben Adrisi-Imam

Brazilians:

Governor Ramon Jorge de Pennamburo of Rio Grande de orte, Brazil
Colonel Pedro Segura, Commander, Army of Rio Grande de Norte

ILLUSTRATIONS

Crew of the Pacific Clipper:

Robert Ford

John Henry Mack

Roderick N. Brown

James Henricksen

John Poindexter

Oscar Hendrickson

John D. Steers

Homans K. Rothe

John B. Parish

Barney Sawicki

Verne C. Edwards

The Clipper Landing:

Pan Am crew at work. B-314 spacious flight deck.

The Dining Room, on of the many luxury features.

Cross Section of nose.

Pilot's seat.

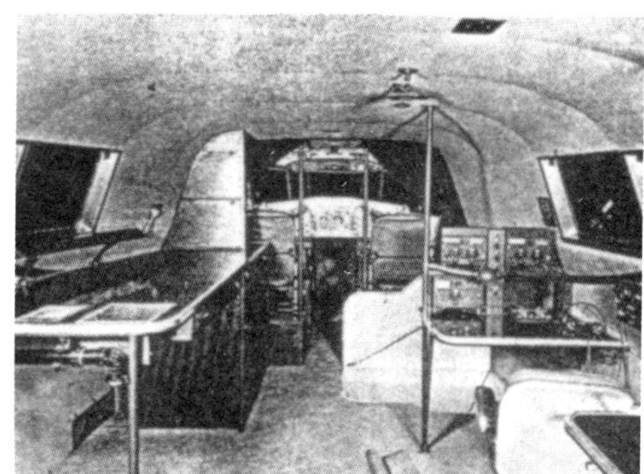

Forward view.

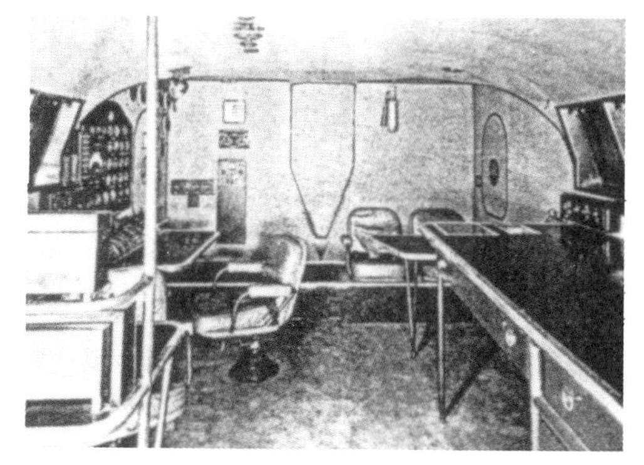

Flight deck.

Radio-engineer station.

Boeing Company--Interior of the Clipper.

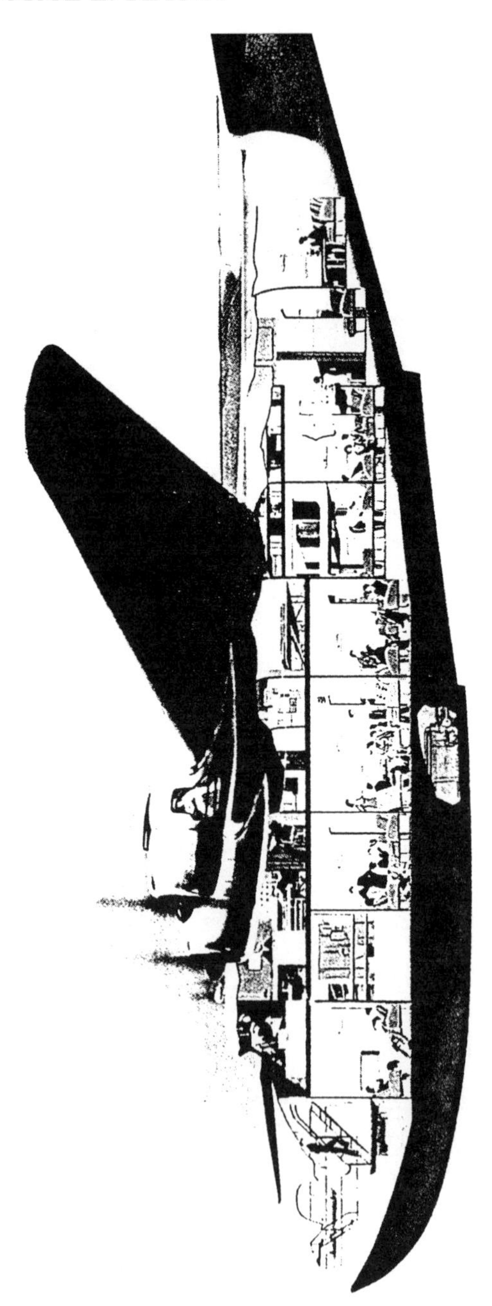

Cut away of Clipper--bow to stern.

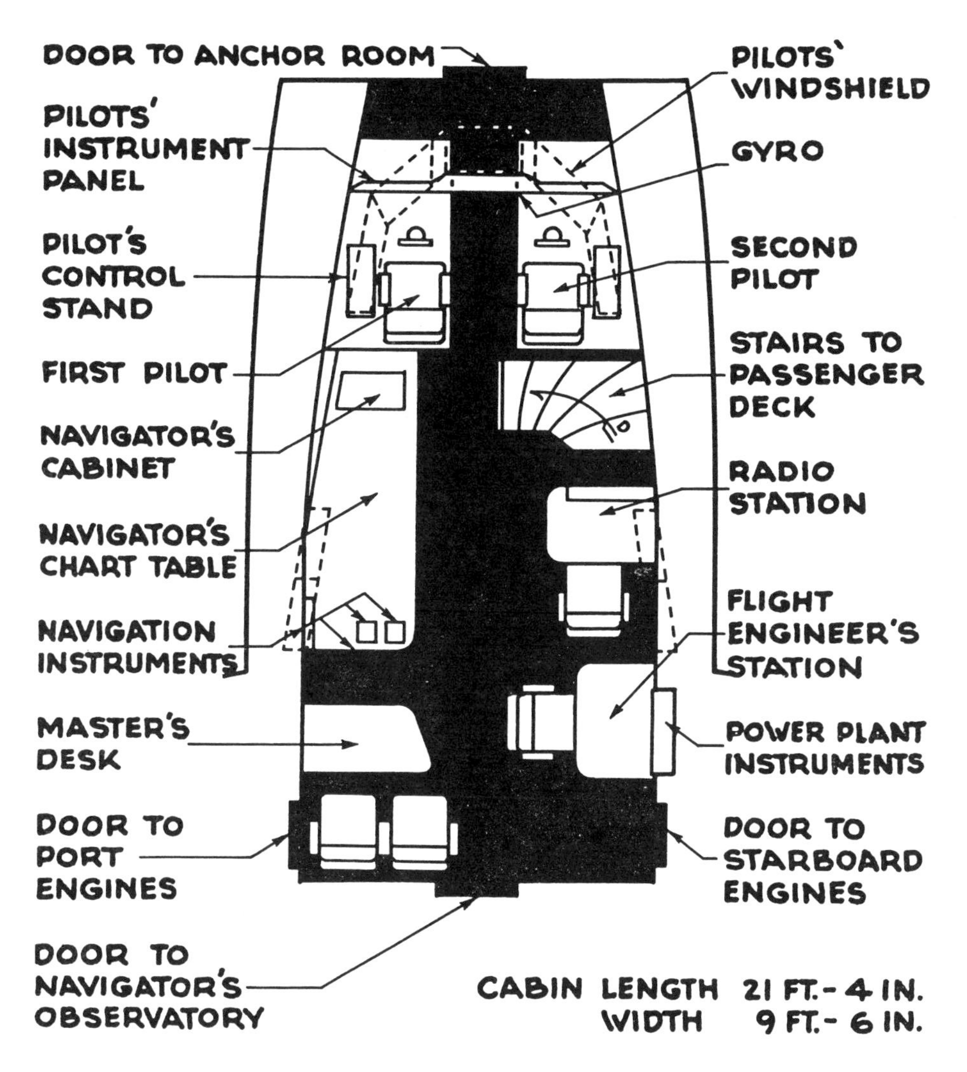

Control Cabin

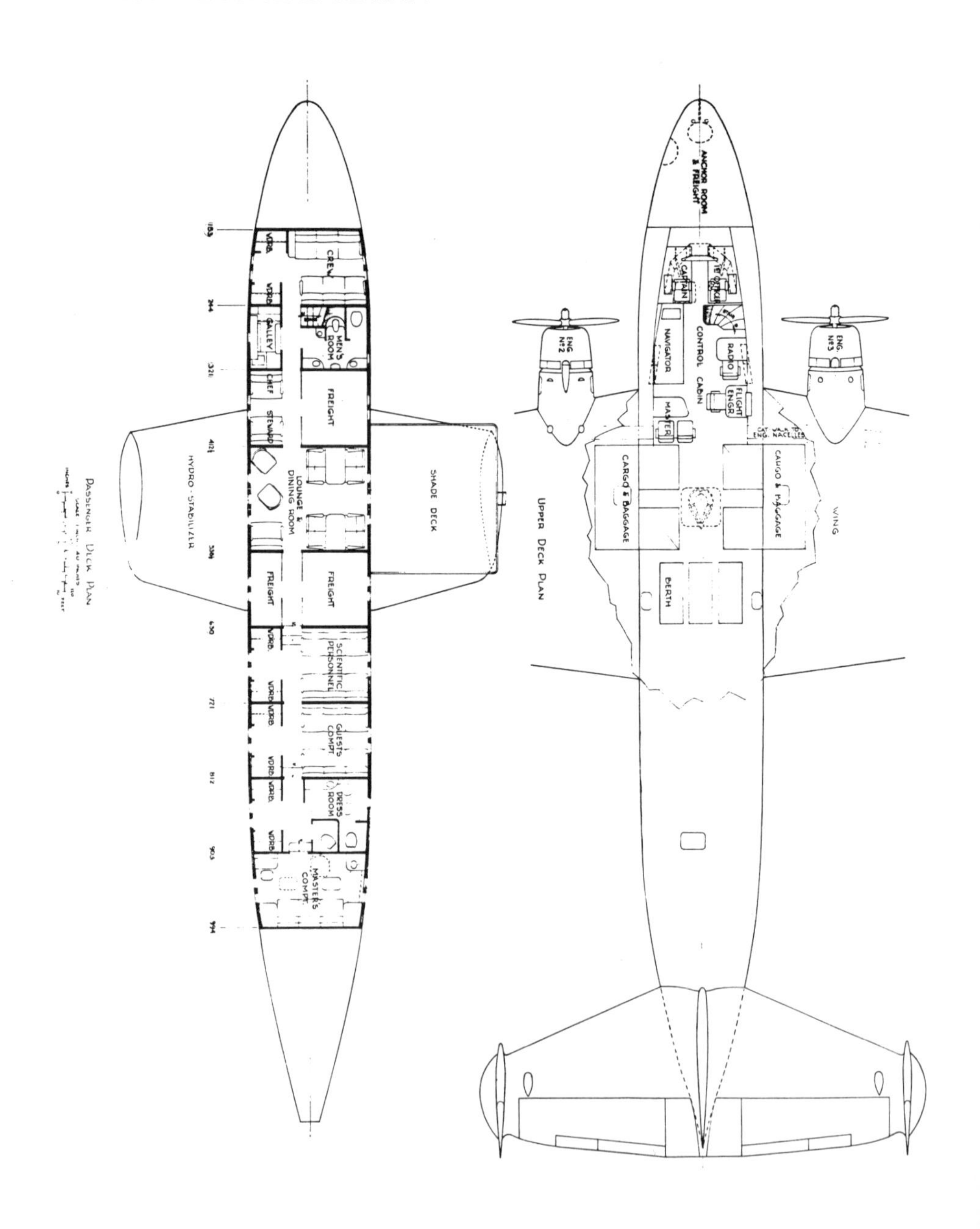

Passenger Deck Plan

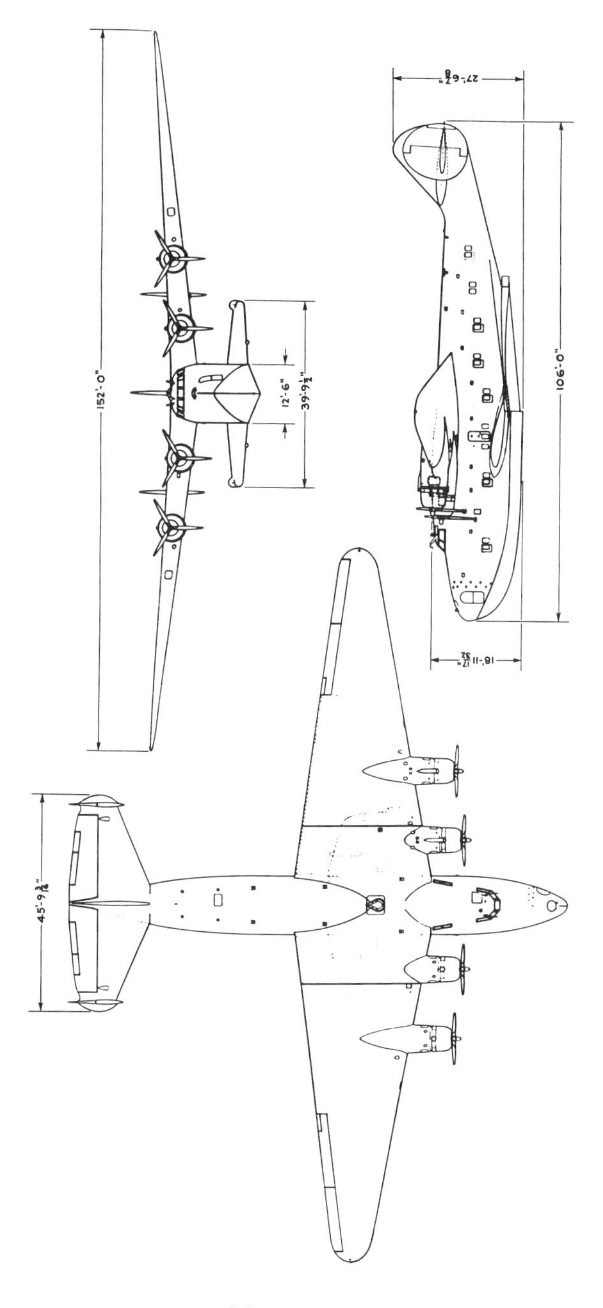

Measurements

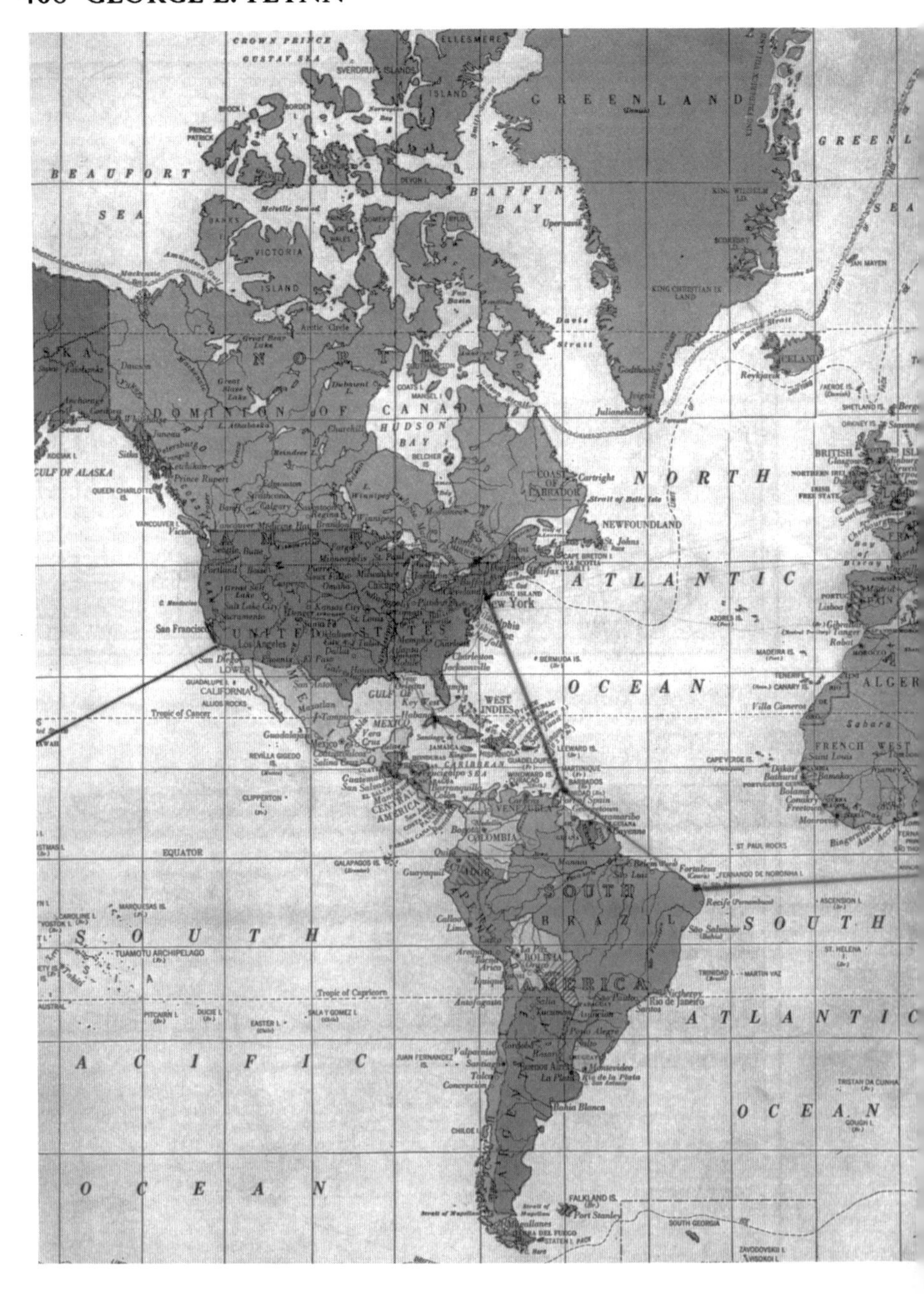
CROWN PRINCE
GUSTAV SEA
ELLESMERE
SVERDRUP ISLANDS
GREENLAND
BEAUFORT
SEA
BAFFIN
BAY
VICTORIA
ISLAND
KING CHRISTIAN IX LAND
ICELAND
Reykjavik
NORTH
DOMINION OF CANADA
HUDSON
BAY
GULF OF ALASKA
Prince Rupert
Vancouver
COAST OF LABRADOR
NORTH
NEWFOUNDLAND
AMERICA
ATLANTIC
San Francisco
UNITED STATES
Los Angeles
New York
BERMUDA IS.
OCEAN
CALIFORNIA
GULF OF MEXICO
Tropic of Cancer
WEST INDIES
CARIBBEAN SEA
CLIPPERTON
VENEZUELA
COLOMBIA
EQUATOR
GALAPAGOS IS.
SOUTH
BRAZIL
Recife
SOUTH
Rio de Janeiro
AMERICA
ATLANTIC
S O U T H
TUAMOTU ARCHIPELAGO
Tropic of Capricorn
EASTER I.
JUAN FERNANDEZ IS.
Valparaiso
Santiago
Buenos Aires
Montevideo
Bahia Blanca
P A C I F I C
OCEAN
O C E A N
FALKLAND IS.
Port Stanley
SOUTH GEORGIA
ST. HELENA
TRISTAN DA CUNHA
FRENCH WEST
ALGER

The Route of the Pacific Clipper.

INDEX